the common ground book of orchards

conservation, culture and community

the common ground book of orchards

conservation, culture and community

CHARITY REG 326335

First published by Common Ground, 2000
PO Box 25309, London, NW5 1ZA
www.commonground.org.uk

© Common Ground, 2000

Illustrations © the illustrators, 2000

Photographs © the photographers, 2000

Design Consultant: David Holmes

Principal writers: Dan Keech with Sue Clifford, Jane Kendall, Angela King, Stephen Turner and Gail Vines
Principal photographers: James Ravilious and Common Ground
Illustrators: see Acknowledgements
Editor: Gail Vines

ISBN: 1 870364 21 X

Design and typesetting on Apple Mac by Stephen Turner and Jane Kendall at Common Ground
Cover image by James Ravilious
This book is printed by Russell Press Ltd., Nottingham
paper: 150gsm Revive Matt - combined Totally Chlorine Free and Elemental Chlorine free, 100% recycled post consumer waste

Common Ground is a registered Charity no. 326335.

CIP catalogue record for this book is available from the British Library.

Common Ground gratefully acknowledges the support of:
The Environmental Action Fund of the Department of the Environment, Transport and the Regions,
The Tedworth Charitable Trust & others

Contents

'THE FRUITE OF APPLES DO DIFFER IN GREATNESS, FORME, COLOUR AND TASTE; SOME COVERED WITH A RED SKIN, OTHERS YELLOWE OR GREEN, VARYING INDEFINITELY ACCORDING TO THE SOYLE AND CLIMATE; SOME VERY GREAT, SOME LITTLE, AND MANY OF A MIDDLE SORT; SOME ARE SWEET OR TASTIE, OR SOMETHING SOWER; MOST BE OF A MIDDLE TASTE BETWEENE SWEETE AND SOWER, TO WHICH TO DISTINGUISH I THINKE IT IMPOSSIBLE; NOT WITHSTANDING I HEARE OF ONE THAT INTENDETH TO WRITE A PECULIAR VOLUME OF APPLES, AND THE USE OF THEM...'

John Gerarde, 1597

Local Distinctiveness

WHAT IS AN ORCHARD if not a wood? It may be more orderly but fruit trees perform the same deciduous miracle of 'dying' in winter only to be born once more each spring. An orchard tells the seasons more frankly than most woods, flaunting its blossom, dropping big fruit, feeding masses of creatures as well as us, demanding attention. This extroversion is reinforced by an intricacy of particularity to place, just as intriguing as a wood, which unravels in complexity as one learns more of culture as well as nature at the local level.

In Cumbria, damson trees keep company with stone walls, in Shropshire they march along hedgerows, as do cherries in some parts of Norfolk. Giant cherry trees, 18 metres high, gather in (the few remaining) great orchards along the north coast of Kent, whilst further south into the Weald squat cobnut plats pick out the ragstone soils of the greensand ridge. Hereford, Somerset and Devon are counties renowned for their cider apple trees, Gloucestershire for its many kinds of perry pears.

Newly planted elder trees are remaking the landscape in corners of Leicestershire and Surrey, as the demand for elderflower cordial undergoes a renaissance which cannot always be met by a wild harvest following the destruction of so many hedgerows. Garden-bound fruit trees hold fast in Hampstead Garden Suburb, mulberries stain the Victorian gardens of Stockwell, relict mixed orchards languish in Cambridge colleges.

> *A valley full of doctor apples,*
> *A valley-stream like flaming straw,*
> *The valley blushing from its roots, and rustling,*
> *The hill-roads cobbled with red fruit.*
>
> FROM THE APPLE BROADCAST *BY* PETER REDGROVE

The trees themselves embody tales of genesis and specificity to place and time. The apple with its powerful symbolisms and rich poetry reveals the intricacy of biological diversity which we have discovered or dabbled into existence and then maintained through grafting; every apple pip contains the potential to produce a new variety, the genes having been newly shuffled, a trick every Somerset cider maker played to advantage, pouring the must from apple pressings around field corners and picking out promising saplings.

The Cornish Honeypin, Cambusnethan Pippin, Norfolk Beefing, Kentish Fillbasket, Stoke Edith Pippin reveal some of their places of origin. The overwhelming revelation expressed in the names of 6,000 varieties of cooking and eating apples (and some hundreds more of cider varieties) reworks the map of Britain you thought you knew. Then there are the damsons, cherries, plums, hazels and walnuts, pears, greengages....

In habitat terms, orchards should be seen as wood pasture, a rich interface, many micro habitats – biodiversity is no less rich for having been gently encouraged into existence or sustained through nurture by many hands. Indeed we should be proud to find around us exemplary cases of how humans and nature can work together; in the case of orchards, we have done so for hundreds of years.

Cider apple orchard in Hele, Devon. Photo: James Ravilious.

Nature loses, culture loses

In orchards we and nature together have created an exuberant and a secret landscape – a treasury of genetic diversity and a repository of culture. For if an orchard is grubbed out for intensive agriculture or development, the loss for local distinctiveness goes deep.

We lose the groves, the tall trees, little ordered woods, the spring blossom bursting when all else is monotone, the shades and greens of summer, the colours and smells of autumn, the winter jobs and mistletoe. As the look of the place changes, nature changes too.

Deprived of the tall, old trees and the grassland at their feet, we also lose the wild life: the buzz of bees and hoverflies working on the blossom, the thrushes, blackbirds and butterflies bargaining over fallen fruit, owl, woodpecker, hare, badger, the lichens, the wild flowers and all of the tiny creatures which offer the first rungs on many ecological ladders. Each assemblage, gathered and particularised over centuries, is specific to locality.

As the touchstones in the everyday disappear, so do the stories prompted by their presence; the songs and customs annually enacted have neither theatre nor reason for repetition.

We may not notice that the Red Rollo or Minshull Crab have been lost to the locality. But with their loss go the recipes that depended on the special properties of these fruits, along with the confidence of long knowledge of the right moment to pick, the length of time to store and the chemistry of mixing and cooking to get the best taste, the most nutrition over the longest period.

The ways of making cider, cherry brandy, perry or plum wine wither, along with the once commonplace skills of pruning, grafting and planting with the peculiarities of these varieties and complementary activities in mind. Generations of hard-won wisdom about aspect and slope, soil and season, nuance of weather and variety dies with people who have nowhere to practise, no-one to tell.

Buildings crumble having lost their use. Ingenious machinery becomes industrial archaeology at best, gets broken and dispersed at worst. The loss of the expertise needed to keep these things going diminishes the local economy and the breadth of interactions. The backbreaking, but social, work falls away, neighbours become strangers, newcomers have fewer working routes for learning how to become a 'local'.

The cultural landscape is both robust and vulnerable. Like nature it needs change to keep it in good heart, but it also needs continuity: the passing on of knowledge, an unbroken chain of care.

Expertise, knowledge, wisdom

Thousands of years of 'empirical research' in almost every corner of the earth has provided us with an extraordinary bank of wisdom about nature; interlinked cultural evolution has borne diverse value systems.

Scientific expertise, in a handful of centuries, has added vast amounts to our understanding and capabilities. But it has focused on facts, replicable states, leaving aside anything difficult to count, cost, exchange or substitute.

The knowledge of scientists is different from vernacular understanding. We need both. Particularly we need to value and keep wisdom practised in its place. Indigenous knowledge, intangible benefits, subjective perceptions, emotional attachments and expressions of value need other languages and other champions.

Note this intricacy: the Kpelle people of Liberia 'carefully match crop strains with the slope, soil conditions and sunlight on each patch of their land. Women of the forest-dwelling Kpelle sow more than 100 varieties of rice, making their fields a jigsaw of genetic diversity' (A. Dunning quoted in United Nations Development Programme: Choices, vol 2, no 2, 1993). In China new research is showing how juxtaposing many rice varieties protects against disease and increases yields. There is safety in diversity. When one variety fails, others succeed; there is still food or income. The trends to monoculture and to growing single varieties of wheat, rice, plums or apples have rendered growers vulnerable to weather, disease, market fickleness and food fashions. We contend that the quest for living for the mutual benefit of nature and ourselves can only be achieved if everyone wants to, and can, join in. In creating or reinventing a benign rapport with nature we need all of our manifold expertise, knowledge and wisdom.

Cherry orchard in north Kent, 1992.

Nature, culture, place

Common Ground was founded on the belief that our relations with nature and the land are fundamental to our everyday and our long-term wellbeing. We are convinced of the ecological imperative, and that humanity and imagination are needed to help us all to create a new ethos of wanting to care. To this end we have worked to help people to stand up for the things they value. Our argument is a plain one – we all need to take responsibility for the ordinary and commonplace things to make our everyday lives better. We need to be involved, so that nature and history are close to us, so that we can have some influence and feel part of a pattern of our own creation.

We have located our activities where nature and culture come together – grounded in place – and we have spread our interest over everyday nature, ordinary histories, commonplace buildings, vernacular landscapes, popular stories, particular legends, great and subtle variegation in cultures.

Orchards are a wonderful example of nature and culture and place – of local distinctiveness. Common Ground's work, in city and country, to help people to save old orchards, to plant new ones, and to create Community Orchards has popularised genetic diversity crucially linked with the importance of keeping knowledge and practice alive in their place – which is real sustainability.

Local distinctiveness

So much 20th-century farming, industry, tourism and development have reduced biodiversity, ironed out variegation and suppressed the personality of places. In the 1980s, Common Ground first elaborated the concept of local distinctiveness: it is about what your place means to you. It links to identity, and encompasses our mostly unspoken appreciation of continuing history and embedded nature.

Importantly it focuses on locality, not region or county or city. It is about accumulations not about one moment in history, about constant dynamism not preservation. It includes the invisible as well as the physical – symbols, festivals, legends may be as important as hedgerows, hills and houses.

Unless a place has meaning to the people who inhabit it and use it, it is unlikely to be well cared for. Little things (detail) and clues to previous land uses and memories of former lives (patina) may be the very things which breathe significance into the streets or fields or orchards. Try to define these things for others or at a grand scale and the point is lost. The connectedness of things makes the richness; we could be talking of habitats and history, building types and breeds

of sheep, landmarks and legends.

Common Ground's founders coined the term 'local distinctiveness' in 1984 in their book *Holding Your Ground: an action guide to local conservation*. Awkward as they seem, the words are descriptively direct; we have found no better way of focusing upon locality to help people to explore and express their views of the things which subtly differentiate one small place from another and endow those places with richnesses not necessarily evident to others.

Damsons are a distinctive feature of the Cumbrian landscape.

Bluebells form a spring-time carpet beneath the trees in a Kentish Cobnut plat on the stony soils of the ragstone ridge between Maidstone and Sevenoaks. Photo: Meg Game.

The importance of the local

Scale is important, as is the question of who defines it. We are talking of the neighbourhood, the parish, the housing estate, the suburb, perhaps even the street. And we are talking of the people themselves, those who live, work and play there, defining the area to which they feel they belong and which belongs to them. They may have always lived there, in a sense the place chose them, or they may have come to this place, have chosen it and be claiming it anew. Both see the place with different eyes, both are important.

At greater scales we can understand patterns in a different way, but to act at these levels risks inattention to people and to the quotidian. For example, to pursue a policy of infill development in villages as part of a district planning policy may mean the loss of all the last orchards beside the old farm houses and the loss of the only open space for wild life and people in the place. A crucial aspect of the personality of the place may be so diminished that people feel they no longer want to live there.

Knowing your neighbours, knowing where and how your food has been grown, understanding the importance of fewer miles travelled by people and products – such deeper engagements with place all suggest the significance of the local.

Smallness and localness should not be confused with simplicity. Locality needs to be defined from the inside, with a natural and cultural base – less abstraction, more detail – which comes with place-based knowledge.

The importance of the commonplace

Our quest has been to move the debate away from the simple domination of experts and action around the rare, the endangered, the spectacular and the beautiful, towards local people standing up for their deeper cultural relations with nature and the land.

Defining beauty as mountains and richness as rarity has not only devalued the remainder, but it has diminished people's confidence to speak out for the ordinary things which focus pride and interest. Most people live, work and play in places for which they sustain an affection through familiarity. And everyday places are as vulnerable as the special. The special anyway has no long-term chance of survival on small protected islands – the everywhere, the commonplace is the vital matrix of ecology as well as our everyday lives.

Places are not just physical surroundings, they are a web of rich understandings between people and nature, people and histories, people and their neighbours. Places carry all kinds of coded messages, some easy to read, some needing a long apprenticeship and humility on behalf of the professional and the incomer.

But we are all guilty of taking things for granted. Once orchards were all around us, not so long ago the thrush and the bullfinch were common. We need to revalue our relations with the commonplace and take more care of the things under our everyday gaze.

Meaning

The significance of a place lingers in the stories and resonances the place holds for those who know it and love it. Many of these will be personal, but many will be shared. Identity is bound up with affection for or alienation from everyday knowledge and the popular understanding of features or the ritual of festivals. The commonplace defines identity – locally abundant plants, specific building techniques, seasonal recipes.

Traditional orchards can continue to provide an important bank of fruits and knowledge for a time when local produce and varieties may be valued in new contexts. They maintain identity and authenticity, and keep intricate local expertise and cultural connections alive.

In 1990 Common Ground invented Apple Day. Our intention was to establish a new day in the calendar, an annual festival, a popular widening of interest and commitment leading to the revitalising of the orchards themselves – linking the apple we eat with the landscape around us as a way of building pride back into the locality and responsibility back into our own actions.

We chose the apple to stand for all fruit because of its many

meanings to us in the hope that the richness of its symbolism would spur people to take the festival to their heart. By 1999 there were 600 or more events all run by local people all reinforcing their own local interests in some way, creating local, self-propelled ritual in homage to fruit and its part in our lives. Traditions have to begin sometime.

Common Ground has also been promoting the idea of Community Orchards, school orchards and city orchards, ways of rethinking what these places could be for, who could benefit and take responsibility for them. Some of them are feeding their fruit and

derived products back into the local food economy, through box schemes, co-ops or farmers' markets, when a decade ago their orchards may have been considered redundant. Other Community Orchards

Giant perry pears holding on in the countryside around Newent and Dymock in Gloucestershire.

Cherry at Cotehele National Trust in the Tamar Valley with its distinctive swelling at the graft union. Photo: James Ravilious.

Overleaf: detail of Parish Map by Gordon Young.

are the richest places for nature or the focus of neighbourhood celebrations. These places are taking on new meanings.

Patina

We should be as proud of our orchards, as protective of the hills and valleys and of the people who support them, and as imaginative about the foods, drinks, songs and stories which they generate, as the French are about their different vineyards and wines, as the Greeks are about their olive groves and the Portuguese about their cork oaks. This does not mean that things stay the same for ever – that is the recipe for demise.

Places are the richer for the accumulation of activities and histories which, of course, implies change. Places must change to stay vital. Nature is always experimenting, and a locality has to be permeable to new people, ideas, buildings, plantings, practices. But crude sacrifices made by large-scale and rapid development demean us and our places. The old and new must jostle on the same stage for us to feel a sense of history in motion.

Fruits too have their histories. Many fruits are traceable to their place of origin, their stories offering real insights into contemporary society and economy. Peasgood's Nonsuch apple was grown in the 1850s by Mrs Peasgood as a child in Grantham. Twenty years later it was being acclaimed and exhibited by the Royal Horticultural Society. Some varieties were simply found, such as the Victoria plum, discovered by chance in the 19th century in a Sussex wood. Several D'Arcy Spice (Spice Apple is one synonym) trees were discovered growing in the gardens of the Hall, Tolleshunt d'Arcy in Essex in the 1780s, while the Yarlington Mill, a Somerset cider apple, grew from a wall by the waterwheel at Yarlington, West Cadbury.

In Herefordshire, it was believed that unless the orchard was baptised with rain on St Peter's Day, the crop would not be good, and it was once common to light fires under the orchard trees on

Midsummer's eve to bless the apples. An Apple Pie Fair has been held in Marldon in Devon on 25 August since 1888, in memory of a farmer, George Hill who gave his workers windfalls every year. They continued to make a giant apple pie for the village, though now many small pies are made and hidden under a big crust. An Apple Pie Princess is crowned. These customs ancient and not so old, particular to their place, savour the local knowledge and history.

Holding on to the old may demand new thinking. What future for the 18-metre-tall remnant cherry orchards around Teynham and Faversham in Kent? These places, breathtaking at blossom time, used as a back-drop for garden furniture in expensive glossy magazines, are not valued as cultural landscapes. Do they have potential as camping sites, for walking and picnics, as open air restaurants, as places for orchard egg production, and other uses for the twenty-first century?

Detail

Much of current gardening and agricultural practice encourages us to believe that we can and should grow almost anything anywhere. And yet we know that plants grow better where the conditions for them occur naturally and that trees make places as much as buildings or the underlying geology. Almost every farm and country house used to have its own orchard, and each of these was as different as the buildings themselves.

Orchards are a manifestation of our long relationship with fruit cultivation. They vary from place to place in the kind of fruit, the varieties, size of trees, the pattern of planting, the domestic animals grazed beneath, the fencing, the soft fruits, flowers and other crops grown under them, the ways and times of pruning, grafting, picking and packing.

Farm cider orchards are a distinctive feature of the Somerset Levels, where they often exist on the drier slopes above the withy beds. The Lake District damsons may be scattered, higgledy-piggledy, along field edges. In Gloucestershire alone, there are about 100 perry pear varieties worthy of note, and each parish produced its own

characteristic single-variety perry or local blend.

In Ryedale in Yorkshire, George Morris has uncovered all manner of detail about the part played by apples in the life and economy of the farms and workers. Orchards were the domain of women, who on marriage would move to their husband's farm bringing graft wood from their home trees to add to the orchard. Along with all of their other work, in the kitchen they concentrated on tasty, nourishing pies, tarts, roasts and dumplings using the fruits of the season. An acre of orchard might contain 16 varieties of apple with a season stretching from August to May, providing apples to eat fresh from the tree or from store all that time. Typically present were apples originating in the county – Yorkshire Cockpit, Green

Balsam, Yorkshire Greening (otherwise known as Yorkshire Goose Sauce), Backhouse Flowery Town (with its pink flesh) Yorkshire Beauty or Hawthornden – together with Keswick Codlin, Warners King, Lane's Prince Albert, Dog's Snout, Catshead, Burr Knot, Striped Beefing, Gravenstein, Lemon Pippin, Northern Greening. The latter are often thrown away now by people who do not realise that their hard and sour early persona is transformed by Easter. George warns that some of the Yorkshire varieties fail to reach their best outside a limited area, adding further to local distinctiveness.

Community Orchards

As economic rapacity, globalisation, supermarket greed, pesticide poisoning, agricultural intensification, ignorance, planning rigidity, development voracity and all the rest claim their victims, small but complex actions such as standing up for an old orchard, inventing a new community place, discovering shared strengths can help us to create a new mutuality between nature and culture, can reintensify local distinctiveness, and offer grounding for evolving ideas of environmental responsibility. What is a Community Orchard? It can be a place run by and for local people, in city, in suburb or in village: a place for communal fruit growing, food production, tree rearing, festive gatherings, playing, quiet contemplation, wild life watching, animal grazing, skill sharing, extending knowledge, building responsibility, nurturing biodiversity, keeping and extending local varieties, championing local distinctiveness.

Common Ground's highest aspiration is to see people reinventing for themselves a relationship with nature and the land which is driven by cultural and ecological sensitivity, as well as economic imperatives. We are all implicated. We can all do something.

From north of Inverness hails the apple Coul Blush – descriptive of the place of origin but its beautiful name is evocative of paradox. Let us not lose what we have sustained for hundreds of years, let us have our apples and eat them.

Community Orchards

COMMUNITY ORCHARDS offer a way of saving vulnerable old orchards as well as opportunities to plant new ones. They provide places for quiet contemplation or local festivities; a reservoir of local varieties of fruit and a refuge for wild life.

In city, town or village, the Community Orchard is becoming the equivalent of the wood in the countryside a century and more ago – a communal asset for the whole parish. But more than that, it can be an additional focal point for the whole village or suburb – the moot, the open-air hall. We could have school orchards, city, museum, hospital and factory orchards open to all. We desperately need more places to relax and play in, and we also need shared activities to enable people of different ages and backgrounds to come together.

Community Orchards help to revive an interest in fruit growing, provide a way of sharing knowledge and horticultural skills and stimulate us into growing food for ourselves again.

Those exotic and unfamiliar sounding places, the French vineyards and the olive groves of Greece or Spain, hold such imagined richness. Yet they are no more interesting or incredible than our own unique but everyday orchards. We just need to recognise the value and the potential of what we have.

An orchard is a collection of fruit trees – mixing fruit trees with other kinds of trees profoundly changes and diminishes the feeling of orchardness. Traditional orchards – with tall standard trees, planted among grass full of wild flowers – constitute places of tranquility, places where you can find continuity in the landscape.

Community Orchards should be open and accessible at all times. They may be owned or leased for or by the community (or held by agreement) by a community group, parish council, or by a local authority or voluntary body. As well as enjoying the place, local people can share the harvest or profit from its sale, taking responsibility for any work in the orchard.

Because their prime purpose is not the production of fruit, we have the opportunity to think creatively about what these orchards can and should be like.

In *Wild Fruits*, the 19th-century naturalist Henry David Thoreau celebrated the special feel of rambling orchards. He described how he loved 'to go through the old orchards of ungrafted apple trees, at whatever season of the year – so irregularly planted: sometimes two trees standing close together; the rows so devious that you would think that they not only had grown while the owner was sleeping, but had been set out by him in a somnambulic state. The rows of grafted fruit will never tempt me to wander amid them like these.'

Most of us prefer rambling old orchards – the ones with trees at all angles, even drunkenly on their sides – to the manicured and regimented ones. In 1790, a single perry pear at Holme Lacy, on the banks of the River Wye, covered a third of a hectare (three quarters of an acre) and produced 5-7 tonnes of fruit. It dropped its limbs, which rooted to produce new trees, and so spread outwards. This is the way that some fruit trees would propagate themselves, if left alone. They seldom are.

The May Queen crowned, Lustleigh Orchard, Devon. Photo: James Ravilious.

Community Orchards offer great potential in both town and country. They can work in housing estates, industrial estates, hospitals and schools. They can enliven the curriculum, improve our diet, and even speed the recovery of the ill and infirm.

The success of a Community Orchard lies in the strength of local commitment to it. Local people are the key to running it and deciding how it is used. These orchards do not have economic fruit production as their *raison d'être*, yet they might just pay for themselves, with income generated through the sale of fruit and other produce – everything from wild flower seeds to mistletoe. In the longer term, fruit wood, as well as coppiced hazel, could generate healthy returns.

Wild life may benefit too. The natural bounty of traditional orchards, with standard trees skirted by hedges and unimproved grassland, is increasingly celebrated by national agencies and local enthusiasts alike.

When establishing a Community Orchard, priority must go to conserving traditional orchards where they exist, as we are losing them so quickly. If you hear that a traditional orchard near you is in danger of being grubbed up, let the owner know of its importance to the landscape, to you and to the local community, that there are grants for maintenance and that there are many ways of adding value to the fruit and the orchard itself – for instance, by letting it out for grazing, local festivals, plays or to campers and caravanners.

Help in picking the fruit, cutting and removing the hay, staking, fencing and pruning can be offered in return for local access.

In many cases, all an old orchard will need is 'gapping up' – planting new trees to replace ones that are dead or diseased. Try not to be overzealous: many fruit trees bear well lying on their sides and make excellent seats, and you can ruin the feel of the place by being too tidy or making woodchip paths. It's worth remembering that stag beetles and a host of other remarkable insects rely on old, decaying fruit wood to survive.

If the owner wishes to sell the orchard, find out if your parish or district/borough council is willing to purchase it for the community. Alternatively, think about setting up a trust to purchase the orchard on behalf of the community or ask your county Wildlife Trust, the RSPB or the Woodland Trust if they would consider buying it.

New uses for old orchards

Camping: Peter and Pat Hinde own a pick-your-own orchard and fruit farm near Iver in Buckinghamshire. Part of their land is used for caravanning, as Peter explains:

My arrangement for caravans is with the Caravan Club who licence the site. I have to have half an acre dedicated to caravans, supply water, household rubbish disposal and a cesspit for disposing of the contents of their WCs. I cannot let any caravan remain for more than 28 days at a time, nor have more than five on the site at any one time. They must be slept in, not stored. I take telephone bookings and customers must be members of the Caravan Club and give me their membership number on booking. I charge £4.50 a night, £28 for seven days. I do not provide electricity though if anyone wants to charge a battery, I show them where the plug is.

Nature conservation: In some counties, old orchards are among the few remaining places where biodiversity is exactly that. There are orchard nature reserves run by the Wildlife Trusts in Worcestershire (Melrose Farm), Hertfordshire (Tewin), Essex (Sergeant's) and Dorset (Broad Oak). On the whole, orchards have rarely been viewed by conservation organisations as suitably wild or natural enough to justify their protection as nature reserves or as subjects for special designation. This is a lost opportunity, since many orchards, particularly old ones which have occupied the same piece of land for many years, may be perfect habitats for rare and common species alike. This notion continues to be borne out following Common Ground's *Orchard Observances* scheme which encourages the keeping of orchard nature diaries by their owners or users. As orchards enjoy greater scrutiny, the more evidence of their value to biodiversity emerges.

Horticultural training: Brighton resident and MIND volunteer Liz Godden had attended an Orchards Training Day in London organised by Common Ground and the Federation of City Farms and Community Gardens. This excited her into thinking about the old orchard at Stanmer Park, on the northern fringe of Brighton.

The 0.4-hectare orchard was once part of the private Stanmer Estate and is now owned by Brighton and Hove Council. While the parkland, house and walled gardens have continued to be used as a public park and council nursery, the orchard had fallen into neglect and the grassland beneath the trees was a mass of nettles, brambles, dogwood and Japanese knotweed. An area directly adjacent to the orchard is used by various voluntary sector organisations and community projects, providing horticultural training for people with learning difficulties and mental health problems.

Liz began exploring ways to restore the orchard for public access and to bring it back into fruitfulness by working with the various groups active in Stanmer and the wider community. She called a meeting of local people and groups associated with the park and the

Making plans for restoration at Stanmer Orchard, Brighton.

local countryside, which resulted in the formation of the Stanmer Orchard Group (SOG). The council were supportive and a management plan was drawn up in 1999/2000.

Three members of the group applied for a BTCV Natural Pioneers Millennium Award to fund training including apple tree care, bird-box making and flora and fauna identification. Clearing some of the vegetation beneath the trees has encouraged an increase in bluebells and the appearance of orchids. Gentle pruning has re-invigorated the fruit bearing of the trees. The work of SOG will make the orchard an attractive place for people to visit, linger in and eat from in the coming years.

Al fresco: The old perry orchard at Warndon is now surrounded by new estates built on Worcester's eastern edge. Huge trees well populated by invertebrates and birds can be admired and enjoyed by their new human neighbours. There is open access at all times and people are encouraged to walk, play and picnic. The locally distinctive perry fruit may not be palatable but offers local home-brewers a new challenge. Visitors to Grantchester, Rupert Brooke's home village near Cambridge, can enjoy a cuppa beneath apple trees in the Orchard Tea Gardens, originally planted in 1868.

Arenas for celebration: Lustleigh Orchard on the edge of Dartmoor anticipated the idea of Community Orchards. It was bequeathed to the parish as an existing cider orchard in 1960 and it sits at the centre of the village. Local people believe that it has been an orchard for as long as there has been settled agriculture in the valley. The orchard is the largest area of green space within the parish and is the focus of community celebrations such as the annual May Day festival, where the May Queen is crowned. The orchard is owned and looked after by the parish council, and as old trees die they are replaced with new stock. An income is gained from selling part of the apple crop (locals are free to take what they like for their own use), letting the orchard to graze sheep and by selling mistletoe. A small donation box on the orchard gate also raises money to help with maintenance.

Restoring old orchards for community use

Since Common Ground first promoted the idea in 1990, many Community Orchards have been created by trusts, parish councils, local authorities and voluntary bodies. Here are some further examples of old orchards which have been restored or nurtured by local people for diverse ends:

Tewin Orchard, near Welwyn Garden City in Hertfordshire, is managed by the Herts & Middlesex Wildlife Trust and is leased from the RSPB. It was one of the first orchard nature reserves, attracting a wide variety of butterflies and birds. Many of its original trees date back to planting in 1933. Restocking of Hertfordshire fruit varieties has continued over recent years. In 1998, following the formation of the Hertfordshire Orchards Initiative, Tewin Orchard started hosting budding and grafting courses and began a rootstock nursery which will supply new local Community Orchards.

The Nuttery in Northamptonshire comprises 0.6 hectares of hazel coppice that has been given to the Woodland Trust. Hazel nuts and snowdrops have been grown commercially at the Nuttery for at least a hundred years. A squeeze gate has been built to give access at all times. There are open days in spring and autumn for the picking and sale of snowdrops and nuts.

————

Gate to Broad Oak Community Orchard, a Dorset Wildlife Trust reserve near Sturminster Newton.

New seasonal uses for orchards: South Petherton folk festival campsite, Somerset. Photo: James Ravilious.

Cleeve Prior Parish Ponds and Community Orchard project in Worcestershire was initiated by Don and Linda Warren who have lived in Cleeve Prior, near Evesham, since 1975. It all began with a village recycling scheme and the formation of the Cleeve Prior Heritage Trust in 1997 with a listed barn as a focus for their activities. Next, the Warrens and other trust members set about acquiring and restoring 2.4 hectares of old orchard, which included Lord Lambourne and Beauty of Bath apples, Damascenes (Shropshire damsons), Victoria, Pershore Yellow Egg, Rivers Early Prolific and other plums and cherries, as well as derelict fish ponds adjacent to the barn. The orchard

had been part of an intensively cultivated patchwork of small strips since the 1920s. In recent years, many of these orchards have been grubbed out and planted with grain or have been developed and what remained was neglected.

Twice-weekly work-parties, usually attracting around 12 villagers, have succeeded in clearing much of the thick scrub from the orchard and from around the newt-laden ponds. The aim is to gradually replant the orchard with local, historically important varieties and a greater diversity of fruits. A mixture of apples, including cider varieties for eventual local production have already been planted.

There is plenty of scope to experiment with new ideas. In years of surplus, fruit could be picked and packed for sale to help with the costs of orchard upkeep. But much of the fruit will go to local people. Volunteers pick fruit for older people in the village and for residents of Evesham. Links with inner-city residents from Birmingham who would like to spend a day in the country picking fruit are another possibility – an historical precedent recalls the seasonal pickers who, until the 1960s, helped with the rural harvest.

The orchard is also a special resource for local schools and those wishing to learn orchard skills. With the ponds and the surrounding hedges and scrub, many species of wild life including dragonflies, damselflies and butterflies, will be attracted to the restored orchard grassland (which contains orchids, adder's tongue fern and centaury) and to its old trees, to feed on blossom or fallen fruit, as well as sheltering under the bark and decaying wood.

The desire to build and maintain features such as signs, seats, gates and displays in the orchard and the adjacent barn and stables offers villagers a chance to contribute practical, artistic and communication skills. There is enthusiasm to be flexible and inclusive about the roles which the orchard, ponds and buildings can support. Already the orchard has inspired Linda Warren and Evesham resident, Bob Woodrofe, to poetry.

Broad Oak Community Orchard near Sturminster Newton is owned

by the Dorset Wildlife Trust and is open all year round. Its two-thirds of a hectare contain mature apple, plum and pear trees that will reward human visitors with almost a dozen delicious varieties in autumn. In summer, its flower-rich grassland contains cowslips, creeping jenny and devil's bit scabious. After the winter gloom the blackthorn hedge illuminates Broad Oak with early blossom. The orchard's wilder visitors include butterflies, a host of birds including woodpeckers and treecreepers as well as ground-hugging mammals that use the grassland as foraging cover. Broad Oak is in good company: two nearby schools, in Sturminster Newton and Blandford Forum, have orchards within their grounds.

Newly planted Community Orchards

Blondin Orchard, in Ealing, West London, covers around a fifth of a 2-hectare allotment that has been owned by the London Borough of Ealing since 1926. Before that it was part of a local family farm estate and from 1750-1834 formed part of the Brentford Nursery, which specialised in fruit trees and held more than 300 apple varieties.

The whole area is named after the Frenchman Charles Blondin, Niagara Falls tightrope walker, who settled here upon retirement. His feats (and a couple of apple varieties) are celebrated in local road names. Designs were drawn up by the council following wide-ranging consultation with residents. Many of the fruit varieties subsequently planted in the orchard were known to have been grown during the time of the Brentford Nursery.

As cultivation of the municipal allotments declined, the council asked local people for their ideas on bringing the area back into community use. More than 150 people expressed opinions, and the consensus was for a Community Orchard within a nature area. The council's aims were: 'to bring a redundant allotment back into active and sustainable community use; to develop the area's interest for wild life; to establish a successful Community Orchard with good fruit production; and to develop the area through ongoing consultation with local people'.

The orchard was planted on 19 February 1997 to commemorate the centenary of Blondin's death. Fifty local people helped to plant 46 apple trees. Individual trees were protected with sturdy wooden cage-type guards. The grassland beneath the trees is mown twice a year by the council. A 50-centimetre clearance is left around each tree when mowing. Local residents have carried out weeding and mulching within the area of the tree guards. A standpipe has enabled people to water the young trees if necessary. A management plan was completed with help from the London Ecology Unit.

A longer-term plan for the orchard will be drawn up by the council and the Friends of Blondin Park. Ideas include fruit production, links with schools, training for new skills, grazing of the orchard by sheep, wild life observances and seating. The orchard may be expanded to take in many of the existing cherry trees within the nature area. Very few trees have been lost since planting. This is partly due to the orchard's location off a main road behind overlooking houses, but also because people enjoy the orchard and see it working. Losses of any trees are replaced.

The establishment of a Friends Group – 50 members at time of writing – has led to collaboration between local people and the council to improve the area. A management plan for the whole nature area, including the orchard, is being jointly prepared. Local people are using a public open space and beginning to work together and think creatively about new opportunities for its social use and its benefit to the local environment. Apple Day has been celebrated in the orchard since 1997. A slow worm was found on Apple Day 1999.

Walbottle Community Orchard is on Tyneside. Encouraged by several successful Apple Day celebrations, the Countryside Ranger Service of Newcastle City Council led a public consultation of plans for a Community Orchard on the edge of Curtens' Quarry in Walbottle, west of the city in October 1997. Four months later local people planted more than 50 apple, pear and cherry trees on a third of a hectare of former grazing land. The orchard has already been included in play schemes and educational visits by local primary schools, and has hosted launch celebrations of the adjacent Walbottle Brickworks Local Nature Reserve. In autumn 1998, thousands of snowdrop and bluebell bulbs were planted between the fruit trees, and these spring flowers will continue to attract people into the orchard while the young fruit trees develop.

Bloomfield Community Orchard and **Lower Common Allotment Orchards** are in Bath. Peter Andrews and Tony Ambrose, local residents whose houses back onto the Bloomfield allotments in Oldfield Park, noticed that four central allotments were untended. They decided to gather support to create a Community Orchard for everyone to enjoy.

At the same time, on the other side of the River Avon, Tim Baines of Bath Organic Group was helping to set up a Community Orchard at the Lower Common Allotments organic demonstration site at Victoria Park. St Stephen's Allotment Society was formed to protect the green, open space at Lansdown in Bath from becoming a housing development. After a long-running battle with the Bath & Wells Diocese which owns the allotments, the group was awarded a £40,000 lottery grant in 1999 to buy part of the land and turn it into a Millennium Green for community use.

Many allotments are underused and Community Orchards can offer one way of keeping them cultivated and producing a communal crop. Knowledge and neighbourly cooperation can continue through the exchange of horticultural tips and recipes as well as through a shared appreciation of the beauty which the fruit trees will eventually contribute.

Establishing a community use for allotments – where a group is involved as opposed to individuals – not only strengthens the sense of community within the area, but helps to protect them. Bath was surrounded by orchards just over 100 years ago. Few old specimens

A Friend of Blondin Park mulching the apple trees at one of the regular maintenance days.
Photo: Sheilagh Hurwitt.

have survived, along with the varieties they bear.

Planting an apple tree is not to be undertaken lightly – standard trees can live for a hundred years or more and during their lifetime produce hundreds of tonnes of fruit. Fruit trees require care, which is especially important as they become established.

Peter Andrews, who has been involved in community projects over many years, was well aware of this when he called a meeting at his house to discuss setting up the Bloomfield Community Orchard.

A number of factors had to fall into place for the plan to proceed. The idea had to win the support of the local authority. Bath and North East Somerset Council allowed the group to secure the four plots at a reduced rate and gave permission for the land to be used as an orchard – there are often local by-laws prohibiting the planting of trees on allotments. At a well-attended meeting at Peter's house, a list of ideas and designs for the project were discussed. Peter takes up the story:

We decided to plant apple trees, a hedge made of willows and various wild plants, to dig a pond to promote wild life and to provide somewhere to sit. The whole project was designed to be light-weight, without tedious meetings. We get together three or four times a year to deal with the business and maintenance and generally have a good time.

The cost of trees is quite high, and as we didn't have any money, we applied to various people for sponsorship. We found this very fruitful, as trees are apparently very non-controversial. South West Electricity Board gave us free rein to choose as many trees as we needed from their nursery. Wessex Water bought the liner and plants for the pond, Shell sponsored

our mower and Marks & Spencer also gave us financial support.

Since 1997, the group have planted apple varieties that will eventually give them fruit from July right through to the following May. These include among others, Beauty of Bath (ready to eat by July), Ashmead's Kernal, Golden Russet, Tydeman's Early Worcester, Kidd's Orange Red and George Cave.

The only real problem was a concealed river – discovered with the help of a dowser – which ran right through the centre of the orchard. Several trees had been inadvertently planted in bog land and had to be moved. Lots of people donated water plants from their own ponds for the orchard pond. Anyone from Bath or the surrounding areas is welcome to come and join us and see how to set up a project like this. I'd love to see Community Orchards on every spare piece of land or allotment countrywide.

On 23 October 1999 (nearest Sunday to Apple Day) and two years since its inception, Bloomfield Community Orchard held its own Apple Day, with those who had been involved in its creation celebrating its success.

Bath Organic Group has been promoting orchards for local communities and is offering a £50 start-up grant to new community orchard groups in the Bath & North East Somerset area.

Gabriel's Orchard at Pilton in Somerset is a new orchard in a rural area where orchards encompass much cultural and social history. In 1996 the first discussions were held to consider what might be suitable projects for Pilton's Millennium celebrations. Village resident Joe King tells more:

Jim and Anne Dowling very generously donated a couple of acres of land on the edge of the village, which had once been part of Pilton Vineyard – on a south-facing slope and well drained.

It was decided that it would be a great opportunity to create a

Apple Day at Tewin Orchard: this pioneering wild life reserve is a remnant of an orchard landscape which once stretched towards the Cambridgeshire border. It has hosted training courses for local people and has begun to sell its apples at farmers' markets.

Community Orchard which would seek to preserve the variety of trees which had been important to Somerset and in particular to Pilton itself. The legal formalities were dealt with and a trust document was set up making the Parish Council the Custodian Trustees, and the day to day management was vested in four Managing Trustees. This format has worked well.

Grants were applied for and this allowed us to fence the area effectively and make our first purchase of trees. These were obtained from Thornhayes Nursery of Cullompton who have a catalogue rich in the older varieties of fruit trees. Planting day came and our volunteers set to and got them all planted. Our aim is to involve volunteers in all aspects of the orchard management and we now set aside the first Saturday morning in the month as a working party to carry out the various jobs that need to be done.

Villagers were encouraged to sponsor a tree in the orchard and the response has been very enthusiastic with nearly a hundred trees now sponsored. Important links were forged with Les Davies, the Mendip Hills Warden, who supervises our annual pruning morning and is teaching us the basics of budding and grafting.

The next step was to identify varieties of apples in the local orchards which were important to preserve. We were again fortunate to make contact with Liz Copas from Long Ashton who is an expert in cider apple recognition, and for the last two autumns we have toured the orchards in the Parish, identifying those trees that are important to preserve. We have now budded seventy young trees in our nursery beds and these will be planted out next year.

All in all, creating the Orchard has been great fun. We are all amateurs but nothing succeeds like enthusiasm. No doubt we still have lots to learn but I've yet to hear someone say that it wasn't worthwhile. Certainly we would encourage anyone to have a go.

New Community Orchards continue to be planted in many different forms and by many different groups around the country. These include school orchards, city orchards, a linear orchard along a cycle track in Gloucestershire, an orchard of local varieties around a caravan site and footpath in Norfolk and in the National Forest in Leicestershire on land around a community hospital.

Support for planting and management

Under the Countryside Stewardship Scheme, started by the Countryside Commission (now Countryside Agency) and taken over by the Ministry of Agriculture, Fisheries and Food, management grants are available in England for the rehabilitation of traditional orchards. Details are available from MAFF regional offices.

Some county and district councils offer support, advice and occasionally grants. Contact the tree officer or landscape section. Also contact your Local Agenda 21 officer who can give advice on ways in which we can live in a more sustainable way. Providing local fruit for local consumption is a good example of this. There are many commercial and charitable sources of small funds. Further details are listed in the appendices.

What to do with the fruit

Throughout the ages people have had the pleasurable task of thinking of ways of disposing of an abundance of fruit. There either seems to be too little or too much. Here are some ideas:

- Cider apples/perry pears – sell them to local cider/perry press – as Stoke Gabriel Community Orchard does in south Devon.
- Fruit for eating/cooking – sell it at the 'orchard gate' or sell it to the village shop, or at fêtes and Apple Day, 21 October. Growing, selling and buying locally helps to reduce food miles.
- Distribute the fruit to those without gardens/fruit trees.
- Make cider/perry or wine with them. Simple fruit crushers, presses and fermenters are available at very reasonable cost from suppliers such as Vigo Vineyard Supplies.
- Make fruit juice. About 20 apples will make one litre of juice. Farmers may be willing to hold 'open days' to help people juice their fruit with their machinery.
- Many varieties of apples and pears can be stored over winter until spring in a cool well-ventilated shed or garage. Alternatively apples can be puréed and frozen or made into jam.
- Use the fruit for cooking a special Apple Day feast.
- Once ripe, cobnuts/filberts can be stored in the fridge in a loosely fastened polythene bag for several weeks. Alternatively, shell them and roast them in a low oven until crisp and eat or freeze, or grind and use as a garnish. Or bury them in a cake tin in the garden till after Christmas, but remember where you put them....
- Orchards can be ideal for free-range chickens, ducks or geese.
- Don't forget to leave some fruit for the wild life!
- Give an apple on Apple Day as a token of friendship.
- Take your fruit harvest to be sold at one of the growing number of farmers' markets, which are operated by growers rather than market traders. The pioneer Bath Farmers' Market celebrated Apple Day during its first weeks. A list is available from the National Association of Farmers' Markets.

Community Orchards should be the focal point for community activities and events which could include:-

- Celebrating Apple Day on 21 October
- Open air plays, storytelling, poetry, meetings
- Barbecues, picnics and great feasts
- Climbing and scrumping
- Open-air classroom
- Beekeeping
- Festivals such as May Day and Wassailing
- Picking and tastings
- Pruning and grafting days
- Community wild life observances.

Saving Orchards

OLD ORCHARDS are the richest kind. Some may have occupied the same piece of land for centuries. The apple and pear orchard at Croome Landscape Park in Worcestershire, now owned by the National Trust, can be traced without interruption on maps dating back to 1707. To allow for continuing harvests, young trees will have been planted to eventually replace gradually ageing or lower yielding neighbours. This continuity of landuse is the basis of the richness of old orchards.

Every farm and large garden would have had its own orchard of mixed fruit trees for domestic use, and farm labourers were often paid partly in cider. The main commercial fruit growing areas were, and still are Kent, Somerset, Devon, Cambridgeshire, Essex, Herefordshire and Worcestershire: Kent for eating and cooking apples, cherries, pears, plums and cobnuts, the eastern counties for apples, the southwest for cider apples, perry pears and mazzards (cherries) and the Vale of Evesham for apples, perry pears and plums. But fruit was grown extensively in other areas too – cherries in Hertfordshire, apples and cherries in Berkshire, damsons in Cumbria, apples in west London and so on.

Orchards, with their tall 'standard' trees, were important landscape features. Standard cider apples were usually spaced at 10 metres, majestic cherry trees were grown at more than 14 metres, and perry pears over 18 metres apart, sometimes intercropped with corn.

Old trees, perhaps up to a century if apple, or over three centuries if pear, may bear fruit pre-dating contemporary fashions in

Cherry picking in the Faversham area of north Kent around 1900. Photo by permission of Bernard Snell, Fine Art Studios, Strood.

taste, now deemed uneconomic by the market. Conversely, fashions may have determined the fruit contained in the orchard. Michael Clark, the Honorary Warden of Tewin Orchard in Hertfordshire, explains that during the inter-war years, many Hertfordshire apple orchards were planted with a selection from Monarch, Bramley, James Grieve, Newton Wonder, Cox's Orange Pippin and Laxton's Superb. Identifying some of these can give clues to the rest and so date the orchard. In this respect old orchards are historical barometers of contemporary tastes.

Variety is the spice of life. Our gentle coercive relationship with nature in orchards over centuries has led to the listing of 6,000 named varieties of culinary and dessert apple in the Ministry of Agriculture's National Fruit Directory of 1971, many of which are alternative names for the same fruit. This range of probably 2,000-3,000 varieties can keep us in apples from July/August through Christmas to Easter. In the months in-between we can munch on hundreds of pears, plums, damsons, nuts, peaches and cherries, all washed down with cider, perry, elderflower cordial, plum wine, mulberry punch and a medley of other orchard brews to keep our summers refreshed and winters warmed. Generations of gardeners have worked within the confines presented by local soils, climate, prevailing weather and aspect to produce fruit varieties most suited to their areas of origin.

Fruit names such as Tom Putt or Laxton's Superb tell us who raised them. Others such as Blenheim Orange or Warwickshire Drooper unfurl banners of place of origin. Commercial orchards grow, in the main, a handful of apple varieties – Cox's Orange Pippin and its derivatives Kidd's Orange Red and Fiesta (aka Red Pippin), as

well as Bramley's Seedling, Egremont Russet, Discovery, Worcester Pearmain, Gala and Jonagold. The advanced methods of refrigerated and controlled atmosphere storage enable shoppers to buy a Bramley at just about any time of year and Cox's, at their best near Christmas, may now just make it to Easter. Older orchards may produce a harvest to reinforce the passing seasons, keeping the grower in fruit for as long as possible until berry fruit and earlier orchard produce such as cherries are ready. The lean months of late spring are the times when quinces and especially wardens, the cooking pears celebrated in medieval banquets, are transformed by months of mellowing and hours of gentle baking from gritty cannonballs to delicate accompaniments to spring lamb or sweet puddings.

Wild and cultivated fruit trees such as damsons, bullaces,

Old orchards needn't disappear under new developments. This is one of two Community Orchards at Highfield Park in St Albans that new and old residents of the neighbourhood can enjoy and eat from.

The magnificent 18-metre standard cherries which once helped to define the north Kent landscape are now a rarity.

plums, cherry-plums and crab apples were commonly grown in the hedgerows as linear orchards for additional crops and as wind breaks. Local preferences led to particular patterns developing such as damson hedges in Shropshire and Kent, cherry-plum in Oxfordshire and bullace in Essex.

The social working of orchards – the need for many hands at harvest time – and the seasonal celebrations which punctuate the orchard calendar have fostered the evolution of songs, recipes and traditions that vary from place to place. Cheshire damson cheese, Somerset wassailing, apple gifting and St Clement's songs have been revived or re-invigorated in recent years, or superceded by new activities such as longest peel competitions, a popular activity at a more recent invention – Apple Day (21 October) initiated by Common Ground in 1990.

Orchard loss

Figures gathered throughout the 1990s from Ministry of Agriculture Fisheries and Food (MAFF), the Countryside Commission and local authorities, the Women's Institute, Wildlife Trusts and a wide variety of individuals, speak for themselves:

95 per cent of traditional orchards lost in Wiltshire since 1945

90 per cent lost in Devon since 1965

75 per cent lost in Gloucestershire since 1945

63 per cent lost in Worcestershire mainly since the 1970s

60 per cent lost in Somerset since 1960s

50 per cent lost in Cumbria since about 1920

40 per cent loss in South Buckinghamshire between 1975 and 1995

The land covered by commercial orchards has declined rapidly too. In 1970 MAFF recorded 62,200 hectares of orchards in the UK. This declined to 46,600 hectares in 1980 and further to 22,400 hectares in 1997. This is a 64 per cent decline in 27 years. It is still continuing.

A traditional orchard amounts to far more than the sum of its parts. Old apple varieties, particular to place or suited to soil, are often found within old orchards and celebrated within the local recipes for pies, puddings or savouries. Locally produced blends of cider are used to wassail the apple trees on Twelfth Night. When a traditional orchard is grubbed up, so much fades away. People lose touch with the land and a visual cue to the passing of seasons. Local pride, power and generations of accumulated wisdom about the soil, the climate, the trees and the fruit are degraded. The blossom, the birds, the bees, countless other invisible orchard residents, and the peace of the orchard simply as a wonderful place to linger, all evaporate. It is reckoned that the British have discovered more ways of grafting than of cooking an egg. The loss of orchards and the standardisation of horticultural practice discourage the development of any more.

Despite the efforts of many individuals, councils, communities and agencies, old orchards are still in a precarious position. We have lost so many in so few years, mainly in the wake of cheap imported fruit, the intensification of agriculture and pressures from land development. British growers have been encouraged to grub up commercial orchards with European grants, even though the money was meant for areas of over-production, such as Italy and France.

Local authorities – strategies and policies

Local authorities need to think more carefully about the impact of their planning and development control practice. Many small, rich orchards have been lost in villages and towns through the routine application of infill policies and through allowing developers to clear land of trees before building. Councils have an enormously important role to play in celebrating the richness that orchards bring to places. Many councils, especially those in counties which have been partly defined by their orchard economies and cultures, have recognised and protected old orchards in strategic policies including Local Plans,

Landscape and Environment Strategies and Biodiversity Action Plans. This ought to be a minimum target for every authority.

As ordinary people everywhere have rediscovered that orchards offer so much, they have looked to local councils to help them make a start to restore and replant new orchards. Cornwall, Somerset, Gloucestershire, Worcestershire, Kent and Shropshire are county councils that provide grants and advice, at varying levels of support, to help orchard owners or Community Orchard Groups to restore, maintain and make better use of local orchards. Some authorities have worked hard, mainly thanks to the efforts and enthusiasm of individual officers, to create circumstances where local fruit varieties are available to residents and orchards are valued within local policies. One such officer is Richard Fawcett, Senior Landscape Officer at Gloucestershire County Council. His own words can best describe his authority's achievements putting orchards firmly back in the frame in Gloucestershire:

Seventy-five per cent of Gloucestershire's orchards have been lost in the last 50 years, mainly though agricultural changes, foreign competition and supermarket pressures. Despite this decline, Gloucestershire still has areas where orchards form strong traditional landscape character. The Berkeley Vale and Dymock areas contain a noticeable number of orchards with many local varieties.

The early 1990s saw an orchard revival, not least with the initiation by Common Ground of Apple Day. Survey work carried out by the County Council in 1991 led to a 'Landscape Strategy'. The plight of orchards became noticed. At the same time public interest awoke.

In 1992 the then County Planning Department began a grant scheme called 'Restoring our Landscape', as a follow-on to the 'Landscape Strategy'. From the 'Strategy' assessment, key neglected landscape features, including orchards, were chosen to become target areas for action. The grant offers up to 30 per cent of the total cost up to a maximum of £500/scheme/year. The main condition is that the proposal must be seen from a footpath or road.

Over the past seven years the scheme has supported the planting of over 2,500 fruit trees. The main problem has been finding local varieties. Despite this, HP Bulmer, the cider makers, and Thornhayes Nursery in Devon are grafting Gloucestershire varieties onto standard and maiden

stems ready to sell. The coming three years will see the creation of Gloucestershire County Fruit Trees, a local public source of distinctive county varieties.

In 1999 Gloucestershire County Council in partnership with Charles Martell, a Dymock farmer and fruit-variety collector, created a collection of Gloucestershire orchard trees as a Millennium project in the form of a Mother Tree Orchard, which is located on a county-owned farm near Cheltenham. Local varieties have been located, identified and propagated over the past 10 years to create a public bank of Mother Trees.

Local people will be able to buy varieties to help restore their orchards or simply plant individual trees. At a later stage, a new Orchard Centre for Rural Interpretation to act as a focal point for education, historical information, demonstration and training is also planned. Meanwhile, the Mother Tree Orchard will safeguard the future of local fruit varieties.

There are 157 recorded Gloucestershire apple varieties of which only 86 are still known to be in existence. There are also dozens of varieties of pear local to the county. Many of the varieties have names that reflect their origins within the county such as Chaxhill Red, Arlington Pippin, Severnbank, Gillyflower of Gloucester and Blakeney Red, a perry pear.

January 2000 saw the first planting in the Museum Orchard. The objective here is to establish all the Gloucestershire varieties as M25 rootstock standards in locations where they will form traditional orchards. To begin this project, the County Council, working with The National Trust, has agreed to set up a project base at The Old Ebworth Centre, near Birdlip. The Centre has the remnants of an old walled orchard which formed part of the grounds of Ebworth House (now demolished). We have planted 46 standard trees as stem builders with a view to grafting Gloucestershire varieties as top grafts in future. Meanwhile, other local varieties will be propagated and grown on by nurseries to be replanted at the other identified locations to create up to six hectares of new orchard to accommodate the county collection.

Ebworth will also act as a future Orchard Interpretation Centre with scope for further research and education of the value of the genetic bank that is being established here. This vision for the return of the county's wealth of distinctive fruit trees starts in earnest in this new millennium. In addition to the grant aid, we have put together an information pack listing local varieties, suppliers and advice on planting. Overall, orchard loss has now stabilised especially with public interest in old apple varieties. Farm shops and markets are also helping re-establish a taste revival, with local apple and plum selections. It will take time to re-educate people's

Bagged cider apples, Iddesleigh, Devon. The fruit is gathered up from the ground once it has fallen or been shaken down. Hand-gathered fruit is in great demand by West Country cider-makers. Photo: James Ravilious.

palates. This is important, as we need to have a market for traditional varieties other than home consumption. But we feel the tide has turned.

Seeing it from the planners' point of view

Many old orchards are grubbed up for development. Sometimes, the permission given for this to happen is granted despite local opposition. In Chestfield near Whitstable in Kent, permission was given by the local council to develop the one small remaining orchard in a parish that was once surrounded by them. Local people felt the orchard should be saved and tried to offer their thoughts on the matter at a meeting on location with the planners and councillors. The trouble was, the development proposals didn't actually contravene any policies in the Local Plan – the document that guides council decisions on planning policy.

So groups fighting to save old orchards need to know how to navigate a way through the planners' world. Amanda Matthews, a landscape architect working for Harrogate Borough Council, explained how orchards are viewed by the planners in her council at a conference, Old Orchards in the Landscape, jointly organised by the Northern Fruit Group, the College of Ripon & York St John and Common Ground in November 1999. Harrogate Council is currently working with a group of local people to oppose the development of an old orchard. Part of Amanda's presentation is reproduced here:

I asked my planning, horticultural and conservation colleagues at Harrogate Borough Council for their views on the role the Local Planning Authority can play in conserving old orchards in the District. The following comments represent the views of officers rather than the views of Harrogate Borough Council since this issue has not been submitted to the Council for consideration.

Those Harrogate Borough Council officers who responded to my enquiries supported the concept of protecting orchards where they are considered to be a valuable resource. Suggested criteria for assessing importance include:

• orchards or particular fruit trees that are an important element of local landscape character, for example, orchards in settlements in the Vale of York (Cattal, Moor Monkton), apple trees at Appleton-le-Moor;

• orchards or particular fruit trees that are an important element of a Conservation Area, for instance, cherry trees at Whixley;

• orchards that contain representative, rare or particularly local fruit tree varieties – for instance, Ribston Pippin at Ribston Hall;

• orchards that make an important contribution to the settlement form and general amenity as 'amenity open space'.

My colleagues also considered ways in which the planning system could protect orchards. These included:

• using existing Local Plan Policies for protection of landscape character, Conservation Area character and amenity open space to cover those orchards identified as important in Supplementary Planning Guidance under these policies. A statement that orchards may be important in landscape character terms can be included in the supplementary/ justification text for these policies at the next Local Plan Review. A specific 'orchards' policy was not considered appropriate, in the same way there is no specific policy for Greens or Veteran Trees;

• identify orchards where these are characteristic and include guidelines for their conservation and protection as part of the forthcoming update of the District-wide landscape character assessment;

• identify and acknowledge old orchards as Characteristic Elements of a Conservation Area in Conservation Area Statements (where appropriate) to make their importance to the character of the area clear. Specific review to include old orchards would not be justified but where the boundary of a Conservation Area needs comprehensive review for other reasons, which we are statutorily required to do 'from time to time', any old orchards within or on the periphery of settlements could be included (if they are not already) which would then confer interim protection to allow a TPO to be made;

• where development is proposed, include existing orchards within the site into proposed Public Open Space where possible. There were different views expressed on this issue: a senior planning officer was concerned that there would be maintenance problems and risk of vandalism, and commented that if the orchard was considered an important feature it would be better to avoid development of the site. A senior officer in the Parks Section commented that various considerations should be taken into account when making the decision whether to retain such orchards,

Traditional orchard, Whimple, Devon. The tall standard trees allow for seasonal undergrazing once they are established. Photo: James Ravilious.

including proximity to buildings – fruit trees are a magnet to children and youths and this can cause major problems for nearby residents – and that it could be necessary to undertake an assessment of the fruit trees to determine if the varieties were worth retaining. He would be interested to see how these areas would be managed. Local authorities have shrinking budgets and if it was necessary to propagate and reintroduce varieties this could be problematic. However, the senior Parks officer commented that although there would be concern about introducing an additional financial burden, if assistance was forthcoming then it would be of benefit to try to retain old orchards.

I asked our Legal Section to clarify the position on TPOs for fruit trees and they said:

A TPO may be made in respect of fruit trees, but the consent of the LPA is not required for the pruning, in accordance with good horticultural practice, of any tree cultivated for the production of fruit. This exemption could apply to most varieties of apple, pear, plums and cherries that are normally pruned to encourage fruit production, but not to ornamental varieties of these species or such trees as Mulberry or Walnut. Confusion on this point has arisen in the past because the 1969 Regulations allowed for the cutting down or carrying out work on fruit trees which were 'cultivated for fruit production growing or standing. . . in an orchard or garden' without the need to obtain the prior consent of the LPA. The exemption in the new 1999 Regulations is much narrower.

A Senior Horticultural Officer commented that Vale Royal Borough Council protected an entire orchard which was subsequently given almost 'heritage' status.

These views demonstrate the acknowledgement by local planning authority officers that old orchards do have an important role in the landscape that we have inherited and that there is a commitment to conserving orchards as part of our future landscapes.

Up against the Crown

Some places, such as Carhampton in Somerset, have orchards at their heart and soul. A long and continuing tradition of wassailing can be traced back to at least 1752 – when the Julian calendar was changed to the current Gregorian – by the celebration of Twelfth Night on 17 January, rather than the sixth day of the month. Wassail Close in the village is yet more evidence of the custom's local prevalence. One old orchard, which lies in the centre of the village by the traffic lights on

the main Minehead Road, and constitutes the only open green area in Carhampton, is owned by the Crown Commissioners and was submitted for planning permission in 1989. Parish Councillor Nancy Holt takes up the story:

Several villagers called a public meeting in our Village Hall. The meeting was packed and we unanimously decided we must fight this application in every way possible. We formed a 'Save Our Orchard' committee, had a collection to help with the expense of the fight, sent objections to the local District Council including all the objections we could think of. Also we sent a petition of objection with 600+ signatures. The committee decided we must give it as much publicity as possible. Huge posters saying 'Save Our Orchard' were erected at either end of the village and we wrote reports to all the local papers. HTV's Points West and Radio Bristol came and made broadcasts and were very interested.

In what we think was a stroke of luck, the Crown Commissioners changed their agents, who agreed to meet with us. We were pleased to find that the new agents were more interested in conservation and complimented us on our publicity, which of course they did not like. Hooray! They withdrew the planning application and we were all very pleased. Still, we felt we must continue to be aware of any similar issues.

Then to our horror we had a terrific gale one night which brought down eight apple trees. After some legal wrangling the Commissioners allowed us to plant some new trees and to prune and stake them on our Apple Day celebrations each year. We feel that Apple Day has helped maintain interest in the orchard and villagers now keep a keen eye on anything happening there.

In 1996 the Crown Commissioners offered to lease the orchard to Carhampton Parish Council for a period of 25 years on condition that a management plan was prepared. A committee was established to pursue charitable status and the Carhampton Community Orchard officially came into being. Wassailing and Apple Day continue and draw in an increasingly far-flung audience.

Weaving orchards into the system

By making room for old orchards within the system, plans can take account of their importance for wild life, local landscape or as places that people value. Finding a way into the many policies and plans which local authorities and others apply can be daunting. Here are some of the most appropriate mechanisms/strategies into which orchards can be written.

Biodiversity Action Plans: After the Rio Earth Summit in 1992, all nation signatories to Agenda 21, including Britain, agreed to work to stop the loss of any more species, to live sustainably without jeopardising the needs of future generations and to enhance the quality of life of their citizens through environmental, economic and health improvements.

Back home at the county level, the first steps towards achieving these aims are being drawn up within Local Biodiversity Action Plans. Orchards feature in a number of these documents as Habitat Action Plans, in counties including Essex, Herefordshire, Gloucestershire, Kent and Worcestershire.

Local plans: Few local authorities make any special recognition of orchards within their planning guidance, partly because of the difficulties in categorising them. Do they constitute farm, horticultural or woodland? Exceptions include Teignbridge in Devon, Exmoor National Park Authority and Taunton Deane, in Somerset. However, councils in Herefordshire and Worcestershire are hoping to include orchards in new Local Plans.

Carhampton residents have worked together to save their orchard in Somerset. Photo: James Ravilious

Landscape strategies: These are non-statutory statements that outline council policies on the local landscape. Orchards have been included in a number of these and some councils, such as Somerset and Worcestershire, have grants to conserve and replant orchards for landscape benefit.

Sites of Special Scientific Interest: SSSIs are statutory designations made by English Nature, and its counterparts in Scotland and Wales, and follow strict criteria relating to the nature conservation value of a place (based largely on the number and rarity of species contained in a habitat deemed 'natural' or 'semi-natural'). Orchards are not currently viewed as being worthy of SSSI status in their own right, although a handful of old orchards survive by accident rather than by design in wider SSSIs in areas such as in the Teme Valley in Shropshire and Herefordshire as well as in Cumbria. The trouble is that the orchards currently included are not valued as orchards per se and are not specifically managed as such. Thus they are often neglected and allowed to become scrub land in a relatively short time. Our 1999 conference with English Nature on Orchards and Wild Life revealed the importance of seeing orchards as wood pasture, given the richness of habitats they can offer.

County designations: Some counties, such as Kent and Herefordshire, have established their own designations relating to wild life which include orchards for their lichen, bird or invertebrate interest.

Local Nature Reserves: LNRs can be designated by English Nature in collaboration with a local authority or, by delegation a parish or town council, who must also have some formal interest in the land in question. Only one orchard, a Community Orchard at Lingfield, has been awarded LNR status as part of a larger reserve. There is much scope for making the most of this designation, and English Nature offers grants to help with LNR management. The leader of the Kent English Nature team, Simon Richardson, has written an Orchards Advice note (No 10 in the Common Ground series) on how Community Orchards can be so designated.

Tree Preservation Orders: Some councils still think that fruit trees cannot be protected by Tree Preservation Orders, but they are mistaken. After much discussion with the Department of the Environment (now DETR) by Common Ground and others, TPOs can now more clearly protect fruit trees, where it is in the interests of amenity to do so. They cannot control tree work in ongoing commercial orchards, but they may be used to protect trees in relict orchards that are no longer cultivated for fruit production. TPO regulations in operation since 1999 have been strengthened in favour of fruit trees (see Amanda Matthews' earlier contribution).

For further advice, contact your local district council's tree officer or the DETR for guidance notes (see appendices for details).

Other organisations: Other agencies with interest in and influence over land use must also play their part. Recent collaborations with English Nature seem to be paving the way for more orchards to be included in

Cross O' Cliff Community Orchard, Lincoln. Photomontage: Claire Peasnall

wild life conservation measures. Through its 'Eat the View' campaign, the Countryside Agency is encouraging the development of new schemes in which local fruit can be woven back into the local food economy. National Park Authorities, including Exmoor and the Lake District, offer grants for orchard research and restoration.

Gathering support

The strong feelings which orchards engender can be their saving grace. Ordinary people all over the country have fought hard battles, and sometimes lost them, in efforts to save old orchards which, it seems, are valued by no-one else and are destined for the bonfire. The story of saving Cross O'Cliff orchard, on the edge of Lincoln, shows something of the difficulties which determination and local support can overcome. The key message is Never Give Up.

In 1991 Lincolnshire County Council proposed planning permission for itself on an area of green land it owned which includes Cross O'Cliff, an orchard containing 60 very old pear trees. Local residents were drawn into the fray barely a month before the planning inquiry started, when they began to realise the orchard's significance and sought expert advice from a local retired engineer, Albert Skinner.

Albert looked at the orchard and from the girth and condition of the trees dated their planting at around 1850. He felt they were all capable of regeneration despite long years of neglect. Claire Peasnall, who has been a driving force behind the initiative to save Cross O'Cliff orchard from the start, continues:

Common Ground urged us to assemble a picture of Lincolnshire's remaining orchards. Fired by Common Ground's and Arthur's enthusiasm we contacted the Countryside Commission (now Countryside Agency) which was about to include traditional orchards in the newly-launched Stewardship Scheme for Historic Landscapes.

Although we knew that only scattered trees survived in the city, county figures from the Ministry of Agriculture, Fisheries and Food were a shock: it seemed that in the post-war period Lincolnshire's orchards had been felled almost to extinction. From Arthur we'd learned that pears at this

latitude have reached their northernmost limit; suddenly we began to see the extraordinary nature of the orchard.

While there was insufficient time before the inquiry for the Commission to make a visit, from our detailed description they were able to indicate to the inspector that the orchard appeared to be the perfect target for Countryside Stewardship. Our own submission, backed by the Ramblers' Association, the Civic Trust, the Lincoln Society, nature and conservation groups and the local schools' inspectorate, argued for the orchard's educational and leisure potential. A survey we had made in 1986/7 illustrated the range of wild life it supports, including many protected species. Our case was, that in the light of current initiatives to preserve England's traditional orchards, it would be irresponsible of the Lincolnshire County Council to sell the Cross O'Cliff orchard for development.

After the inquiry, while Claire and her colleagues waited for a decision, the Countryside Commission steadfastly backed their plans and confirmed their eligibility for a 10-year restoration and maintenance grant. During the summer of 1992, local residents gathered more information about the orchard, including the arrival of the cuckoo and the turtle-dove 'and refuting', in Claire's words 'for our own satisfaction the preposterous assertion by the County Council at the public inquiry, that there were 12 orchards still standing within a 7-kilometre radius of Lincoln.'

Residents also explored the possibility of alternative ownership via the Woodland Trust and from maps in the British Library established the orchard's age at a minimum of 122 years. The orchard was also prominently featured on Woman's Hour on BBC Radio 4, for the considerable role women played throughout.

In the autumn Arthur, with help from Nottinghamshire fruit-grower

John Hempsall, identified 19 varieties of pear, plum and apple including three Lincolnshire apples. One, the Custard apple, boasts a pedigree which dates back to the 13th century.

Finally news came that planning permission was to be granted, and not long afterwards Arthur sadly died. John Hempsall made preparations to salvage some varieties from the orchard to be replanted at his own fruit museum. Six months later a new County Council was elected and the residents were encouraged to make a fresh approach by Common Ground. Reinforced by the Countryside Commission, coupled with a press campaign which yielded articles in *The Guardian*, *The Independent* and *The Daily Telegraph*, rumours turned into reality: the orchard was saved. At a meeting with the council it was a terrific reward, after almost four years, to hear every claim and proposal the campaigners had made for the old orchard upheld.

Individual opposition to the bureaucratic machine will seem difficult. It is best to gather local opinion and form a strong group containing people with a variety of talents including practical skills, knowledge of natural and local history, people who are willing to write to the press or lead fund-raising efforts. Cross O'Cliff orchard is now being managed by the residents' group under the Countryside Stewardship Scheme and has been saved from development for all to enjoy. Residents have organised regular workdays to clear old scrub and plant boundary hedges and new fruit trees. A focus for Apple Day celebrations, the orchard is becoming increasingly valued by people in the vicinity and from further afield as well as by wild life, which includes visiting nightingales and nesting woodpeckers.

Old orchards are a rare testament to the commonplace. Their age is a celebration of continuity in an increasingly transient world. Some orchards are like museums of living artefacts, within which more

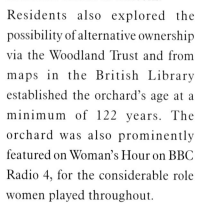

A young campaigner lends his support to efforts to stop a Totnes orchard being turned into a car park.

Former orchard, Eggesford, Devon. Grubbing grants encouraged many growers to throw in the towel. Now grants are available to restore old orchards, rather than destroy them. Photo: James Ravilious.

life thrives. Their greatest asset, however is their inspiration for the future. They offer suggestions for better land use, for social collaboration and for the continuation of learning. The feelings which old orchards can release within us have inspired artists and underscore local distinctiveness – imagine Somerset or Kent or Cheshire without their very different orchards. There is something of the mysterious about old orchards, too. Not darkly brooding, like an ancient wood, but welcoming, warm and often fragrant. It is vital that the experiences that old orchards inspire persist so that places, people and nature can continue their conspiracy.

Planting New Orchards

ORCHARDS CAPTURE people's imagination as a marriage of the cool serenity of woodlands with the ordered abundance of gardens. In recent years, a new impetus to plant has emerged, not least through the interest generated by Common Ground's Apple Day and Community Orchards work. Orchards take time to come into being. We need to plant now a succession of new orchards – as well as gapping up established ones – for the future. The experiences of all these new orchardists can reveal some of the opportunities, problems and processes that you may need to consider when deciding when, where and how to plant a new orchard.

In 1998, the Hertfordshire Orchards Initiative was set up to celebrate the value of the county's orchards and fruit varieties. Its first conference attracted almost 100 people. At the first opportunity, a member of the audience raised the problem that, without appropriate skills, ordinary people could not help to restore flagging orchards. No sooner said, and Neil Holmes-Smith, a horticultural lecturer, was on his feet offering to lead a training course in pruning, planting, grafting and budding. Within a few weeks, 12 people had signed up for 10 monthly classes at Tewin Orchard where a rootstock nursery was grafted with local apple varieties or those growing happily in East Hertfordshire.

In the autumn of 2000, the first Millennium Orchards were ready to be planted with the young apples, pears and cherries. A request has been submitted to the Ordnance Survey to identify the Millennium Orchards on any new maps.

Before planting new orchards, try to carry out local research. Perhaps the first question to address is: 'why do we want an orchard?' Community Orchards are not planted solely with an eye to making a profit, and so offer opportunities that are quite different from commercial enterprises. Many basic skills needed for successful planting and husbandry are likely to be present within the group of people proposing the new orchard. Help and advice may be available locally, as well as horticultural books by the library-full. The advice will raise as many questions as it answers, all of which need to be discussed communally. For example, some people may

> *The holes were already dug, and they set to work.*
>
> *Winterbourne's fingers were endowed with a gentle conjurer's touch in spreading the roots of each little tree, resulting in a sort of caress under which the delicate fibres all laid themselves out in the proper directions for growth. He put most of these roots towards the south-west; for, he said, in forty years' time, when some great gale is blowing from that quarter, the trees will require the strongest holdfast on that side to stand against it and not fall.*
>
> from *The Woodlanders* by Thomas Hardy, 1888

This 48-hectare perry pear orchard at Combe Florey, Somerset, was grubbed out in 1992 with £30,000 worth of pears to make way for subsidised arable crops. It was one of the biggest of its kind in the country. Photo: James Ravilious.

advise planting dwarfing trees for ease of maintenance, while others may recommend vigorous standards that will feed the whole street, attract birds and look wonderful. Think hard about how to re-inforce local distinctiveness.

A good way of gauging local opinion is to have a public meeting, perhaps linked to an orchard visit, to introduce the idea. Ask a local orchard owner to host an Apple Day or invite someone from another town or village to talk about their own experiences. Many counties have active new orchard societies who could give presentations. Ask the County Record Office or local archive library to show you early maps of where orchards were. Most people are surprised to find the spectres of lost orchards on old maps.

Ground rules

Before spending anything up to £20 on apple saplings, make sure the land you have chosen for the orchard is suitable. In 1995 the people of Hatherleigh in North Devon were disappointed to experience the death of their new Community Orchard because water-logging had drowned the trees. Apples like well-drained soil, while pears and plums don't mind damper, heavier soils quite so much, although both need more sun and shelter.

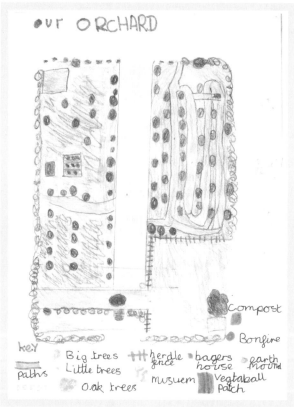

Pupils of Gurnard School on the Isle of Wight mapped the orchard they adopted in 1994.

Walnuts don't like light sandy soils, where cobnuts may do better. It's best to ask local gardeners and allotment holders what will grow well locally, and walk around to discover which fruits are locally productive. Plums and pears flower early, usually late March and April respectively, so care must be taken not to plant these fruits where they may be affected by late frosts. Choose sunshine! Southern slopes are good for apples, providing them with most sun and good drainage. South-western or northern slopes can be even better because they allow slow defrosting of the blossom before the sun is at its strongest. If your blossom suffers a late frost, the damage will occur from sun-scorching which is magnified through the ice, not from the frost itself. Avoid the east!

Choosing varieties

Plant what grows best in the locality – perry pears in Gloucestershire, cherries and cobnuts in north Kent and so on. Try to grow local varieties that have been raised in local conditions. There will be plenty; after all, we have named 6,000 varieties of apple alone. Choose some at least from your county and any which were raised locally. They will help to reinforce local identity and bolster local pride as well as being suited to local soil and weather conditions. For example, some west-country cherries display resistance to canker, while their Kentish cousins are better at coping with mildew and the east wind. The Cox may dominate the commercial scene in Britain, but this delicate apple won't thrive in many areas without cocktails of pricey chemicals.

Blaisdon Red plums are reputed to 'flourish with the health and vigour of a weed' within a five-mile radius of Blaisdon in west Gloucestershire, 'but with few exceptions it does not thrive elsewhere', according to local writer and grower Humphrey Phelps. Varieties such as these may be growing unsung in the surrounding gardens and farms. The local horticultural society or nursery may be able to provide root suckers (of Blaison Reds or Dittisham plums, for instance) or take grafts for you or show you how – it is surprisingly easy. These grafts need to be put onto vigorous rootstock to produce standard or half standard trees. Alternatively, try taking cuttings. The fruit from trees that are not grafted onto rootstock is reputed to taste better.

Planting distances vary with different kinds of fruit, different varieties and local practice. Local enthusiasts such as gardeners, farmers and nurseries could provide valuable advice.

If the orchard is to be grazed, stock-proof fencing and tree guards need to be put up, and the stock will need a supply of water. But if your orchard is not grazed, the hay should be cut and removed after the wild flowers have set seed. The less you use in the way of artificial fertilisers, herbicides and pesticides, the more wild flowers, insects, birds and mammals you will attract. Pest control could be easier too. One ornithologist has observed that dock is one of the favourite food plants of bullfinches, and its removal from orchards may be one of the reasons why the birds resort to the buds of pears and other fruit trees. The variety you choose could also make a difference. In *The Cultivated Fruits of Britain*, Frederick Roach writes: 'The buds of Conference, Williams' Bon Chretien and Merton Pride are particularly attractive to bullfinches, whereas those of Doyenné du Comice and Beurré Hardy are often left alone.'

Orchards are ideal places for bees and for keeping hives. They help to pollinate the fruit and provide you with orchard honey – another source of good food and income.

Remember that Community Orchards have different objectives to those of commercial growers. How you look after them will depend on the orchard in question, but it should be as much for people, wild life and the landscape as for fruit production.

If you can't find what you want, a number of quality nurseries will carry out grafting to order, given time, and deliver plants through the post. To help you choose which fruits you like, visit local farms, attend Apple Day tastings or refer to the section of fruit suppliers in the back of this book. The Community Orchard Group will appreciate a trial run of beefings, beurrés and burcombes, perhaps washed down with perries, ciders, cordials or plum wines made with varieties which you can grow locally.

Lingfield and Dormansland Parish Council in Surrey was concerned that its local apple, the Lingfield Forge, had suffered great losses in the Great Gale of 1987. A search of garden trees unearthed just a few old specimens. Action to save this parish pearl was needed, but no nurseries seemed to stock the local variety. Finally, cuttings from existing trees were taken for grafting at the Brogdale Horticultural Trust, and a new Community Orchard of mixed fruit including the Lingfield Forge was planted in 1999 as part of the Centenary Fields Local Nature Reserve.

Basic steps for planting

Here are some tips for buying and planting standards – the tall, vigorous trees found in traditional orchards – compiled with the help of Chris Fairs of Bulmers.

Where to plant: Learn from history. Visit your local studies library and have a look at first-edition Ordnance Survey or old tithe maps. These will show where orchards used to grow and could indicate areas of good drainage, shelter or frost resistance. Tithe maps often have commentaries that may describe the fruits grown. The traces of old nurseries or fruit farms around towns may indicate suitable soils and guide your choice of varieties which may have been raised there.

As a rule of thumb, make sure the fruit tree is planted in well-drained land. Choose areas that provide shelter from the prevailing weather direction and enough sunshine to ripen the fruit. If your intended area is prone to frost, plant late-flowering varieties. If you are planting on a slope, plant early-cropping varieties. Hillside apple harvests can get very messy in November. Don't plant in ground prone to water-logging. Seek out suitable plots of land and sympathetic landholders. Ask your local council if it has any potential land in its ownership (such as disused allotments).

It may be necessary to form a trust to look after any land bought by or donated to the parish or community. Ask the parish clerk and/or a solictor for advice. It may well be better to buy or lease a field that fulfils your needs, rather than to accept land that is given for a Community Orchard if the conditions are wrong. When selecting a place for a Community Orchard, try to find somewhere that is close to the centre of the community. Is there easy access to water and protection against browsing visitors such as wild deer?

Buying tips: Buy from a reputable nursery. Order well in advance if you want unusual varieties. When buying a young standard tree – that is one which will grow tall with one main, thick trunk – be sure to save yourself later work by buying a 'feathered maiden'. These will have a well-balanced crown, with perhaps four or five young branches coming off the leading vertical shoot.

Make sure you buy the right rootstock for your situation. Rootstocks come in a variety of degrees of vigour, ordered within a numerical system that seems to make no real sense. For example, M25

is a traditional and very vigorous rootstock good for growing standard trees. MM111 and M2 are also good for standards or half standards, while M9 and M27 rootstocks will produce dwarf trees that will require staking throughout their lives. Seek advice from a good nursery. You might also consider growing a tree on its own roots (discussed later in this chapter).

When to plant: Plant in winter if you can, when the tree is dormant. Anytime between December and February should do, but planting before Christmas usually means the soil still has some warmth, which helps the tree to establish.

Planting tips for full-size standard trees: Drive a tall stake, 2.5-3 metres high, into the ground leaving around two metres above the ground. The stake should be about 10 centimetres thick. Dig the planting hole to the lee of the stake. For example, if the wind is normally south-westerly, dig your planting hole to the north-east of the stake. This will allow the stake to do its job well.

If your orchard is not grazed by stock, you could try using a smaller stake. A stake protruding only three-quarters of a metre or so above the ground will be enough to steady the sapling but will let it be blown around by the wind and weather. This buffeting will encourage it to establish firm roots. Some now argue that planting a small tree without a stake challenges the sapling to really good roothold as it rocks in its first winter winds.

A stark warning: how not to plant, Scott's nursery, Somerset.

Planting the new Community Orchard where the farm orchard once grew by the Friends of Horsenden Hill, Perivale, west London, with help from Yvonne Sharp of Oaklands College.

Dig the hole 30-40 centimetres deep or as appropriate for the root ball. If using a stake, it should be in line with the centre of the hole. Try to plant the tree about 10 centimetres from the stake. Rotate the tree in the hole to obtain the best fit. It is vital to plant the tree at the same soil level as it was in the nursery (you can tell this level by the soil mark left around the base of the trunk). All roots should be adequately covered with soil mixed with well-rotted manure or organic fertiliser. Trim away any damaged roots with sharp secateurs and do not leave any roots that are up-turned.

Do not put coarse turf into the hole. Shake the tree gently while filling the hole and carefully firm the earth with your heel (paying special attention to the area between the stake and the tree) to avoid air pockets forming around the roots. Do NOT cover the rootstock union (where scion and rootstock meet) or you will kill the tree. Make a note to wassail the tree between Christmas Eve and Twelfth Night, according to local custom.

Hole dont's: Don't dig holes too far in advance of planting

Don't leave holes open overnight

Don't plant in wet holes

Fitting a tie: Make a tie out of a strip of strong flexible material such as old bike tyres or old tights about 50-60 centimetres long. Nail or tie this three centimetres down from the top in the rear centre of the stake. Pass the tie around the tree in a figure of eight. Fasten the tie so that it holds the tree firmly upright and allows no chafing against the stake. The tie will have to be slackened as the tree grows to prevent it cutting into the trunk.

Rabbit/sheep/deer guard: To fit a stock-proof guard made of chicken wire, either staple the wire to the sides of the stake, or make three snips in one of selvedges and loop ends through the opposite side, fitting the guard between the tree and the stake. Ensure the base of the guard is gently bedded into the soil. Make sure the top spikey ends of the wire are turned slightly outwards. Place some upside-down turf strips around the base of the guard to allow for sinkage.

Mulching: Mulch an area of up to one metre around the base of the tree with suitable material such as clippings or chippings or well-rotted manure. This will keep competing weeds at bay and help to retain soil moisture and warmth.

Aftercare: Pour a bucket of water immediately over the planted area. This will help to drive out any air pockets. Keep well watered, especially during the first summer and occasionally thereafter if necessary. Don't forget to slacken the ties as the tree matures and remove the stake altogether when the tree is strong enough to support itself and its guard. Finally, wait and watch....

Shelter belts: Orchards in windy areas will benefit from shelter-belts. Commercial plantations commonly plant rows of fast-growing poplars or alders to break the breeze. These species are vigorous and are cut to encourage upright, dense growth. In a Community Orchard it may be more manageable to plant a mixed fruiting hedge that will prolong the flowering season for pollen-seeking insects including honeybees. Don't cut out elder or bash your brambles if these are thriving in an existing hedge. Brambles may tend to get a bit rampant but blackberries are a must for apple pies, and elderflowers make lovely cordials and can be fried in batter. Their purple berries make a mellow wine. In Leicestershire elders are being grown in orchards in their own right.

Access: In the early years of establishment, young fruit trees are delicate. Vandalism can be an expensive problem but usually happens in places where the vandals have no connection or affection for the orchard. Rangers in the London Borough of Barking and Dagenham are working through the Local Agenda 21 network to get young people into Mark's Gate Community Orchard, an old mixed-fruit orchard surviving on a strip of land adjacent to the A13. It is a remnant of a much larger fruit farm that once supplied Covent Garden.

It is dispiriting to have to spend precious funds on new trees that keep being broken. Apple Day is a good way of getting people of all ages interested in orchards, through social celebration and making sure there is plenty of work for idle hands. Antisocial behaviour, just like depression or ill health, can sometimes begin to be tackled by offering the chance of using the orchard and contributing to its care. *Planting from pips:* The surest and quickest way of achieving the variety you desire is from a grafted sapling. Another method that is finding favour because of the strength of the resulting tree is planting fruit trees from pips. This is actually nothing new. Some of our best-loved varieties are chance seedlings. Keswick Codlin, a dual-purpose apple from Cumbria, was found growing among rubbish behind a wall in Gleaston Castle in the 18th century; Bramley's Seedling, the best-selling British cooker, was raised from seed by Mary Anne Brailsford in Southwell, Nottinghamshire, almost 200 years ago. The original tree still survives, having fallen over and rooted itself on an elbow. Phil Corbett of the Own-Root Fruit Tree (ORFT) Project now under way in Gloucestershire outlines some of the benefits and bounties behind raising a Jones' Pippin or a Singh's Superb.

This project is based on the unpublished work of Hugh Ermen, formerly of Brogdale Horticultural Experimental Station and now retired and breeding new varieties of fruit trees. Unfortunately, Hugh's own-root trees at Brogdale have now been destroyed for redevelopment of the site. The ORFT Project is busy propagating own-root trees for planting in our trial grounds at Ragman's Lane Farm in Gloucestershire.

Hugh discovered that there are several advantages in growing apples on their own roots – that is, not grafted onto a rootstock. The graft union, which is a union between two genetically different individuals, always creates a degree of incompatibility. Not having this incompatibility, own-root trees were found to have better health and better fruit quality. The only disadvantage of own-root trees is that most varieties are more vigorous than is usually wanted. This means that trees may make a lot of wood at the expense of fruit bud production, giving big trees that take a long time to come into crop. Conventionally this vigour is controlled by grafting onto a dwarfing rootstock. With trees on their own roots, however, a number of traditional techniques can induce early cropping. Once cropping begins, the tree's energies are channelled into fruit production and growth slows down to a controllable level. The techniques that are usually sufficient to bring about cropping are:
• withholding nitrogen, which would stimulate growth, and withholding irrigation, except in serious drought;
• tying down one- and two-year-old branches to the horizontal. This induces fruit bud formation;
• prune in summer to stimulate fruit buds to form, and avoid winter pruning which stimulates regrowth.

Once cropping has begun, a normal feeding and watering regime can begin. The average cropping own-root tree can be maintained at a size very similar to the same variety on MM106 rootstock.

Own-root fruit trees may be just as 'coppice-able' as other trees, and may be useful where damage from gales, animals or vandals is likely.

Coppice-ability is also the basis of our 'Coppice Orchard' which we began to

plant in winter 1998/99. This consists of about four-tenths of a hectare of own-root trees planted in rows running north-south. When the canopy of the orchard closes, a north-south row will be coppiced and the land in the row used for light-demanding crops – for instance, vegetables on a no-dig system, while the trees regrow. The trees either side of the glade will have higher light levels on their sides and produce more fruit buds. The next year another north-south row is cut but not the immediate neighbour as this will have the extra buds, so the next row for coppicing will be next-door-but-one. In other words, this will be alternate-row coppicing. This process is repeated every year, creating a series of parallel, sheltered glades. Eventually the rows of trees forming the avenues between the glades will also be coppiced in turn,

but by then the 'glade' trees will have regrown to form the avenues. As the trees regrow there will be glades at all stages of regrowth until the cycle repeats itself, and niches for plants suited to full light, semi-shade or heavy shade, creating opportunities for different types of land use.

Apart from apples, the main planting sites of the orchard also have own-root pears and plums, hazelnuts, and nitrogen-fixing trees and shrubs. Instead of

In December 1999, pupils from Walnut Tree Walk School in Lambeth planted four espalier apple trees in the adjacent Roots and Shoots Community Garden.

Fan-shaped apple tree, Royal Horticultural Society Gardens at Wisley.

just producing fruit, the coppice orchard can produce a wide range of crops – small wood, fruit, soft fruit, vegetables, possibly cereals, fungi and the more traditional bees and poultry.

There is an old Chinese proverb that says 'fertility follows in the footsteps of the farmer' which is reworked as the permaculture principle 'Fertility Follows Attention'. In the coppice orchard, there is the potential for producing a great range of our needs in a single system, and productivity should benefit from our attention not being divided between vegetable plot, orchard and woodland. The rotation of crops avoids disease build-ups, and if all residues are returned there should be a build up of fertility. The plan is to include nitrogen-fixing and soil-conditioning plants, plants to support useful insects, nestboxes for birds and bumblebees, small ponds for amphibians and hedgehogs, and generally to maximise the natural diversity, and yields.

Planning a new orchard can be as rewarding as planting it. Researching horticultural considerations will probably unearth a bushel of other information: tales, traditions, recipes and tips. There will be a job for everyone from pouring over maps, interviewing farmers or gardeners and negotiating the availability of land to ironing out conflicting views, fund raising, publicity and buying tools and trees. Many new friends stand to be made along the way, all of whom will benefit in just a few seasons from the fruits of their labours.

When the planting day does arrive, most groups find their horticultural skills can be easily dusted down and used to good effect. Make sure plenty of juice, cider or cakes are on hand for regular rests. The day will be a celebration in itself which may not stop when the last tree is planted.

City and Country

ORCHARDS CAN and should be the centre of communities: city orchards, no less than village and suburb, should offer quiet retreat as well as destinations for learning, working and eating. There is also room for orchards on city streets – not just flowering cherries and ornamental crabs, but real fruit trees from which people can eat. Yet the thought of such communal places engenders dread imaginings in some town halls, of errant youths lobbing fruit at pensioners' windows, or of escalating costs incurred to clear windfalls from the road.

By contrast, many places make much of their municipal orchards and would be much poorer without them. In Seville, for example, the famous bitter oranges (which only the British seem to value for marmalade) lend beauty and much-needed shade to central squares and neighbourhood courtyards. In Britain too, city authorities have celebrated the deep-rooted link they enjoy with fruit growing and which endures in municipal remnant orchards in the hearts of places such as Exeter and in Worcester. New orchards with open access are being planned and planted in city parks and close to housing estates in Manchester, Sheffield and London.

Norwich was described (possibly by Bunyan) as 'either a city in an orchard or an orchard in a city, so equally are the houses and trees planted'. Norwich may not have been unique. Walk around Dartmouth Park, near Highgate in north London, in late April and

Park as orchard at Devonshire Place, Exeter. Photo: James Ravilious.

Crest of Worcestershire County Council, clearly showing the Black Worcester pear. Reproduced with permission from WCC.

you can see, through gaps between the houses, mature pear trees in full bloom. A rooftop vantage-point reveals what seems like an orchard of pears enclosed by the fences and hedges of many back gardens. When the houses were built in the second half of the 19th century, could they have been built around an existing orchard, or did new residents all decide to plant pears? Either way, the neighbourhood is alight with blossom each spring, and in glut years trays of pears marked 'help yourself' appear at gateways .

Old orchards, rural or urban, have proven particularly vulnerable to the developers' chainsaw. Yet alternative outcomes are easily imagined. Developers are usually obliged to provide open spaces within new housing plans. Local authorities need to be encouraged to argue for the retention of the orchard as open space, rather than allow the grubbing up of a neglected but possibly mature orchard of standard trees to be replaced by an off-the-shelf amenity grassland elsewhere in the new estate. New community buildings such as hospitals, schools and local authority offices could include orchards for recuperation, curriculum use and as a supplementary source of fresh fruit.

The residents of a new estate in **Abington, Northampton,** have, over the past five years, negotiated the protection of a 1.2-hectare orchard for neighbourhood use. The orchard, which was part of Billings Mill Farm, survived, with help, the building of 200 new houses by Persimmon Homes between 1994-97. While options for the future of the orchard land are being considered by Persimmon, the new residents enjoy informal access to the orchard, its blossom and fruit,

sharing it with badgers, butterflies and deer. Recently, Persimmon explored the possibility of selling the orchard in lots to adjacent residents. People on the rest of the estate worried that this would exclude them from the orchard and would not guarantee the survival of the enclosed trees. They were supported in their case by Northampton Borough Council's Planning Department, which outlined the orchard as a Green Space in the Local Plan. Collaborations with a local environmental co-op include the possibility of providing advice for residents who are keen to care for the orchard to improve its health and its value to wild life.

Before catching a late summer flight from **Stansted Airport** in Essex, holiday-makers can drop their vehicles off at the long-stay car park and reach up for a Discovery, just one of the varieties of apple, plum and pear trees growing among the cars. Tourists may savour its juicy crispness as a last taste of England before exchanging it for that of exotic olives, peaches or mangoes.

Pre-Reformation monks were commonly buried in orchards, as a place of peace and rest (a return to Eden, perhaps). A visit to **Teynham Church** near Sittingbourne in Kent offers a similar effect, although the apple and cherry orchards that surround it and light up the landscape in spring are outside the graveyard walls.

Corn Close Orchard in Riseley, Bedfordshire, covers 0.6 hectares of glebe land planted with apples by local coppicer Mark Powell in the winter 1995/6. Much of the parish glebe land has been given over to arable farming and both Mark and his vicar saw the orchard as a way of keeping the land available to the parishioners, who are welcome to visit the orchard. Income from the sale of 10 varieties of apple to local shops adds to the patchwork of Mark's living.

New trees are being planted among the century-old veterans at Girton College, Cambridge.
South-facing house walls at Aynho, Northamptonshire, are ideal for growing apricots.
An old orchard survives within suburban gardens in Exeter.

In **Aynho** at the southern-most tip of Northamptonshire, the south-facing walls of ancient sandstone cottages offer support to trained apricots. The cottagers gave the fruits to Lord Cartwright, the local squire, in part-payment for their rent. Flowering in April and still harvested in September, the fruits can be difficult to grow, but the Aynho apricots show that there is nothing new about the notion of orchards in housing estates. This example helps to reinforce the challenge to find room for fruit. Many of the older, courtyard-and-balcony style blocks of flats offer sunny aspects and warm walls for trained pears, figs or apples. Courtyard planters of plums and apples, under which people can come together, sit and relax with a eye towards their playing children, are a feature of the community gardens of some Berlin blocks. Balconies are great places for staked miniature pot-trees, which with very little effort will brighten your view and fill your pie dish. In a dense city block, imagine the enchantment of a small green space with espaliered fruit trees against the walls.

Orchards are everywhere. In Cambridge, the old orchard within the grounds of **Girton College** dates back to at least 1904, when the first reference to it appears in college records. Paul Read, who in recent years has been responsible for mapping and identifying the trees, feels that some of the trees may pre-date the decision to plant the orchard. Most of the oldest specimens are regionally prevalent cookers such as Norfolk Beefing, Peasgood Nonsuch and Bramley. It is quite likely that these trees may be the closest surviving ancestors of the varieties they represent, and the Chivers Seedling (probably a Chivers Delight) may have been supplied by the famous nursery at Histon, now gone, a

few miles up the road. The Blenheim Orange growing in the old orchard is said to be a cutting taken from the original at Woodstock.

In 1943, the trees of Girton's Old Orchard, which include plums, quince, apples and pears, were regarded by the garden steward, Chrystobel Procter, as 'wearing out and no amount of patching can put them right again'. The new orchard was planted in 1948 as a replacement for the old, but the old trees were (thankfully) never grubbed out. Today 400 Girton students can walk in the orchard and help themselves, in competition with the fellows and College staff. Occasionally fruit from this intriguing Cambridgeshire orchard ends up in the college kitchen.

Mapping local orchards

Ilmington, in **Warwickshire**, echoes Norwich, for it seems like a village built within an orchard, and there are apple trees right at the heart of the place, clustered around the church. For some years on Apple Day the Ilmington Women's Institute has been celebrating the environmental, historical and gastronomic delights of the apple, which once played an important role in the local economy.

In 1996 the WI organised an exhibition with maps showing the extent of the existing orchards and historic photos. Guided walks were led through the orchards, grafting and cider-making demonstrations were held, and villagers were refreshed after Apple Day games with appley food. Warwickshire Rural Action, who supported the Apple Day in Ilmington, also funded an artist to work with local people to produce a tapestry of the village showing all the

orchards in blossom. Unveiled in 1999, it is on display in the church. Common Ground's *Apple Map of Britain*, inspired June Small of **Charlton Orchards** to investigate the apples of Somerset and put them on a map. The large number of orchards in Somerset and the range of traditions and folklore attached to apples made the mapping a difficult but interesting task, as June explains:

Apples were associated with magic, with fortune telling and used as a cure for many ills. They were named after Somerset people and places and orchards of cider trees abounded for centuries. A few trees remain and the colourful fruit with wonderful names such as Sheep's Nose, Slack-ma-Girdle, Hoary Morning and Gooseberry Apple can be still found. Avalon, the Isle of Apple Trees, where dead heroes are buried, Carhampton, where the trees are wassailed on Twelfth Night and the modern road names of Bramley Close and Laxton Road are all depicted on the map. Many orchards and cider makers too are to be found and the insects, good and bad for the trees, are pictured.

In September 1989, the **Hampstead Garden Suburb** Horticultural Society organised a 'Great Apple Hunt' to identify garden fruit trees planted by the Garden Suburb Trust and Dame Henrietta Barnett 90 years earlier. More than 40 varieties were found, and a display was exhibited at the first Apple Day in Covent Garden in 1990.

Barbara Bender, a Common Ground board member and resident of **Branscombe** in **Devon**, heard from older villagers that the place was, pretty much, an orchard only fifty years ago. Most local farms included small orchards of cider apples. Many fell gradually into neglect and grubbing grants encouraged many growers to pull them up completely. Yet Barbara and many of her neighbours felt that the relationship between orchards and Branscombe ran too deep to abandon.

She organised an exhibition about orchards which included old maps dating back to the 1790s through the nineteenth century to the present day. The older maps showed more orchards and traced a picture which reflected the memories of the older residents. One man took people on an imaginary walk around the village remembering where the orchards stood. Another resident described the local technique for making cider. Remaining orchards and apple trees were marked on the modern map.

Since the exhibition, at least three orchards have been replanted, by residents and by the National Trust, which owns land in and around Branscombe and have set aside a small patch for apple trees planted by the village school pupils.

Many county groups dedicated to the conservation of old orchards and their fruits are mapping their local orchards in various ways. Some groups, such as the **Northern Fruit Group** and the **Marcher Apple Network**, are independently developing a computerised identification key for their respective county apples. They are also collaborating, along with a number of other counties, on a statistical survey of orchards, based on random sampling of 10-kilometre squares. Added together, these surveys should complement knowledge of how many old orchards remain.

Another approach, pioneered by the **Hertfordshire Biological Records Centre**, gathers historical data from old maps. The record centre first tackled Dacorum, one of 10 district councils, and uncovered references to hundreds of old orchards. Seven of the districts have now been completed including the urban boroughs of Stevenage and Watford, which was an important transport hub for the local cherry culture. Field workers then visit the sites of the old orchards to find out what remains. In time, the records centre aims to map all the county's orchards that conform to agreed specifications.

Not only are places made richer by the presence of orchards, many places have fruity roots. One of the finest dessert apples, the Claygate Pearmain, was discovered growing in a hedge near Claygate in the 1820s. The versatile Newton Wonder was found growing in thatched roof of the Hardinge Arms Inn at King's Newton, Derbyshire in 1870. The river that flows near

Dunster, within the Exmoor National Park, is called Avill, which means apple. The village crest of Paulerspury in Northamptonshire includes a pear. In 1993, with funding from Rural Action, Dorothy Hinchcliffe and Dan Colley, two residents of **Appleby in Westmorland, Cumbria**, produced *Apples from Appleby*, a history of local fruit growing. The book describes some of the oldest trees and offers plenty of local recipes. The village's roots are clear: 'Records of

---

The orchard of plums, pears and apples at Kentish Town City Farm is thriving on a steep railway embankment and is undergrazed by sheep just two-and-a-half miles from Trafalgar Square.

Ebley Linear Community Orchard, Gloucestershire, separates cyclists and walkers from the road.

This orchard, a striking interface between city and country.
Photo: Chris Goddard.

Apelbi of 1130, or Eppelbi in 1308 may not go back as far as the Garden of Eden, but do underline the long history of this small market town, established on the banks of the River Eden.'

Only about 15 trees of the Plymouth Pear survive in Britain, chiefly in the hedgerows of industrial estates in **Plymouth**. It is so rare that most people have never have seen it and probably wouldn't recognise it if they did. There is little (except perhaps the reputedly fishy smell of the blossom) to reward admirers because this is a wild pear that produces gritty, diminutive fruits. Attempts by Plymouth City Council to propagate the tree may mean they will appear in more public places in the future and earn the affection of locals. Until then, the location of these few pears and their cousins in Truro remains strictly secret.

Youth hostel orchards: Orchards in youth hostels can offer perfect places for relaxing after a day's hike, or provide the focus for outdoor social gatherings. In 1993 the hostel at **Welsh Bicknor** took part in the Youth Hostel Association Conservation and Amenity Orchards Scheme and planted 22 fruit trees. John Kingsbury of the YHA remembers the positioning of some of the oddly named fruits within the grounds:

Ten Commandments was placed next to the church gate, while a precocious ruddy Calville (Calville Rouge Precoce) lurked behind the bike shed. Some larger, semi-standard cider apples such as Bulmer's Norman and Frederick went in close to the cider press and the orchard was interplanted with attractive smaller trees such as crab apple John Downie (with fruits appreciated by winter wild life) and the Black Worcester Pear: excellent for cooking.

Perhaps the warden plans to put the press back to good use in due course. At **Badby Youth Hostel** in Northamptonshire, 'the orchard is the last remaining one in the village', says Ruth Alcock for the Central

Region Countryside Committee of the YHA.

In the early days of the hostel it was well looked after by regional volunteers. One of their delights was an apple-picking day at Badby; and some of the fruit found its way into apple pies supplied to hostellers. For several years now the Northampton Local YHA Group has organised biannual working parties on the garden and this has included cutting the grass in the orchard and picking the apples in the autumn.

Since 1998 the old orchard has been pruned and gale losses have been replanted with varieties including the Farleigh damson, and Monarch, Egremont Russet and Wyken Pippen apples. Hostellers are welcome to enjoy the orchard fruit when visiting.

Linear orchards: After years of planning, British Waterways received a helping hand from celebrity gardener Monty Don who performed the official opening of the restored lock cottage orchard at **Soulbury Locks** on the Grand Union Canal in Warwickshire. Many lock keepers will once have planted fruit trees in their tied cottage gardens, and canalside orchards remain visible around Braunston and Blisworth in Northamptonshire. Perhaps the organisers of the many boat rallies on inland waterways could negotiate with owners to offer canalside orchard walks, fruit sales and picnics.

Apple Day in 1994 saw the start of the planting of the **Ebley Linear Community Orchard** near Stroud by Gloucestershire County Council. This is England's first orchard alongside an ex-railway line, now a cycletrack. Seventy standard trees along half a mile or so of the track have been planted. This will make a powerful landscape feature in the future. Each variety, some of which are quite rare, sports an information board giving its date of origin and uses of the fruit. Gloucester Underleaf, Ashmead's Kernel and Gillyflower of Gloucester are just some of the varieties planted, and each will provide a refreshing free bite for cyclists to sample.

A few hundred metres from Parliament, across the river at **Lambeth**, a linear orchard, albeit a small one, was planted by the borough's mayor in one of his favourite Community Gardens, Roots and Shoots. The mayor was assisted by almost 30 children from the next-door school in Walnut Tree Walk. Other fruit trees such as the flourishing kiwi and two pineapple guavas enjoy south-facing walls and reflect the cosmopolitan nature of the local community.

Along most motorways and main roads, linear orchards of sorts are best seen when in flower, in April and May. These wildings travel with us up and down the country and set root from munched apple cores thrown from passing cars and lorries. They grow to form bushy trees with beautiful blossom that will often yield small, sweet reminders of their parents.

Orchard wells: The India of the Raj had much to teach the British about the value of orchards, as the curious tale of the **Maharajah's Well** at **Stoke Row** in Oxfordshire reveals. In 1857 Edward Reade, fifth son of the Squire of Ipsden, Oxfordshire, was serving in India as Lieutenant-Governor of the North West Provinces for the East India Company. The Maharajah of Benares was deeply impressed by Mr Reade's personal dedication and by many other things English, so much so that he expressed a wish to endow a charity as a token of his

Merton Beauty was one of a dozen varieties raised in the south London suburbs in the early 1900s.

Common Ground's Apple Map of Britain, published on Apple Day 1993.

appreciation. Mr Reade suggested that the Maharajah's charity could be used to supply a free and public well in the Oxfordshire village of Stoke Row. But the lucky village was about to get an orchard as well as the well. The Maharajah stated that 'the public should have the privilege of taking water free of charge, in all time to come'. So to finance the well's maintenance, the Maharajah donated the purchase price of a good-sized orchard, just over one and a half hectares, to be stocked with cherries. He even provided the funds needed to buy a cottage for the Well Warden, who would be responsible for ensuring access to the well and its maintenance. Thanks to the generous nawab, the village adopted a time-honoured Indian solution – supporting a free well with the profits of a local fruit harvest.

The number of trees in the orchard is gradually declining through old age, and they are not being replaced, but there is still open access to those that remain. Perhaps this story could encourage municipal park authorities to provide the shade and bounty of fruit trees around new drinking water fountains.

The village pub in Stoke Row is now called The Cherry Tree, although once it was known as The Traveller's Friend – not least because it provided board for the many cherry pickers who

journeyed from Reading and Oxford to harvest the local orchards.

Allotment orchards: Allotments are entering a renaissance in some areas, particularly in cities where urban dwellers relish the opportunity to escape the concrete environment. In suburban and rural districts, however, the take-up of the plots may be slow, perhaps because more people have gardens. Fruit trees can make a great contribution to allotments – city or country – by offering shade, blossom and fruit. Many allotments have the odd wilding, sprung up from a discarded lunch-break core, or border cherries or damsons, which no-one in particular owns and from which everyone collects. Other allotments have had orchards purposely planted within them to fill long-vacant plots or to create a communal open space to chat, rest or harvest fruit. Don't forget – it is vital to secure formal permission from your council if you plan to plant fruit trees on municipal allotments.

For a few years the local council in Watford, had been anxious about the long-term vacancies on a number of its municipal allotment plots. When Mary Reid became chairman of the Allotment Society at **Oxhey**, a village just on the edge of Watford, she decided to carry out a survey of the members to explore alternative green uses of vacancies.

More than 80 per cent of the villagers responded to Mary's survey, in June 1999. Two ideas were most popular: to create a wild flower meadow and a Community Orchard. Mary knew that by negotiating a new mowing regime with the council, they could have both and concentrated on consolidating enthusiasm for the orchard, calling a public meeting in October. Almost immediately this was followed by a grant application to the council for £1,000, most of which would pay for 40 fruit trees including apples, plums and morello cherries. A ground preparation day was attended by a good turnout of local children and their parents.

Planting followed in November and December, and finally in January a mulberry was planted and wild flower seeds were scattered, again with help from 5-year-old pupils from the local school, who sang a planting song, an adaptation of 'Here We Go Around The Mulberry Bush'. At school, pupils had been assigned a particular tree, which they had to find in the orchard. They drew the trees and identified leaf and fruit buds. Mary hopes to encourage the children's involvement as they grow up and will invite them to return regularly, to visit the trees, picnic and enjoy the fruits.

A neighbouring countryside group, the Friends of Attenborough's Fields, lent the Oxhey Allotment Society many of their tools and horticultural machinery, which saved a lot of money. Watford Borough Council has also maintained its support. The council has extended a hedge to shelter the orchard from winter winds and waived the rent on the five plots that the new orchard occupies.

The orchard is always open – a policy that originally caused a few grumbles from some society members – and has been added to the annual Oxhey Gardens Trail. Two beehives are kept near the orchard and a new pond already supports a variety of wild life.

The prevalence of orchards, sometimes in the most unexpected places, not only reflects the positive collaboration which many people, councils, schools, farmers or all sorts of other groups have achieved, but also shows that orchards can satisfy so many different needs. Scrumping, fruit throwing or autumn mush on the roads are challenges no different from graffiti, litter or getting to know your neighbours. There is plenty room for orchards if we offer them space and learn to value their potential.

Michael Brunt's South Petherton allotment appears as if it had been cleared from the surrounding orchard landscape, which could only be in Somerset. Photo: James Ravilious.

Orchard Fruits

THE APPLE, with its deep symbolism, can stand as champion for all orchard fruits. Its diversity, its place in our culture and landscape, gives the apple its status as an emblem of all things fruitful. In the same vein, while Common Ground invented Apple Day – 21 October – as a celebration of apples, we always envisaged it being prefaced by All Fruits Eve. Here we explore the richness of other orchard fruits, familiar and new, the places where they grow and the people who nurture them. We also go in search of the origins of the apple.

The coming years may see changes in the way orchard fruits are grown in Britain. Economic trends will play a key role, as reviving interest in seasonality and local varieties jostles with the pressures of relentlessly commercial growing. Supermarkets may respond to demand for organic produce while farmers' markets increasingly provide local outlets for small growers. Other influences on our orchards – notably climate change – are harder to anticipate. Projections vary, but most climatologists agree that at the very least we should expect more unpredictable weather. Wetter, milder winters, strong winds, late frosts and hail in the fruiting season could all make fruit growing more of a challenge.

As one response, a tendency towards fruit monoculture may be supplanted by a shift towards mixed growing, to spread the risk, and to take advantage of new growing conditions. Damson growers well understand the impact of a late frost; the effect of summer hail on apples can be the difference between profit and loss; fireblight can rip through a pear orchard in one season. We need to re-examine the benefits that stem from more extensive and mixed orcharding, taking lessons from other countries as well as from our own history of rotational landuse and underplanting.

Social change continues apace as well. Ours is a dynamic society, constantly enriched by new tastes, recipes and horticultural techniques. As such knowledge filters from the margins to the mainstream, the domestic vernacular grows ever more capable of adapting creatively to the changes that lie ahead. The Community Orchard at Chinbrook Allotments in Lewisham, a culturally diverse part of southeast London, contains traditional Kentish apples and cherries as well as figs, olives and vines. Childhood memories of grafting Jamaican mangoes will come in handy for some residents of the Maiden Lane estate, a few miles north in Camden, when the tiny orchard within the community centre is restored as part of a popular seasonal gardening course.

More widely, our growing urban communities – already 80 per cent of us live in towns or cities – will need to slash energy consumption, reduce food miles and seek to become environmentally sustainable. The planting and cultivation of many more orchards in towns could help communities to achieve some of these goals.

Cherries

The sight of a standard cherry orchard in full bloom is literally breathtaking. For a start the trees are so enormous. Towering up to 18 metres, it seems strange that these timber giants live only to produce tuppenny-sized fruit, albeit about half a tonne of them. During late April, the countryside seems hidden under snow in traditional cherry-

---

Fallen fruit in a Somerset cider orchard. Photo: James Ravilious.

growing centres – landscapes such as north Worcestershire (not far to the south along the Wye Valley their wild cousins dot the hillsides), the Tamar Valley in Cornwall, the north Kent coast and formerly Hertfordshire. Cherries produce a delicate, white, seductive blossom in great profusion. Framed by a blue sky, the blossom lights up the landscape, while the dark peeling tree bark lurks below.

Harvesting cherries was a highly skilled and potentially dangerous business. Skilled men especially hired for the task hauled immense spruce ladders from tree to tree. Each ladder had at least 40 rungs, diminishing in width as they rise up to give a wider base for stability and a narrow top for precise positioning. Prerequisites for the job were strength, balance and a good eye so no branches were damaged as ladders were set against the trees. In the Tamar Valley pickers climbed up with deep round baskets which they hooked onto the ladder rungs to pick a 'coose' or course of cherries. In her delightful book on these Cornish orchards, *Burcombes, Queenies and Colloggetts*, Virginia Spiers describes how a grower 'liked to hear his workmen whistling as then he knew that they were not eating too many'.

Tall standard cherries are a challenge for any commercial grower. They take up to a dozen years to produce a decent crop and as many again before the initial outlay is returned. Cherry skin is prone to splitting after heavy rain, and must be harvested by skilled pickers to survive intact. Even then, the delicate fruits still have to make it to market. Many varieties are prone to disease, and damage by birds can be a big problem. During the Second World War, the Tamar Valley orchards had a brief respite, as avian scrumpers were frightened off by the booming of the big guns above Plymouth Sound. Canny orchardists in the Valley planted sweet cherries on the edges of woodlands adjacent to orchards. These sacrificial trees acted as delicious decoys for birds who found them a safer prospect from which to feed.

In recent years the English cherry industry has declined almost to the point of disappearance. Health and safety regulations along with the scarcity of tall-tree pickers has fuelled a move to dwarf trees that can be easily netted against marauding birds and sprayed against pest and disease. Tapering ladders are now redundant, as are the underplanted crops or grazing that once flourished below the tall trees.

The decline of cherry growing in standard orchards has amounted to quite a loss in the landscape, not just of the snowy spring-time blossom. Valuable and hard-won knowledge of complex inter-relationships in nature has gone too. The grass once grazed by sheep in cherry orchards, while initially competing with the young saplings for nutrients, also removes nitrogen from the soil which can in turn reduce the risk of diseases such as bacterial canker.

Many orchards, including scores in Kent and Cornwall, were planted with varieties suited to their place on wild rootstocks. In the Tamar Valley, municipal ditch tenders as well as men who worked in the local woods frequently came across gean or wild cherry saplings among the trees or in the hedges. The men grafted favoured varieties onto these saplings at a height of two metres. A year later, the sapling could be dug up and planted in the orchard. Already the young trees were of a suitable height for underplanting with soft fruits or flower bulbs. If the land under the trees was to be grazed instead, the animals would be unable to reach the shoots. This practice produced the large boles – the bulbous swellings that mark the graft union in mature cherries. A more common way to propagate cherries is the same method except back to front – gean saplings are transplanted to the orchard first and left to establish for a year before grafting on the fruit variety.

Local Tamar varieties such as Burcombes or Birchenhayes were named after the farms where they were

Standard cherry orchards, here beside the A2 near Sittingbourne in Kent, are under particular threat from building development in the over-populated southeast.

first grown. Both these varieties are resistant to bacterial canker, the cherry's bane, and their small fruits tend not to split in the damp Cornish climate. Although it is wet in the southwest, it's also milder and Tamar Valley cherries were prized as an earlier crop than those from upcountry. Cherry orchards were planted to face the north to delay the time of blossoming until the risk of frost had largely passed. May frosts can spell disaster for the crop. The southeast-facing slopes on the Cornish side of the Valley were particularly prized for strawberries. The Devon side, by contrast, was more reliable for apples.

All traditional orcharding, not least for cherries, is a social if laborious activity, and the conclusion of a harvest is an event worth celebrating. Virginia Spiers notes: 'Such was the celebration of the cherry that Pentillie estate, downriver from Cothele, held an annual cherry feast when huge cherry pies were cooked for local children invited to the castle for sports and entertainment. This festival has recently been re-established at St Mellion....'

In Kent, some 200 miles away, Harriet Festing coordinates the Stour Valley Farmers' Market in her role as Environmental Co-ordinator for Ashford Borough Council. In 1999 the second of the monthly markets, which have since become weekly, included a cherry-stone spitting competition attracting 60 competitors. Kent has been famous for its cherries since at least Roman times, and wild cherries still grow along Watling Street, the Roman road that runs along the route of the A2. Journalist Rebecca

Hubbard, herself from Kent, takes up the story:

At first, cherry-growing was limited to monasteries and private gardens where they were grown for medicinal purposes as well as for consumption. But as early as the fourteenth century they were hawked in London to the cry 'cherryes in the ryse' (on the twig). In Kent, cherry production received a boost in the sixteenth century when King Henry VIII's fruiterer planted 'the sweet cherry, the temperate pippyn, and the golden reinette' around Teynham. During the same period, the Earl of Leicester planted 30 acres at Sittingbourne, where the fertile brickearth was said to yield an incredible thousand pound's worth of fruit in a season. As commercial growing took off, it became the practice to interplant young orchards with hops and filberts. Later, these were grassed down and up until this century sheep were brought from Romney Marsh in autumn to graze under the trees. Odd orchards around Faversham, Sittingbourne and Teynham are still planted with old, large-treed Kent

varieties of cherry – dark, juicy Early Rivers, pale chewy Emperor Francis and the distinctive flavoured Amber Heart. But it is hard to get hold of enough cherriers (pickers) with 'ladder skills' for harvesting the trees. 'There used to be plenty of wizened little men who could handle forty foot of ladder like a feather,' lamented one grower with trees as tall as houses.

Few standard cherry orchards remain in North Kent today. One ancient survivor, mouldering away quietly off Cherry Tree Walk in the middle of Rainham, supports a thriving population of stag bettles and is owned and managed for nature with public access by Medway Borough Council. Local people remain active in its use and care, which includes replanting with local cherry varieties, having already saved it from development.

In Hertfordshire at Croxley Green, Stone's Community Orchard (named after a former owner) is a 1.4-hectare relic of an orchard once nearly four times as large. Such orchards formed an important element of the local economy a century ago. 'Cherry Sundays' were fairs held in July in many orcharding villages in south-west Hertfordshire and combined picking, sales and picnicking in local orchards including Stone's. Today, new saplings of the dark Carroon (Kerroon) and Hertfordshire Black cherries, as well as local apple varieties and plums, stand among the still flowering ancient giants which Walter Stone may have planted.

Apple and pear orchards sometimes persist for centuries in the

Mazzards frame the Landkey Festival banner, reflecting their prominence in the life of the parish.
Pears are one of the many orchard crops grown in the productive Kent soil for centuries, along with cobnuts, cherries and apples. Orchard near Offham.
Photo: Simone Canetty-Clarke (for Common Ground, South East Arts and Photoworks nee CCPM).

same spot, but cherry orchards move about. When old trees die, the whole orchard may be replanted in another field and the old orchard grubbed out for grazing. Old maps suggest that orchards march around the countryside over time. This transplantation removes the risk of transmitting bacterial infections from the rootholes of old trees to those newly planted. Typically, a mixture of cherry varieties are planted. Because cherries rely on the wind to pollinate their flowers, it is best to include varieties that have overlapping blossoming times to achieve the longest possible pollination period.

Poet Simon Fletcher, who grew up on a Wyre Forest smallholding in the 1950s, remembers picking at least five varieties of cherries:

Whiteheart, Ironside, Morello, Early Rivers and Waterloo – we were never short of fruit through the summer. In the 1950s and 60s we used to pick 50-100 chips of cherries per season and sell them to a fruiterer from Birmingham. If there was fruit to collect, Dad tells me, they used to leave an empty chip at the gate so that the driver would know to call. His itinerary included the villages of Heightington, Clows Top, Far Forest and Bliss Gate. A chip was 12.5 lbs. The numbers of cherries picked declined into the 70s and 80s, as the trees declined, and some were cut down for firewood. Cherry has a gorgeous sweet scent when burnt and my old English master used to say he always knew when he was in the forest because of the scent of burning cherry. In the 1930s 'Gladderbrook', our smallholding, was owned by the Dolloway family who ran fruit and vegetable shops in Smethwick and Birmingham. Brummies used to travel out to Wyre to cherry pick in the summer, just as the Eastenders of London used to go down into the Kent hop fields. One thing that used to intrigue me as a boy was the black band around the trunks of the mature cherry trees. This was, of course, to deter the depredations of the winter moth. We did however use 'bangers' in the trees to keep the birds off. Grandad did make some very potent cherry wine.

North Devon mazzards: Locals maintain that mazzard cherries, sweet and dark, are indigenous to Kent, Devon and Cornwall. They're such delicious fruit, it's not surprising that people are eager to claim them. Dark juicy varieties have been, in places, generically termed mazzards, but the name has also been applied to the wild cherry or gean. In any case, in North Devon, the cultivation of mazzards reaches back over 400 years when mazzard scions may have been brought here by Huguenots fleeing persecution. Grown on 15-metre trees depending on the variety, North Devon mazzards are Big Dun, Small Dun, Green Stem Black and Bottlers, the latter used for fermenting in bottles. Most farms would have kept a small 'mazzard green', as the orchards were known locally.

At Goodleigh in North Devon mazzards were 'yielding great abundance' in Tristram Risdon's county survey carried out between 1605 and 1630. At Westacott, in the parish of Landkey near Barnstaple, part of the crop of a 2.4-hectare mazzard orchard was sold to gypsies who in turn sold it from pony and trap in South Moulton and Chulmleigh. There were also mazzard greens, at Swinbridge and Harford. They covered around 54 hectares in Landkey a century ago, but this had been whittled down to barely one. Cheaper imports from Kent and the continent became feasible as transport improved after the Second World War. Old orchards were not replanted and eventually they died.

Since the 1970s Landkey Parish Councillor Dick Joy has explored the possibility of saving the mazzard from extinction. His ambitions have been realised with help from the Dartington North Devon Trust and Landkey villagers. Cuttings of the four varieties were collected from surviving local garden and orchard trees and grafted (not without some difficulty) in 1994 and propagated in a nearby nursery run by the Trust. In 1999, 20 new trees were planted on ground within a quarry. A second mazzard green has been planted on land purchased with help from the Countryside Agency as a Millennium Green, ensuring that future generations of Landkey people will be able to enjoy the fruit, perhaps in the fabled mazzard pie, which most local people born after 1950 will not have tasted.

Plums, gages, bullaces and damsons

Plums have a wonderfully convoluted and exotic origin, despite the familiarity of plum pudding, a 'plum' job and a plummy accent. The domestic plums we know are probably descendants of natural hybrids between the common sloe, that mouth-puckering miniature that enriches winter gin so well, and the cherry plum – which, like the apple, hails from Central Asia. Similarly, damsons, cultivated today mainly in Shropshire, Cheshire and Cumbria, have cultural tap-roots, betrayed in their name: they have been grown in Damascus since pre-Christian times from whence they came to us, originally as damascenes.

Bullaces are closely related occidental members of the plum family and grow wild in many a hedgerow. These small plumlets are, like their damson cousins, a little drier and tarter or bitterer than cultivated plums. They sucker and hybridise freely with their relatives which, in some places, made them useful hedge plants. In east Hertfordshire and west Essex, bullaces offer a late-summer hedgerow harvest. They are possibly hybrids of cultivated plum prunings struck into hedges.

In a few places on the Fal Estuary in Cornwall, the Kea plum, which takes its name from the village of the same name, grows in rambling orchards and even on the beach, where it is not affected by the salt-laden rain and south-westerlies. Historically, the plum has represented an important contribution to the livings of the villagers of Kea, Coombe, Cowlands and other Fal villages, where it contributed to the household alongside oyster fishing and bark stripping for tanning. The estate-owned houses were let with plums trees, and tenants were expected to replace trees as they lost their fruitfulness.

The Kea is a jamming plum, a little too tart to eat fresh, and with a glut only every third year, it typically satisfied only local consumption. However, in the past few years a number of Cornish producers and cider makers have been diversifying into commercial Kea jam, ice cream and wine production. The National Trust at Trelissick Gardens has sold Kea plum jam for a number of years. 'Grey' Kea, perhaps from bullace parentage, produce translucent crystals while others, classified as 'reds', could be damson descendants.

The Westmorland damsons of the Lyth Valley near Kendal are a little smaller and sharper than their Shropshire relatives. The trees are scattered all over the valley – along stone walls, in field corners, near the school yard – anywhere where the thin soils allow. Like the Kea plum, these damsons continue to be sold locally for pickling and jamming. They can be enjoyed fresh and make a good-flavoured ice-cream. Wine and beer production is on the increase, and the beer is sold in bottles in the Mason's Arms in Cartmel Fell. Marketing the

Kea plums grow on the shoreline of the Fal Estuary, Cornwall.

damsons has become the job of the Westmorland Damson Association. Each April thousands of visitors celebrate its Damson Day, started in the 1990s, to sample last season's produce. Dotted about the country, scores of local plums still persist, though their future is far from secure. The Aylesbury Prune is now a relatively rare hedgerow plum which Aylesbury Vale Council has made efforts to conserve.

The Blaisdon Red produces prodigiously in the area near its Gloucestershire home, but poorly when further afield. By contrast, the commercially successful Cambridge Gage is a reliable, high-quality cropper grown in many areas. The Yellow Egg, grown as a processing plum around Pershore in Worcestershire, has also enjoyed commercial popularity.

Plums and Pershore are an old couple. The local authority, Wychavon District Council, has for a number of years formalised what generations of Midlanders have always done by setting up a blossom route for motorists which guides visitors through some of the Vale of Evesham's finest countryside. Once, a train ran from Pershore to Stratford called 'The Pershore Plum', offering similar seasonal views. The planting and restoration of traditional fruit in Worcestershire is now being supported by the county council and MAFF's Countryside Stewardship scheme, with the active encouragement of the Worcestershire Traditional Orchards Forum, set up in 1998.

Since 1996 the town of Pershore has hosted an annual Plum Festival on August Bank Holiday. Masterminded by John Edgely and

Kevin O'Neill of Pershore College, the festival aims to boost interest in local plums, including the Yellow Egg and Marjorie's Seedling, and the local orchard economy. Cakes, fruit, jams, chutneys, wines and juices are offered along with growing tips, renditions of poetry in dialect and exhibitions. It's like Apple Day with warmer weather, and looks set to continue.

In Shropshire and Cheshire, damsons were often planted as a hedgerow species, rather than in planned orchards, and received little attention. Yet their productivity provided a welcome harvest and an income in certain years. Fruit was not only sold to eat but juiced to dye cloth purple. Cottage gardens commonly contained damsons, and during Wakes Weekend at Sandbach – the first in September – the appearance of the season's first damson pies coincided with the annual visit of the fair.

Gages, or greengages, are the epicure's plum – green or yellow, with sweet, soft and juicy fruit – a real chin-dribbler. Some, the transparent gages, have translucent skins that reveal the stone inside. Gages tend to grow relatively true from seed, which means these attributes can be passed on by parents. The gage first came from Armenia, via Greece, Italy and France where it was named after the Queen, Reine-Claude. Its Italian name, Verdocchia, was anglicised by the 1600s to verdoch. The fruit's modern name was a chance occurrence: in the early 1700s Thomas Gage of Suffolk received a shipment of Reine-Claudes that had lost their label, so his gardener named them Green Gage.

The Cobtree pub sign at Ightham, Kent: before, showing an incongruous Welsh cob pony and after, following successful negotiations with the brewery to reflect the pub's true celebration of the local crop.

Prunes, once an all-too regular item on school menus, are dark plums that dry well thanks to their wealth of fruit sugars. California is a source of many imported varieties and Agen in France is renowned for the delicate quality of its prunes, delicious eaten dry.

Cobnuts

Cobnuts have a distinctive place in Kentish culture, as Meg Game of the Kentish Cobnuts Association explains:

A fine spring day sees a strange activity in Kent. The grower of Kent cobnuts is in his orchard tapping each tree with a stick. Each tap produces a waft of fine pollen from the long yellow catkins dangling in the wind. The cloud of pollen drifts leisurely on the breeze, and by chance a few grains will land on the bright red stigmas of the female flower, allowing fertilisation and the production of nuts.

In 1939 my parents bought a Kentish farmhouse. Soon they found themselves with hungry evacuees to feed, so they purchased the adjoining cobnut orchard, where they could keep a pig and some ducks, and gather nuts, of which they now had an abundant supply. The purchase of that nut plantation was to have quite an influence on my life.

When I was a child, my mother and I would search for wild flowers in the nut plat, as these orchards are called, progressing to the apple, cherry and pear orchards on the farm. This instilled in me an early but lifelong interest in botany. Now, alas, the farm landscape is different. Today the farmer is ruled by supermarkets and paperwork. The cherries are long vanished, and the pears and apples going; most of the ground is sprayed with herbicides. However, our cobnut plat remains, cherished for its old trees and the plants and animals they support, and enjoyed by visiting friends and customers alike.

Cobnuts and filberts are kinds of hazelnut. World-wide, there must be several hundred varieties in cultivation or in collections, differing in characteristics such as taste, size, vigour of the tree and time of ripening. Until the 19th century White Filbert was the chief variety planted, with several hundred acres around Maidstone in 1794. Many old plats still contain a scatter of White Filbert trees. Lambert's Filbert was introduced in about 1830 by a Mr Lambert from Goudhurst, whose splendid house still stands, along with assorted nut trees in the garden. Lambert's Filbert is very well suited to England's climate, and was soon being planted throughout the Home Counties. By the end of the 19th century it had been so widely established in Kent, especially on the thin sandy soils of the ragstone ridge, stretching between Sevenoaks and Ashford, that it had changed its name to Kentish Cob, and poor Mr Lambert was all but forgotten. Most surviving old plats are predominantly of Kentish Cob.

In Kent a unique system of pruning and orchard management was developed. In 1834 John Rogers advised that 'as respects the pruning of the filbert, the reader would not be so wise in his whole life as a visit to Maidstone would make him in one hour'. It was remarkable, he said, that the system had been brought to perfection by the 'untaught, unlettered Kentish peasant', and had been passed down from father to son for generations. The principle was to check the growth of the tree, keeping it to a mere five or six feet high, within easy reach for picking. Such hard-pruned trees bore fewer but larger and more accessible nuts compared with a free-growing tree twenty or more feet high. Although the trees were kept low-growing, the branches were trained outwards to such a degree that the tree could eventually reach twenty feet in diameter.

In essence it is still quite widely practised today. England is probably the only place in the world where hazelnut trees are managed in this manner. However, trees with the most extreme near-horizontal branches are sadly becoming a rarity, the victim of mechanisation, especially the need to get mowers or other machinery between the trees. I still delight in a few trees which are far wider than they are tall, which I try to maintain: I can do as I please, since for me growing nuts is a hobby.

It seems incredible now, but nut plats used to be dug annually, to remove weeds and to expose the larvae of the nut weevil, a troublesome pest. Digging was carried out using a three-pronged plat fork or 'spud', and a whole layer of earth was moved by inverting each forkful in large clods, leaving it to be broken down by the winter frosts. Further cultivation was carried out with a hoe, and some plats were maintained virtually weed-free year round. Plats were also regularly manured using material such as wool or fish waste. One grower used turkey feathers after Christmas until the 1980s; the ground was covered with white down for such a long time that a visitor in June mistook it for an extremely late snowfall.

Cobnuts used to be sent to market in 'sieves', round baskets about a foot in depth and one and a half feet in diameter, often made of osiers. The nuts were covered with paper pegged down with wands or cleft sticks; green bracken might be laid over the paper. The crop was mostly conveyed to London by river along the Medway and Thames.

With the success of the variety Kentish Cob, cobnut growing was thriving by the end of the 19th century. An agricultural census of 1913 estimated the national area of cobnuts at 7,325 acres, of which the bulk was undoubtedly in Kent. However, a relentless decline followed the Great War. By 1936 the estimated national extent had shrunk to 1,855 acres, with Kent contributing 1,385 acres, Gloucestershire 71 acres and Worcestershire 56. By 1944 the estimate was down to 1,230 acres in Kent, falling to 730 acres by 1951. After this, cobnuts were no longer thought worth including in the national statistics. By the early 1990s I estimated that the area in Kent had declined to 200-250 acres, including plats so derelict that most people would not have recognised them as such.

The reasons for this decline were several. Home produce had to compete with imported fruits and nuts, which became increasingly available due to improvements in transport and refrigeration. Better packaging and treatment kept foreign nuts in prime condition. Nuts had been profitable on relatively infertile land, but as fertilisers and pesticides became more generally available so other crops, such as strawberries and apples, became more economic. Cobnut cultivation is particularly labour intensive, and as wages rose so did the price of nut cultivation. The Second World War caused the demise of some plats in the Dig for Victory campaign, and the expansion of Maidstone and other towns and villages have taken their toll. Removal of trees to make horse pasture has been a particular recent cause of loss.

In the late 1980s I became seriously concerned at the number of plats which were being destroyed or neglected, and set about charting the last ones. I was amazed at the wealth of flora the plantations support, now that they are no longer dug. About ten years ago several Kentish growers came together, intending to form a producers' co-operative. Originally this focused on commercial growers, who were interested in EC funding, but it soon widened to include all aspects of nut growing. I recall being astonished when membership topped 30, but now the Kentish Cobnuts Association, as it became, has about 150 members. Many have only small plats, or even just a few trees in their garden, the latter sometimes all that remains of a larger plat which was developed for housing. The Association is an entirely voluntary organisation which, like so many similar bodies, relies on a few dedicated enthusiasts – nutters, perhaps – to run it, and its members to cough up the annual fee. The Association provides training and technical information; produces a newsletter; arranges outings and events for members; keeps in touch with relevant legislation; promotes cobnuts through publicity material, including factsheets, exhibitions, recipe leaflets, photos and material for journalists and occasional press events; attends shows; and provides advice and assistance for members to market their produce. Derelict plats have been restored, often with the help of Countryside Stewardship grants, and new ones have been planted. We have been astonishingly successful in attracting publicity, and this has gone some way to raise the profile of cobnuts, although much remains to be done.

From my point of view, another vital achievement of the Association has been to bring growers together. Many members own small plats, which are always at risk of neglect or removal. I hope that such people may now feel their cobnut plats should be treasured, not destroyed thoughtlessly.

Meg's nut growing keeps another old association active – that between Kent produce and the seasonal invasion of Londoners. For many centuries, residents of the capital have spent summers in the county picking seasonal fruit including cherries, apples and hops. Their coming was part escape from the city and part an opportunity for extra income. Today the Turkish residents of Hackney and Lewisham continue this tradition and Meg is noticing the same faces year after year who come, not just to gather nuts but to enjoy a family picnic

Turkish residents of Hackney and Lewisham continue the traditional association between Kent produce and seasonal London pickers. Photo: Meg Game.

Pick your own: a popular pastime across cultures and generations, Crowhurst Farm, Borough Green, Kent. Photo: Simone Canetty-Clarke (for Common Ground, South East Arts and Photoworks nee CCPM).

among the trees. The Turks are huge hazel enthusiasts and produce the majority of the world crop. In Britain they can keep this affection in good heart in the cobnut plats of Kent.

Pears

Pears can be the longest-lived orchard trees, thriving and productive for upwards of three centuries. In Britain we are towards the northern edge of their range. Yet thriving northern varieties such as the hardy Hessle, from East Yorkshire, have accommodated to local conditions over the years. The largest collection of pears in northern England is conserved near Barnsley in South Yorkshire at Canon Hall. Some of the espaliers have almost two dozen tiers. Pear Day is celebrated there every year in September, a month before Apple Day, which inspired it. Southeast Scotland was similarly good pear country during the 1800s and it is certain that pears have been cultivated from Norman times in Britain, if not before. Soft, juicy eating pears owe much to their cultivators in France and Belgium who first developed Cuisse-madame (my lady's thigh) or Doyenné du Comice.

Early pears, many varieties of which remain, were hard and gritty, notably the wardens. These tooth-busters need long storage until April or May and will still be too hard to eat raw. A warden has become the generic name of a cooking pear with such characteristics but the original warden may have been grown at Warden Abbey, near Biggleswade in Bedfordshire. Next door at Southill, a new Community Orchard was planted including wardens in the winter of 1999/2000, and a spring-time walk around Warden village will reveal pear blossom in several of the gardens.

Jim Arbury of the Royal Horticultural Society at Wisley suggests that the Black Worcester pear may well be the original warden variety and that its ancestors arrived with the Roman invasion. In Worcester the pear is celebrated on various coats of arms including the county and city councils and the County Cricket Club. Anxious

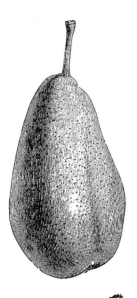

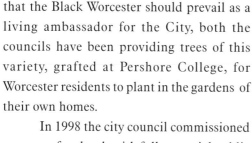

that the Black Worcester should prevail as a living ambassador for the City, both the councils have been providing trees of this variety, grafted at Pershore College, for Worcester residents to plant in the gardens of their own homes.

In 1998 the city council commissioned a survey of orchards with full or partial public access within the city limits. More than 20 were identified, many containing perry pear trees, which, like the cider apples, formed an important crop in the Three Counties of Worcestershire, Herefordshire and Gloucestershire. Regional perry varieties have been planted at the Three Counties Showground in Malvern to reflect this. Small and unpalatable, perry fruits generally make a lighter and more delicate drink than cider. At its best, perry is a rival to wine. Not before time, perry production is undergoing a revival in the region, both commercially and on a domestic scale.

Rough-cut compared to the urbane dessert pears, perry pears have fantastic names, some of which hint at the effects of consumption: Bloody Bastard, Blakeney Red, Merrylegs and Lightning Pear (reputed to go straight through).

Local perry makers reckon that perry pear trees grow best in the red sandstone soils found on the Herefordshire-Gloucestershire border, within sight of May Hill.

Gloucestershire pears are a muddle of local names that change from place to place – the county is said to be home to some 100 perry pear varieties known by well over 200 different names.

The fluidity of local nomenclature is brilliantly captured by Gillian Faulkner and Ray Williams, writing in *Perry Pears*: 'If one asks to see specimens of Red Pear in Blakeney, one will be shown Blakeney Red, which is quite a different variety: and to obtain samples of Rock it is necessary to ask for Mud Cap in the parish of Arlingham, for Black Huffcap in Highnam, for Brown Huffcap in Tibberton and Red Huffcap in Newent.'

Pears are grafted onto a variety of rootstocks, including seedling pear for vigorous growth and quince for earlier and better fruit. Hawthorn was also used or even crab, both of which produce very gritty fruits. Some varieties are not compatible with quince stock and so have an intermediate graft called a stem builder, which forms the trunk onto the top of which the fruit scion is grafted. This grafting technique is common practice for cider apples, too.

Walnuts

The walnut is another of our Persian love affairs and is aptly named from the Old English *wealh*, meaning foreign. While walnuts in one guise or another may be consumed with gusto in every dinner course, from the salad dressing to the cheese board, they are tricky croppers. In the 16th century, when walnuts were more popular than today, a great deal were being imported from Italy. In 1988, according to Martin Crawford's treatise *Walnuts - Production and Culture*, 6,000 tonnes of walnuts were imported into the UK while our domestic commercial crop was nil. Nevertheless Yorkshire, Devon, Somerset, Dorset and Lincolnshire remain walnut-growing areas, and many old gardens boast a beautiful tall walnut tree.

The difficulty may be pollination, which is achieved by the wind. While the trees sport both male and female flowers, the universal male tendency of premature enthusiasm is also suffered by this species. The Persian variety, most commonly grown here (there is also a Polish), is both self- and cross-fertile but the brain-shaped nuts, which were once sympathetically consumed against headache, will take upwards of a dozen years to appear.

There is an old notion that walnuts and apples do not mix and in fact walnuts do poison apples, strawberries and many other plants. The toxic chemical junglone is contained within its roots and leaves which can make even rain run-off problematic. So undercropping needs to be carefully considered. Thankfully, blackcurrants are happy to provide an interim crop beneath walnut saplings.

The nuts are a versatile crop. In addition to their delicious taste and high levels of essential polyunsaturated fats, the hard woody shells can be finely ground and used like chestnut flour. Forester Peter Dewey, remembering his nut-hunting childhood in Leicestershire, advises the carrying of a darning needle when out and about in late June/early July. At this point the green husks are still soft and the shells inside them has not yet become woody. Peter's needle, if it passes the whole way through the nut, will indicate its readiness for pickling. Doing it yourself allows experimentation with gentler recipes than the industrially acidic product on sale in supermarkets.

Quince

The quince resembles a beautiful mix between pear and apple. Portugal, one of the most familiar varieties, has been cultivated in Britain for almost 400 years, and others have been here since at least the 13th century. Initially, the colour of lemon, the fruit turns to orange when ripe. Immediately striking is its intense and delicious aroma.

At Oxburgh Hall in Norfolk, Portugal quinces from the walled orchard are a great attraction. An oasis among the local agricultural landscape, the orchard is visited by hares and rabbits, deer, chaffinches and pied wagtails. Wrens nest in the quince and a pair of barn owls hunt over the estate. People too find it just as appealing. One year, visitors to Oxburgh were so impressed with the quinces that they took away a crop and made more than 100 kilograms of jam. The proceeds were returned to the National Trust to support the gardens fund. Head Gardener Graham Donachie recommends another traditional use of the fruit: placed in a bowl of sawdust or soft tissues, quinces are said to effectively counteract any odours in the best room.

But most of the orchard crop goes to the Hall kitchens run by Alison Sloane. Quinces are inedible – bullet hard and sour – straight from the tree, but they offer up a grainy foil to rich savouries, and a luscious, but tart cooked dessert that has echoes of pear. The Oxburgh quinces do not keep for long, and Alison boils the ones she does not immediately need into a quince syrup which is then used throughout the year in quince and almond tarts.

Biennially, Oxburgh hosts a quince evening on Apple Day, at which Alison prepares a variety of quince dishes, including stews, tarts and Turkish Delight. Tastings are followed by a lecture from Graham on the cultivation of the fruit.

Graham's colleague Barry Champion at the National Trust's Trelissick Gardens, near Falmouth, has planted an orchard of Cornish apple varieties. The young orchard also includes quince and medlar, which he says is traditional in Cornish apple orchards.

Quinces grow wild in the Middle East but varieties have been successfully cultivated in Britain from America, the Balkans and southern Europe. In France a commercial quince culture has existed for centuries, not just for fruit but also to provide rootstocks for pear trees, a practice subsequently adopted by the British. Although it thrives with cross pollination, quince is self-fertile and has beautiful white flowers, like large apple blossom.

The habit of baking orchard fruit has declined, which is a great pity considering the potential rewards, especially from quince. Their rarity has turned them into an expensive and unfamiliar pleasure.

However, Britons of Turkish, Iranian, Spanish and Portuguese origin have retained their affection for the quince, and shops serving these communities often sell the fresh fruit or marmelada paste, which is also gradually becoming available at some supermarket cheese counters.

As well as their culinary and aromatic usefulness, quince trees are very beautiful and have a long tradition of aesthetic planting (often in the company of medlar). Several accounts of quinces associate them

with love and fruitfulness, to be eaten as tokens of such at weddings. Could there be room for a few quince trees in the quietest corner of the Community Orchard under which courting couples, during blossom-time, can anticipate a nuptial menu?

Most varieties are ready to be picked by October. Store them

Picking apples at West Bradley, Somerset. Photo: James Ravilious.

The Nuttery at Newnham in Northamptonshire is owned by the Woodland Trust. Its nut cultivation is achieved along traditional coppicing lines which also produces hazel poles.

on straw and away from other fruits that will affect their aroma and flavour. They will be ready to enjoy in four to eight weeks.

Medlars

Medlars look like overgrown, brown rosehips, which earned them the pseudonym *open-ers* (arse) as long ago as Chaucer's *Reeve's Tale* of 1387. Medlars also came to us, via the monasteries, from the bountiful border where southern Europe and Asia meet. Their beautiful white flowers, dark trunks, heavy shade and strong autumn colour made them a natural choice (often with quince, mulberry and walnut) for gardens and orchards. Old trees are most frequently found in walled gardens or estate collections, and they are making a come-back in Community Orchards as lovely additions to the main planting. Their fruits are delicious and taste like baked apple – although they are edible only after the first frosts have softened them, by which time they may be half-rotten on the tree. All the same, these intriguing fruits can be made into a good jelly.

Wild fruit trees

Orchards, at their best, are a bargain made between humankind and nature, each profiting from the other, as long as our interference remains sensitive and benign. It is fitting, then, that many fruit trees retain an intimate connection with wildness.

Elder is alternately valued throughout history for its usefulness as a fast-growing hedge-gapping shrub, or grubbed out as a short-lived straggling weed. Either way, its fruitfulness has long been celebrated all over the country in elderflower cordial or champagne, elderberry wine and even chutney. Its umbels make delicious battered fritters. A growing interest in natural products and high-quality tastes has helped to propel elderflower cordial into fashion. On Hampstead Heath in May, Londoners wanting a crop need to keep a close eye on the umbels. As soon as they are ready they're picked. (The same goes

for winter sloes, which appear in the warmer city microclimate a little earlier than they do in the countryside.) A small Gloucestershire company producing cordial, Bottle Green, buys umbels collected by upwards of 600 local people who gather the florets freely from hedges. In Leicestershire the Belvoir Cordials company has moved from a reliance on the hedgerow crop to planting 32 hectares of their own elder orchards.

Today, relatives of wild crab apples are planted at regular intervals in commercial orchards to serve as vital pollinators. But they also punctuate many hedges, where their massive profusion of florets helps to attract many more insects into the orchard. Their fruits, sometimes as sharp as sloes, are a challenge to the stomach fresh off the tree, but they make a marvellous jelly, best for rich meats and cheese. Left to its own devices the native wild crab has a peculiar tendency to occur alone in woodland. Oliver Rackham records only one crab per 10 acres, about 4 hectares, for East Anglian woods.

In search of the wild apple

Dr Barrie Juniper, tutor in Plant Sciences at St Catherine's College, Oxford University, has for many years had a special interest in apples. In the summer of 1998, he leapt at the chance to fulfil a long-held ambition, and with two intrepid colleagues set off on an expedition in search of the apple's birthplace.

The ancestors of apples as we know them were brought here by the Romans. So they have enjoyed life in this country for barely two thousand years. Molecular biology tells us that they – the apples that is, not the Romans – almost certainly have nothing whatsoever to do with the very rare and native apple, *Malus sylvestris*, which again almost certainly most of you have never seen and is spiny and inedible to boot. The Romans arrived in this country, took one bite of the local apple, probably felt sorry for the pigs and sent back immediately to Rome for the scions of good juicy sweet fruit. But the amount

Common Ground has chosen the apple to stand as the champion for the panoply of orchard fruits which grow on these islands. Photo: James Ravilious.

of germplasm the Romans could have brought to this country was small; hence the search for the source to reinforce matters.

But where then did the apple come from originally? The Romans thought it came from Syria and confessed they had learned the techniques of grafting from the Greeks. The ancient Greeks neither wrote nor said anything on this topic, but an educated guess is that the Persians invented grafting and so evolved the technique of conserving and spreading chosen varieties, since apples don't come true from seed and cannot be grown from cuttings. Syria was, therefore, not a bad guess – at least in the right direction – but the molecular biology research was pointing to regions far to the east, possibly even into China itself.

The provinces of southern, central and western China are immensely rich in tree and shrubby species of plants, never having suffered in recent geological time the devastation of total glaciation. If you took away all the true Chinese species of plants from the gardens of St Catherine's College there would be almost nothing left but bare earth. The Chinese have over twenty true wild species of apple (cf. the British Isles with one) but most of these are small-fruited, often no bigger than a cherry. How and where, then, did the evolution to the big, round, red and juicy things we enjoy take place?

There were hints that the answer might lie somewhere within the old autonomous provinces of the Soviet Union, such as Uzbekistan and Kazakhstan. Yet nobody in Russia seemed to be able to provide a definitive answer and virtually no westerner and certainly nobody from Britain had attempted to penetrate into most of this region. Nevertheless, some two hundred e-mails, faxes and letters later we had all the necessary permissions. Some of the funds were provided by the Leverhulme Trust, who had already backed our successful molecular investigation.

Three of us flew to Almaty in Kazakhstan. Almaty means the 'place of apples'. We supposed, in our naivety, that we might find wild apples in abundance just up the road. Not to put too fine a point on it, however, the whole of the central section of Kazakhstan and most of Uzbekistan has been wrecked, in the botanical sense, by several thousand years of nomads' goats and Stalin and Khrushchev's virgin lands projects.

So was there any intact forest left? On the third day of our visit, after vigorous negotiations supported by the $ sign, two Russian-built jeeps arrived, with two middle-ranking Kazakh soldiers as our permanent, but frequently hilarious escort, two drivers (one of whom was a former Russian jet-fighter pilot out of a job), an interpreter and a local botanist. The jeeps on offer to us were rugged and effective but lacked some of the finer details in the design of the suspension.

We drove, in equivalent, from Oxford to Aberdeen. We had passed through Russian control posts, since Russia still locks an iron ring around the borders of its former possessions. The Russian squaddies, with their red stars on their

floppy field caps, were outranked by our Kazakh escort and saluted smartly as we passed through. (If it moves – salute it – is obviously a world-wide army response.) We passed a huge forward strategic airbase with lines of Migs in full war paint on the runways. Our escort indicated, in response to our anxious glances, that none of the planes had moved for many months due to a lack of aviation fuel.

In the gathering dusty darkness we arrived, somewhat bruised and emotionally drained, at the lower mountain slopes of the Djungarian Alatau, an outlier of the great Tien-Shan range (the heavenly mountains), just north of the Illi River and looking over into China.

In the morning as we emerged from our yurt (yes, and very comfortable they are too), we realized that we were surrounded by fruit forest of which the world knows very little. Apples, pears, plums, apricots, with other berrying trees like hawthorns and rowans abound. Dismiss your view of apples in a gentle Kentish meadow! Real apples we found up to 6,000 feet enjoying 30°C in summer and minus 30° of the same in winter. Tiny fragments of this forest still exist, preserved by the accident of political and military whim which has kept all but the most suicidal of travellers out ever since the world began. This area is, after all, the other side of the vast frontier of the Great Game. Wherever the goat and cow could penetrate, the forest has gone. The tsars, the Soviets and now the Kazakh government have ensured that a few tiny fragments remain. But for how long?

So how did the big sweet apple, which was all around us, evolve? Part of the answer is the 4.5 million-year-old ancestry of the Tien-Shan, on which we stood, heaved up into the air, and still growing, by the Indian orogeny which first forced up the Himalayas and Pamirs to the south. The tiny, bitter invading Chinese apples creeping up from the south-east never got a moment's peace. Could they, unconsciously, have been selected too by the sweet tooth and acute sense of smell of the bears which abound in those mountains? The bears' autumn 'droppings' are stuffed with the pips of apples, plum stones and hawthorn seeds.

Then came the Silk Roads of the last ten thousand years, which pass just by on their great journey to the east and west; laden caravans with their camels, horses and mules. And then perhaps came Alexander's cavalry to carry unwittingly the selected seeds back to Macedonia. Even the great Alexander was beaten back by the robust Kazakh nomads, and turned south to the softer target of the Hindu-Kush, but he got into the edge of this region. A horse's teeth and guts, like those of a bear, do no harm to an apple pip, and at least the seeds are planted in a fertile medium. The Romans brought the whole

evolved package to Britain. They grafted their own sweet scions on the stocks of the bitter native crabs. We can still, by virtue of this technique, grow Roman varieties in our orchards. In the British climate the 'new' apple set seed and proliferated into the world's finest collection of dessert, culinary and cider fruits. From a chance seedling of unknown but distant Roman parentage, in a Berkshire orchard some 180 years ago, arose the Cox's Orange Pippin. It has come a long way.

At least three influences – hybridisation, our position of the edge of the range of many fruits and the melding of many cultures and cuisines – have provided us with a huge range of fruits. These rich wellsprings of diversity, along with the probability of changing climate patterns over the next half century, will continue to shape the orchards in which they are grown. Like the Bengalis of London's Brick Lane or the Poles of Peterborough, fruits have set root in particular locations and become part of that place. Some orchards are maps through history, as the rings of their trunks mirror the patina of place. History lives on in the varieties of fruit. Court Pendu Plat, an apple dating from the 15th century, is still grown today, and as Roach tells us of the Romans: 'it seems likely that some of their numerous varieties must have been tried by Roman gardeners in Britain'. Orchards are very good at capturing the imagination of people. Any interest paid to them will offer rich rewards, not all of them edible, and will be a good starting point for celebrating local distinctiveness.

Reg Holland at his farm in Chulmleigh in Devon. Photo: James Ravilious.

Sharing with Nature

HAD OUR FOREBEARS set out to create havens for wild life, they could hardly have bettered traditional orchards. 'Domesticated', deliberately shaped by human ambitions, old orchards may be – but they're no less wild for all that.

Nature revels in the sheer variety of these places – orchards defy tidy categorisation. Neither woodland, grassland, hedgerow or wood pasture, they rarely feature in habitat surveys. Yet the wonder of these places stems from the fact that they can be all these habitats at once. At their best, orchards offer a patchwork attractive to everything from beetles and bats to badgers and butterflies. On the scaly bark of old Bramley trees in No Man's Orchard, Kent's first Community Orchard, sharp-eyed botanists have spied at least 33 species of lichens and mosses – a world in miniature that testifies to the wholesome air enjoyed by walkers on the North Downs Way, as they pass by the orchard.

Orchards' history as valued places is central to this natural bounty. 'Biodiversity' thrives in places that are themselves diverse, and have been that way for a long time. Old orchards are living signs of continuity in the landscape, and most species, like most people, appreciate places with a bit of history to them.

In some favoured spots, old orchards are enduring features of the landscape. Even though the trees themselves are relatively short-lived, orchards may have occupied the same piece of land for centuries. As fruit trees are periodically replaced and replanted, a diverse *mélange* gradually develops. Underneath the trees, a flower-rich grassland carpet evolves, reflecting years of grazing or hay-making. The combination proves irresistible to a myriad of pollinating insects which in turn attracts birds and bats, and much more. The web of interconnections has yet to be fully charted.

If the orchard is surrounded by an old and varied hedge, all the better. The hedge itself may contain locally distinctive fruit trees, such as damsons in Shropshire or cherries in Norfolk, while it provides another refuge for nesting and feeding.

Traditional orchards of tall-stemmed trees offer the best opportunities. Full-sized fruit trees harbour valuable spiders, grubs and beetles for trunk feeders such as nuthatches and treecreepers, which will find rich pickings under the bark flakes of apple and in the crevices between the chequerboard scales of pear. Orchard trees, with the exception of walnut and pear, rot relatively quickly, allowing colonisation by hole-dwelling birds including woodpeckers, which are among the most common orchard birds. Other species that find refuge among the rotwood are starlings, tits, tree sparrows – now a rare species in Britain – and, on the continent, the hoopoe and wryneck.

Orchard blossom, and the fruit itself of course, acts as a magnet for wild life, and an amazingly diverse range of creatures will be pleased to help you harvest the crop. As birds and insects in particular take their tithe of fruit, they more than repay the favour, as blue tits hunt over apple trees to pick off quantities of codling moth caterpillars and wasps tackle aphid pests. Even the depredations of the bud-eating bullfinch, until recently killed by commercial fruit growers under license from the Ministry of Agriculture, Fisheries and Food (MAFF), has become something to be welcomed. This beautiful bird, prized as a cage bird by the Victorians, is now in serious decline, having lost some three-quarters of its population in the past 30 years.

Not a moment too soon, conservationists are beginning to take a closer look at old orchards. One of Britain's first orchard nature reserves is Tewin Orchard, near Welwyn Garden City in Hertfordshire. Leased from the RSPB, it is managed by the Herts & Middlesex Wildlife Trust. The great variety of creatures it attracts embraces bats, a badger colony and 20 types of moth, including, in spring, the privet hawkmoth. Butterflies abound, including the marbled white and the white-letter hairstreak. It has not been sprayed since 1958, enabling a healthy grassland to develop. Wild flowers such as bird's foot trefoil, field scabious and various cranesbills flourish there.

Three types of uncommon bats feed in the orchard: the serotine, the noctule and the long-eared. The long-eared bat in particular enjoys feasting on the insects feeding on over-ripe fruit, particularly the plums, at an important time before hibernation.

A wide range of birds enjoy the orchard too, including large numbers of tits, greenfinches, bullfinches, linnets, goldfinches, yellowhammers and blackbirds. In winter, flocks of fieldfares and redwings, sometimes 700 strong, feed on the fallen fruit. The abundance of songbirds provides sparrowhawks with a reliable food source. In the summer, the overgrown cordons are an attractive breeding habitat for a range of warblers, notably the garden warbler, lesser whitethroat, willow warbler and blackcap. Reed buntings have started to visit in summer as well as winter, and bramblings turn up occasionally. Hobby, goshawk and buzzard are rare visitors.

The hop aphid also has a penchant for plum.
Increasingly rare bullfinches can now be something to celebrate in the orchard.

The Wildlife Trust carefully manages Tewin Orchard to enhance the diversity of the habitats available to wild life. But the most important rule of thumb is to avoid being overtidy. Above all, never cut down a tree until you really understand how the orchard works. Gnarled old branches and trunks, pocked with rot holes and covered in peeling bark, may not look like much to us, but they provide dream homes and lavish catering for a host of interesting creatures.

For instance, the aptly named little owls, about the size of starlings, like nothing better than an old orchard as home base. 'All ornithologists think of little owls and orchards together,' says Colin Shawyer of the Hawk and Owl Trust. In north Somerset, Faith Moulin and her fellow orchardists are keeping a close eye on local little owls as part of their Two Hoots Biodiversity Project. The sparse trees and grassy turf of a good orchard resemble the traditional farmland and parkland that are their favourite haunts on the continent, from whence they came to Britain. Once sacred to the goddess Athene, little owls were successfully introduced into Britain in the 1870s, by one Lord Lilford of Northamptonshire, perhaps in the hopes that they might feast on bullfinches, that notorious consumer of fruit buds. The owls were certainly intended to be some sort of biological pest control. Since then, the diminutive owls have gradually spread throughout England and Wales, though they prefer insects, earthworms and voles to small birds. If an old orchard has rotted hollows that form suitable nest holes, and there's short grassland about for feeding, there's a chance you'll see a little owl even in daylight, a grey blob perched on a wall or post. Listen for the repetitive loud piercing _kEEoo_, rather like a mewing kitten.

James Marsden's Herefordshire orchard is home to little owls and much else besides. A general manager with English Nature, he owns and manages about two hectares of traditional orchards at Gregg's Pit in Much Marcle, Herefordshire, for the benefit of local wild life and to produce his own cider and perry, as he describes:

With the right management, the biodiversity of mine and my neighbour's adjacent orchards will continue to grow. Luckily, the old orchards are already rich in standing dead and decaying wood. The heart rot, hollows, holes and sap runs, which, rich in sugar and yeast, provide rich pickings for wild life. Green, great and lesser spotted woodpeckers feed on the rich invertebrate life, and find nesting holes, as do little owls, starlings and jackdaws. Tawny owls and spotted flycatcher nest in my neighbour's orchards. Other frequent avian visitors include numerous tits and finches, spotted flycatcher, pied wagtail, yellow wagtail, treecreeper, blackbird, woodpigeon and magpie. Buzzard prey on rabbits, while sparrowhawk use the orchards to capture fruit-eating birds. Large mixed flocks of fieldfare, redwing and starling feed on fallen fruit during November and December.

Bats roost in some of the old trees too, and fly in to eat the moths and chafers. No wonder traditional orchards are an important component of 'bat landscapes', providing feeding habitats for greater horseshoe, brown long-eared and pipistrelle bats. Other mammals frequent orchards too, including fox, brown hare, rabbit, stoat, weasel, hedgehog and badger.

Gregg's Pit Orchard contains a marl pit, which gives it its name, from which it is said the lime mortar was made to point the stonework of St Bartholomew's Church, Much Marcle. The marl pit forms a shallow pond, surrounded by mature scrub comprising goat willow, crack willow, elm, hawthorn and field maple. Mallards and moorhens frequent the pond, which is also home to both great crested and palmate newts.

Giant puffballs and field mushrooms mysteriously erupt in late August and early September, while bracket fungi grow on mature trees. Within older trees, a multitude of less visible fungi are hard at work advancing the process of decay which provides important habitats for invertebrates.

As a (very!) amateur entomologist, I have confined myself to recording butterflies and have been impressed by the numbers and variety of species attracted to my orchard. During September 1999 ripe plums inspired a feeding frenzy of butterflies, and on one sunny day I saw seven species in the orchard – comma, large white, painted lady, red admiral, small copper, small tortoiseshell and speckled wood. My records for purple hairstreak date from a month or two earlier in the year, when I saw these attractive butterflies feeding on oak in the orchard hedges, in perry pear and cider apple trees, and following the setting sun due west up the orchard on two warm evenings.

And let's not forget the wild yeasts. These helpful but wayward microbes leave a distinctive taste print on each traditional cider and perry, as they challenge the maker to achieve that ever-elusive quality, consistency.

Mixed orchards producing fruit of many types and varieties can offer the best mix of habitats for some moths and butterflies. Big cherry or apple trees cast shade, but they are usually widely spaced to allow patches of open ground to encourage wild grasses and flowers such as vetches, which are important food plants for caterpillars or provide nectar for adults. Plum orchards can be particularly rich in sun-loving butterflies and moths because they cast a much lighter shade than cherry or apple. By contrast, mature pears, being more upright than spreading in their growth, offer ideal conditions for speckled wood and orange tip butterflies and other dappled-shade-loving species.

Ideally, trees in an orchard should also be of mixed age. Young trees allow plenty of light to reach the ground plants while older trees provide an abundance of food and shelter. Ironically, dead and decaying trees can be the most valuable of all to everything from nesting woodpeckers and roosting bats to unusual lichens and rare beetles. If the sight of a slowly dying tree disturbs you, don't rush to find a chainsaw – why not clothe it in ivy to make it look more interesting? The ivy itself makes a first-rate wild life resource. A good roosting and nesting place, it also provides food at just the right times of year. Flowering late, in September and October, ivy supplies nectar to butterflies, bees and other insects when other sources have dried up, and then fruits late in March and April, to nourish desperately hungry wood pigeons, thrushes and small mammals.

You can boost the diversity of life that can make use of an orchard by creating a patchwork of habitats, fitting to your locality, even if only on a small scale. Encourage a flower-rich meadow, for instance, perhaps by directly planting wild flower plugs or seeds sourced locally, as well as devising a sustainable grazing or cutting regime. Stunning bee- and butterfly-friendly flowers such as primroses, cowslips, knapweed, scabious, fleabane and wild basil could become established in your orchard. Your local Wildlife Trust may be able to offer advice. Try to find out what works best in your neighbourhood. Grazing by sheep, cattle, pigs or even hens can be beneficial to local flora and fauna, but only if carefully managed – hungry herbivores can rapidly strip a meadow and damage the trees themselves, if stocking levels are too high or the timing is wrong. Tree guards are recommended.

Plant a hedge with native hawthorns, holly, yew, blackthorn, bramble and crabs, peppered with perennial wild flowers of the locality, and a surprising array of animals will notice the difference. Among the first to respond will be the insects. Buckthorn will attract the brimstone butterfly, while elms, still distinctive hedgerow plants in the eastern counties, attract the comma and white letter hairstreak. In counties such as Hertfordshire and Norfolk, where plum and cherry prunings were often struck into hedges, butterflies such as the black hairstreak and the cherry-bark moth may flourish.

Butterflies readily attract human admirers, but thousands of other invertebrates deserve our attention too, not least because they form the foundations of food chains that sustain more photogenic creatures. What's more, an insect-rich orchard also comes equipped with nature's own pesticide squad – a complex array of natural predators. Recent research shows that this natural armoury can, in the long term, keep pest species at bay much more effectively than any chemical spray ever can.

Lichens soon develop on trees where spraying has ceased, especially where air quality is good. In recent surveys of some 30 Yorkshire orchards, naturalist Albert Henderson has discovered dozens of lichens. At Bingley, Bradford, he found 26 species of lichen in just one orchard. Further north, in particularly fine traditional orchards,

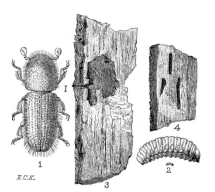

Flat-celled shot-borer beetles relish plum wood.

species counts reach as high as 33 at Parceval Hall and 35 at Ampleforth – on a par with prime orchards in Devon and Fermanagh. So far, he's found a total of 44 lichen species living in Yorkshire orchards, and expects to find still more. Most typical of the best orchards are lichens with an overall green-grey tinge. A noticeable presence of yellowish orange lichen is usually a tell-tale sign of extra enrichment by nitrogen from agricultural fertilisers or car exhaust pollution.

Woodland lichens flourish too in an old orchard at Yeldon Farm near the Wyre Forest in Worcestershire, says Andrew Fraser of the Worcestershire Wildlife Trust. Here, new cherries are being planted in gaps within the old orchard; venerable lichens growing on the trunks of old trees may be able to colonise the new ones. In the Vale of Evesham – which Oliver Rackham suggests has been unwooded since about 1000BC – old orchards stand in for the vanished wildwood. In one orchard, now a reserve managed by the trust, a typical woodland fungus hints at the long continuity of landuse: one blewit fairy ring is some 20 metres in diameter.

Exceedingly rich grassland flora can also be found within traditional orchards on the limestone soils of the Cotswolds or on the liassic limestone soils underlying parts of Worcestershire. In fact, one of the main areas for bee orchids in Worcestershire is in the old plum orchards in the Vale of Evesham, Fraser says. And one of only two known places in the county where lesser broomrape grows is on clover in a plum orchard near Evesham.

Hidden away in the city of Worcester are 20 old orchards, some with glorious flower-rich meadows and mature mixed hedgerows, according to a recent survey by wild life consultant William Watson, commissioned by Worcester City Council. The small orchard next to the farmhouse at Hornhill, part of Hornhill Meadows Local Nature

Reserve, has old apple trees, perry pears and damsons, festooned with wild-life-friendly ivy. Dense scrub nearby welcomes nesting whitethroats, warblers and tits. At Barland Orchard, veteran perry pears still stand, and might just date from 1753, when the orchard first appears on a map. In the standing dead wood a local entomologist spotted an interesting woodworm beetle that is found only very locally within Worcestershire. Mistletoe thrives on 26 apple trees at seven sites – among the highest density in the country – while impressive lichen colonies are well established on 35 old trees in almost a dozen orchards in the city. At Aconbury Orchard, an old farm orchard with veteran perry pears, Colin Harris of Warndon Villages Wildwatch Volunteers has kept a diary of the birds he has seen. Over the past few years he has spied 29 species, including green woodpeckers, fieldfare and redwings – three species designated as 'associated species' of traditional orchards within Worcestershire's Biodiversity Action Plan.

In recent years, several local biodiversity action plans have explicitly included orchards. These plans, drawn up at the county level, are intended to set targets for practical nature conservation schemes across the country. Such official recognition of the conservation value of orchards has happened especially in the West Midlands, where traditional orchards are still integral elements of the local economy and landscape. Here, birds associated with orchards include spotted flycatchers, tree sparrows, fieldfares, redwings, song thrushes and all three British woodpeckers. In Devon old orchards help to provide the kind of mixed grassland enjoyed by cirl buntings, once so common as to earn themselves

the nickname 'village buntings'. Wrynecks – slim and sinuous relatives of woodpeckers named for their habit of twisting and craning their necks into quite bizarre poses – are now extremely rare in Britain but have been associated with Kentish orchards in the past. While the loss of old orchards cannot be solely responsible for the bird's decline, it certainly hasn't helped. These birds relied on old pastures rich in ants to feed upon.

Hawfinches too are in decline, with some 15 per cent of the remaining British pairs nesting in old orchards. Hornbeam is, with cherry, the mainstay of their autumn diet and their decline in Kent must surely be associated with the virtual extinction of the once-common standard cherry orchards.

Intensively managed commercial bush plantations offer, on the whole, fewer opportunities for birds, with the exception of seed- and fruit-eating finches such as yellowhammers and bullfinches which prefer the bushy refuges offered by spindle and bush trees. The bullfinch has been persecuted by commercial growers for its tendency to eat its way over a fruit tree, eventually venturing deeper into the orchard, rather than flitting from tree to tree.

Stewards of Community or wild life orchards need not worry quite so much, but if the bullfinch is disturbing your efforts to raise prime fruits, bear this in mind: they generally prefer the buds of pear, plum and apple, in that order. Bullfinches will even display preferences for varieties within fruits, for example, Conference over

Old orchards offer rich pickings for wild life. Clockwise from top left: bird hole in perry pear, Aconbury Orchard, Worcester; bracket fungus on apple at Home Cottage Farm, Bucks; lichen on apple at Cotehele, Cornwall; invertebrate holes in cherry at Stone's Orchard, Croxley Green, Herts.

Comice pears. Planting 'sacrificial' varieties may distract them from the main body of the orchard. As ecologist Ian Newton of the Institute of Terrestrial Ecology noted in the early 1960s: 'in a mixed orchard at blossom time, Conference trees may be almost denuded of flower, while the adjoining Comice are in full bloom.' An abundance of other seed food in orchard borders, such as ash, coupled perhaps with a generous gap to the nearest fruit tree, may also help keep the finches in the hedge.

Commercial orchards are of less interest to bird life, although nest boxes can help. The spindle or bush trees are usually grubbed at around 15 years or earlier and so have no deadwood or rot holes, and their short trunks hold no quarry for trunk feeders such as treecreepers or beetles. What's more, the orchard floor is usually sprayed with herbicides to allow young trees to establish quickly without competition, so obliterating nectar-rich wild flowers.

You can't help but notice the difference should you visit James Marsden's orchard, at Gregg's Pit, Much Marcle, in Herefordshire. The land deeds show that it dates from at least 1785. Pests may never have been much of a problem, simply because the orchard is so rich in natural predators, as Marsden explains:

Diversity offers intrinsic protection from pests. Old orchards like mine often contain a number of trees of considerable age – perry pears that are more than 150 years old, for instance, and cider apple and cherry trees more than 60 years old. Because of the replanting that has gone on over many years, a great mixture of trees of different varieties and ages are dotted throughout the orchard. The result is a highly valuable wild life habitat very similar to the better-known lowland wood pasture.

The mixture of fruit species of early- and late-flowering fruit species reduces the risk of damaging outbreaks of pests or disease. In Gregg's Pit orchard, flowering starts in late March with damsons, plums and perry pears and continues until early June with the last of the apples.

And because few if any chemical sprays are used in many traditional orchards, natural predators of pest species – ladybirds, hoverflies, earwigs as well as tits and finches and more – build up numbers high enough to combat any potential problem. In effect, ladybirds and blue tits act as nature's insecticides. Potential pests such as codling moth, apple sawfly and aphids may be present, but not in high numbers.

Healthy populations of beneficial insects may also be encouraged by the presence of livestock grazing the orchard sward, especially in spring and early summer months. But even more important is the presence of grassland and hedgerows rich in wild flowers. The richer the botanical diversity of your orchard, the greater the complement of insects that act as natural pest control agents. For instance, nectar-rich flowers provide vital energy in spring and early summer for a host of parasitic wasps which in turn attack pest species such as aphids.

Research has also shown that orchards with rich plant communities are remarkably free of codling moth – whose larvae are the 'maggots' in apples – even though the orchards have not been sprayed. Most of the larvae are dealt with by their natural insect enemies, including various sorts of ground beetles. The beetles hunt down and eat the larvae as they overwinter in the soil.

Boundary hedges around the orchard provide protection from wind and frost, food and nesting habitats for many species, and a home for natural predators of orchard pests. Brambles, for instance, are known to support substantial populations of beneficial predatory mites.

What's more, beneficial bird species that eat caterpillars and other insect pests – the tit species and tree sparrows, for instance – favour traditional orchards too. Bullfinches, on the other hand, often regarded as a significant

> JUST AS MEN FROM VARIOUS CAUSES CONGREGATE IN PARTICULAR PLACES, SO THERE ARE SPOTS IN THE FIELDS — IN THE COUNTRY GENERALLY — WHICH APPEAR TO SPECIALLY ATTRACT BIRDS OF ALL KINDS...THIS ORCHARD AND GARDEN AT WICK IS ONE OF THE FAVOURITE PLACES. IT IS LIKE ONE OF THOSE EASTERN MARTS WHERE MEN OF FIFTY DIFFERENT NATIONALITIES, AND PICTURESQUELY CLAD, JOSTLE EACH OTHER IN THE BAZAARS: SO HERE FEATHERED TRAVELLERS OF EVERY SPECIES HAVE A KIND OF LEAFY CAPITAL
>
> from *Wild Life in a Southern County*, Richard Jefferies, 1879

orchard pest, turn out to be more frequent in modern bush orchards.

In a recent study of 109 orchards in Herefordshire, more than twice as many birds were counted in traditional orchards, compared to modern commercial ones, and the range of species seen in the old orchards was significantly more diverse as well. The traditional, unsprayed orchards were particularly attractive to tree sparrows, wood pigeon, great tit, jackdaw, long-tailed tit, mistle thrush, spotted flycatcher, little owl, treecreeper, starling, great spotted woodpecker, stock dove and collared dove – not least because many of these species nest in holes in old, standard trees and feed on invertebrates.

So the less intensively you manage an orchard, the more species it may support and the greater the opportunity for a build up of natural predators. Blue tits and other insect-eating song birds are adept in the biological control of orchard pests such as aphids, and will themselves attract birds of prey including buzzards, sparrowhawks and peregrines. Control of voles – which sometimes damage young tree roots – is best achieved by hole-dwelling owls including tawny and little.

Traditional orchards tend to be less intensively managed, mainly because they satisfy a number of land uses such as grazing or haymaking, as well as fruit production. In any case, spraying a standard orchard requires expensive equipment and chemicals and in the case of cider, perry or juicing fruit, there is no need for blemish-free specimens.

Instead of using sprays, wise growers are also experimenting with ways to reinforce the natural predators' good work by broadcasting a scented pheromone, the pests' natural chemical signalling device, to disrupt their mating. One recent study in California showed that an array of automatic puffer machines hung in walnut trees, and set to release a puff of pheromone every 30 minutes for a week, prevented up to 98 per cent of the male codling moths finding females. Meanwhile, British researchers are actively investigating the use of aphid pheromones to disrupt mating in

The red admiral is one of many butterflies that will feed on fruit.

orchards. 'If we could divert them from the trees, so no eggs were laid in the autumn, it might be the long-term, environmentally benign solution to these pests,' says insect ecologist Simon Leather of Imperial College London.

The more benign pest control techniques of the pre-pesticide era might also be worthy of re-discovery. When DDT was first introduced in the US in the 1940s, to control codling moths in the apple orchards of Washington state, growers summarily abandoned a host of effective but labour-intensive techniques that had once kept pest populations at bay. Clues to this lost knowledge are tucked away in old manuals and technical treatises such as Eleanor Ormerod's *Handbook of Insects Injurious to Orchard and Bush Fruits with Means of Prevention and Remedy*, published in London in 1898. A Fellow of the Entomological Society of London, she was also a member of similar societies in Stockholm, the US, Canada, Australia and 'Cape Colony'. To tackle codling moth she

recommends shaking the boughs of the trees onto cloths spread underneath, 'for thus a good proportion of the infested Apples can be gathered up before the grubs have time to get away'. The damaged fruit 'can be thrown at once to wet manure' or fed to sheep, she wrote, from her study at Torrington House in St Albans, where she worked with her sister Georgiana. To stop the codling maggots climbing up or down the trees she tells orchardists to 'wind a hay-rope in three coils round the trunk of a tree at a little distance from the ground,' and also to the larger branches.

To deal with other pests, Eleanor Ormerod often advises removal of the offending bugs or affected parts by hand – on cherry trees you might 'send a boy up the tree to nip out the nests'. But at the right time of day and season more shakings could be on the cards, perhaps 'over an old umbrella placed the wrong way up and daubed inside with adhesive mixture'. The timely arrival of a flock of hens or 'the attendance of the pigs might also be invaluable and save the trouble of spreading anything beneath the trees to collect into'. Bear in mind, she advises, that 'birds of various kinds – as rooks, thrushes, blackbirds and especially starlings – have been found to be of great use in keeping the grubs in check, and should on no account be driven away'. Throughout she reminds growers that the 'best methods of prevention lie in the regular measures of good cultivation' – healthy trees can generally weather the onslaughts of their insect visitors.

It is well worth thinking too about growing local cultivars that are resistant to diseases that are likely to be the greatest problems in your region. For instance, Cox has become a widespread apple variety, yet ironically it is one of the hardest to grow, being vulnerable to a range of diseases. Commercial apple growers may routinely spray a dozen or more applications of fungicide each growing season just to prevent one disease, scab – but good scab-resistant varieties are available and could be grown instead. An end to these sprays would bring an added bonus: in a fungicide-free orchard natural populations of beneficial predatory mites can recover, and then help to keep infestations of damaging mites at bay.

Above all, encourage diversity in your orchard, and don't worry about a few spots or holes in your trees' leaves. In fact, such depredations could even be the trees' secret weapon, as research on tomatoes suggests.

Biologist Steve Wratten, now at Lincoln University in New Zealand, has found that tomato plants respond very quickly to insect attack, producing chemicals in the afflicted leaves that move caterpillars onto other leaves. The result is lots of leaves with a few holes in them. This is a happy outcome for the plant, Wratten suggests, because insect-eating birds such as tits notice all the holes and come looking for caterpillars.

Fruit trees may well behave in similar ways in order to recruit their own natural defenders: the take-home message could be: don't panic, holes in leaves are a sign that the tree has everything under control. Further research into the mysteries of plant defences could be 'very rewarding', reckons Simon Leather, who specialises in the study of insects on cherry trees.

How the apple tempted the bee

We do know, at any rate, that whatever the leaves may be up to, the flowers of fruit trees are decidedly masters in the manipulation of beneficial wild life. Long before Eve, the apple's forebears found a way to make themselves irresistible to insects. They hit upon an ingenious way to reproduce, enlisting these six-legged allies as go-betweens to ferry pollen, the male sex cells, from one flower to another. This outlandish scheme was a tremendous success, not least because an apple blossom offers its insect visitor a gift of nectar – a high-energy drink that perfectly complements the tasty pollen, which bees and beetles consume as a rich source of protein. The apple bears the loss happily – not all will be eaten. There's plenty to go round.

Indeed, as Charles Darwin suggested in 1876, it's likely that apple trees deliberately make far more flowers than will ever set fruit. The profusion of flowers is well worth the effort, because it enhances the tree's attractiveness to pollinating insects. To test the idea, a researcher in Oregon in 1909 painstakingly removed the petals from all 1,500 flowers of one apple tree: only eight bees visited the tree, and only five flowers set fruit. Another pomologist, working in New Jersey in 1924, removed the petals from 250 apple flowers; he found that no bees visited and none set fruit.

Unspecialised beetles, wasps and flies probably pollinated the very first flowers – which looked a bit like a modern magnolia. But this basic model was soon joined by thousands of novel variations, brightly coloured and bizarrely shaped. Pollinating insects kept pace, evolving body shapes to suit the new floral anatomies. Thanks to 150 million years of fevered negotiation, our planet is now home to a huge variety of bees, wasps, butterflies, moths and hoverflies, each equipped with tongue or proboscis custom-made to reach the nectar hidden deep within some fantastic flower. You could say that in temptation lies the origin of Eden, not its demise.

Beekeeping was born when early humans discovered that house-hunting swarms of honeybees would accept an artificial abode. From the start, orchards were deemed good places to lodge the hive – wild bees themselves might choose the hollow of an aged fruit tree to set up home. Not so long ago, few orchards were without at least one beekeeper's hive.

European honeybees *Apis mellifera* make good pollinators of apple and other fruit trees, especially when the worker-bees collect pollen to feed to the young brood. The light honey they make from the nectar of fruit blossom is said to have an excellent delicate flavour and fine aroma.

When the Romans invaded Britain, they found the locals tending dome-shaped hives made of willow or hazel twigs and plastered inside and out with cow dung. This kind of hive survived in parts of Britain until the 18th century, when it was gradually replaced

Beehives in an apple orchard near Teynham, Kent, where the bees' foraging will cross-pollinate the blossom. Commercial bee farmers move their colonies seasonally, following flowering crops, but mixed orchards with diverse grassland or hedgerow species can support sedentary hives.
Illustration: codling moth with 'maggoty' apple.

by the straw basket hive or 'skep', which persisted well into Victorian times. To shelter the straw hives from the weather, recesses were built into walls, often in orchards. Commonly known as bee holes in Yorkshire and bee boles in Scotland, these recesses still persist in places such as Packwood House, a National Trust property in Warwickshire.

Traditionally, orchards were stocked with about two hives to the hectare, and even today many old orchards have at least one hive. But high-density commercial apple orchards typically rely on mobile bees – 'flying squads' – hired in from April to early May for about £30 a hive.

'Migratory beekeeping' has become a thriving industry. Every year several thousands of hives are moved into fruit orchards in Kent and the Vale of Evesham, as well as East Anglia and eastern Scotland, with Kent alone providing work for 1,700 mobile hives, according to the Bee Farmers' Association. By mid May or early June, as the fruit blossom fades, the bees are trucked off to pollinate oilseed rape, field bean and mustard.

By contrast, in old orchards, traditional beekeeping is sometimes still practised, and here the bees need access to a wide range of wild and garden flowers once the fruit blossom is over.

Even in perfect conditions, however, it can be a mistake to rely entirely on honeybees as pollinators, if only because they are always vulnerable to the spread of diseases or deadly parasites such as the imported mite, Varroa. Given the right environment – a healthy landscape with plenty of places to feed and nest – wild bees can do the job even more effectively than domesticated honeybees. Bumblebees – six out of 25 species are still widespread in Britain – take to the wing even when it's too cold for honeybees. They work fast too, clocking in as many as 20 apple flowers per minute. Because they're big, bumblebees tend to pollinate the flowers more effectively than honeybees do. And because they have longer tongues than honeybees, they are vital pollinators of scores of deep-throated perennial wild flowers as well as field bean and red clover crops.

Thirty years ago, John Free of Rothamsted Experimental Station in Hertfordshire, writing in his *Insect Pollination of Crops*, noted scores of studies showing fruit set better in orchards grown in good countryside hospitable to bumblebees. In the late 1980s, enthusiastic young members of WATCH, the junior wing of the Wildlife Trusts, carried out a valuable national survey of bumblebees' flower preferences. Apple blossoms turned out to be a particular favourite of a beautiful gingery bumblebee, sometimes known as a carder bee; its Latin name *Bombus pascuorum* means 'of the pastures'.

Solitary bees – wild bees that don't form colonies – can also be important pollinators of fruit trees in Britain. But like all the wild bees, they need to find suitable nesting places close to prime feeding sites. Tussocky old pasture and banks alongside flower-rich hedgerows and orchards are bumblebee paradise.

Cherry aphids provide food for many orchard birds; the caterpillars of the spectacular goat moth sometimes tunnel into orchard trees exuding a powerful goat-like odour; while the rare Camberwell beauty butterfly has been sighted feasting on early windfalls in plum orchards, and bumblebees pollinate apple blossom even more efficiently than honeybees do.

Bees get most of the credit, but apple-blossom pollen is spread about by other less glamorous insects too. The apple's inviting flowers attract a remarkable diversity of flying insects. Keen-eyed observers of apple blossom have spotted fungus-gnats, aptly named for their penchant for mushrooms, as well as St Mark's flies (*Bibio* spp). Look in an orchard around St Mark's Day, 25 April, and you're likely to see these largish black insects drifting lazily about with long legs dangling. Other visitors include the sluggish fever flies (*Dilophus* spp) and the bee-flies *Bombylius*, which look rather like small bumblebees equipped with a permanently protruding proboscis. Representatives of the house-fly and blowfly families regularly put in an appearance, as well as small flower-beetles of the family Nitidulidae.

The feast at the fallen fruit

On any autumn day, you might see a noisy, colourful flock of fieldfares, hundreds strong, perhaps, descend on an orchard full of ripe fruit. It can look like the arrival of marauding hordes. But the feeding frenzy doesn't worry the trees. After all, fruit is designed to be eaten. It's a tree's way of ensuring that its seeds are distributed far beyond its reach. It's not by accident that an apple tree encloses its seeds in sweet, succulent, conspicuously coloured flesh. The eye-catching packaging is a deliberately fashioned advertisement. Birds in particular are eager consumers. Ground-feeding insectivores, particularly the thrushes – redwings, fieldfares, mistle and song thrush, as well as blackbirds – are joined by members of the crow family to feed on windfalls in autumn and winter.

Plum orchards provide windfalls well in

advance of most apples and pears, and it was among the plums that butterfly enthusiasts recorded the most early sightings of the rare Camberwell beauty in 1995. Red admirals and commas feeding on over-ripe fruit are a common sight. By dusk that fruit is equally attractive to moths. A visit with a torch can reveal large numbers of feeding moths. The species most often encountered are the sallows, silver Ys and large yellow underwings. Rotting fruit seems particularly important to species preparing to hibernate as adults such as the chestnut or the satellite moths. The buff arches moth is said to be powerfully attracted to the essence of the delicious Jargonelle pear.

Orchard owners wishing to attract fruit-eating birds ought to include crab apples in their orchard. Not only will the crabs help to pollinate the domestic apples, they also hold their fruits for longer, perhaps offering winter food for smaller birds with less fear of predation or robbery on the ground. A number of domestic apples, such as Dymock Red, Bismark, Arthur Turner and Sturmer Pippin, to name a few, share this quality, even well into the frost season.

Abundant in autumn and winter, fruit is there just when birds in particular need high-energy foods. Once eaten, the seeds usually pass undamaged through the digestive tract or else are regurgitated some distance from the mother tree. If you see a blackbird or robin 'heaving', chances are they are about to bring up a lump of seeds that have collected in their crop. But life is never simple, and, from the fruit tree's point of view, some birds undeniably cheat. Finches, for instance, typically digest the seeds, while tits often just peck at an apple or pear, avoiding the seeds inside. But, braced for the loss, the fruit tree responds by ensuring a supply of more than enough seed.

Sometimes birds eating windfalls get more than they bargained for. David Norman of Liverpool University has seen fieldfares swaying about near fruit farms at Daresbury, in Cheshire. 'They were highly disorientated and intoxicated from the effects of eating fermenting apples,' he said. 'Twice, I caught drunken birds by hand. They only sobered up and flew off after spending half an hour in a darkened room.' As the fruits decomposed, wild yeasts had turned the sugars to alcohol. Sturdy starlings, however, may be immune to the effects. Researchers in Frankfurt University fed captive birds a diet laced with alcohol, but in half an hour the birds appeared stone-cold sober. The biologists discovered that the enzyme that breaks down alcohol, alcohol dehydrogenase, works 14 times faster in starlings than in humans. So these lucky birds can consume as much fermenting fruit as they like without becoming incapacitated.

Reports of tipsy mammals are thin on the ground, but hedgehogs, hares, deer and badgers certainly visit orchards in autumn and winter to feed on the trees' largesse. Hedgehogs have long been said to carry away fallen fruits by rolling and impaling them on their spines. It's a remarkably persistent story, recorded by the Roman historian Pliny some 2000 years ago, and widely repeated in mediaeval bestiaries throughout Europe. It even pops up in China. The fruit being gathered ranges from apples and figs to grapes, pears and strawberries, and in some accounts the hedgehogs are said first to climb trees to dislodge the fruit and then to hurl themselves down on the fruit of their labour. Modern-day biologists are deeply sceptical, however; Nigel Reeve concludes that while hedgehogs may appreciate fruit, it doesn't constitute a major component of their diet. They have never been known to cache fruit for themselves or their young, nor has tree-climbing been observed. Biologist Maurice Burton, reluctant to condemn such an enduring tale out of hand, has suggested that hedgehogs might just conceivably pick up fallen fruits on their spines by accident, should they be stimulated to 'self-anoint' as they passed under a tree. Burton himself had a tame hedgehog that indulged in this unique behaviour when it smelt or tasted, among other things, dead leaves. When self-anointing, a hedgehog foams at the mouth and flails about trying to spit saliva onto its back and flanks. Conceivably while so energetically occupied it might also spear the odd fruit, as Burton's hedgehog did, when it happened under a crab apple tree.

Fruit is a particularly important source of energy for badgers in late summer and autumn, when the animals are trying to build up fat rapidly before winter, according to British badger expert Ernest Neal. Badgers are particularly fond of sweet succulent fruit, picking off ripe blackberries from brambles neatly with their mouths. If badgers can visit orchards, however, they will happily eat whatever fruit is available – windfall apples in particular, but also pears, plums, cherries and peaches.

Hares and deer may also venture into orchards at harvest time, an attraction that has been exploited by wild life vets. Researchers placed apples injected with a worming compound called Davosin at forest edges close to the paths used by hares. According to a 1993 report in the journal *Nature*, the hares consumed the apples and so protected themselves against intestinal parasites. The same trick worked for roe and red deer too.

Orchards, particularly those with apples, are often host to another source of winter fodder – the berries of the semi-parasitic plant known as mistletoe. A recent survey for the Botanical Society of the British Isles and Plantlife has confirmed apple as the favourite host of this useful and decorative species – indeed, apples are home to more than 80 per cent of mistletoes in the country. Most common in Herefordshire, Worcestershire, Gloucestershire and parts of Somerset, mistletoe particularly likes the open habitats of orchards, where it is a valuable resource for many overwintering birds, as botanist Jonathan Briggs explains:

Berries develop through the summer months, first as green fruit and finally ripening to white. Mistletoe is our only native white-berried plant, which presents it with problems: many birds that might spread its seeds don't recognise white berries. Luckily the mistle thrush, aptly named after the plant, relishes the berries, and guards them over the winter against other potential consumers. Blackcaps, which increasingly overwinter in Britain, also have a taste for the berries.

These two birds eat the berries in quite different ways. The mistle thrush swallows the berry whole and later excretes the seed, while the blackcap tries to wipe the seed from the sticky berry flesh onto the branch of the tree. The blackcap method is probably much more successful in spreading mistletoe from tree to tree and helping it germinate in the right spot. But no doubt people too have lent a helping hand. Its fame as a Yuletide decoration has ensured its spread into formal parklands in London, Lincolnshire, Norfolk and even Scotland.

In Kent, many old cobnut plantations, called plats, provide another sort of harvest that forms a welcome foodstuff for a variety of hungry birds and mammals, as Meg Game of the Kentish Cobnuts Association describes:

Grey squirrels visit nut plats in numbers not appreciated by the grower. Luckily even their voracious appetites can rarely strip an entire orchard before harvest. By contrast, cobnuts are deliberately fed to red squirrels; in the north of England and Scotland enthusiasts purchase up to a tonne of nuts for this purpose. In Kent, many nut plats also support dormice. Cobnut shells are rather thicker than those of wild hazel, but dormice seem to be able to open them, and are rewarded by larger kernels than those of hazel. Old trees provide a cornucopia of holes, nooks and crannies near the ground for hibernating.

Mistletoe, seen here in several clumps on a Herefordshire tree, favours apple to the other fruit trees as its host.

Cobnut plats, with their lack of undergrowth and large nuts, are not particularly attractive to many birds, although their array of small branches suits cup-shaped nests. All the same, cobnuts are greatly enjoyed by nuthatches, which seem unusually abundant in nut-growing districts.

Many plats contain shade-loving plants more often found in ancient woods, such as primrose, moschatel (town hall clock), sanicle, barren strawberry, wood anemone, cow-wheat, orpine, twayblade and pignut. Pignut is so abundant in one plat that the former owner complained that it invaded her garden. Rarer plants in Kentish nut plats are early purple orchid, broad-leaved helleborine, bird's nest orchid, heath spotted-orchid and toothwort. The latter is parasitic on hazel, though it seems to do little harm to the trees. It is rather rare, being largely restricted to old woods and hedges. However, it is found in at least five cobnut plats, where it thrives to such an extent that two commercial plats hold probably the largest populations in the country. Even more surprising is that both of these plats are sprayed with herbicide. Presumably the toothwort, having no green parts, is unaffected by the chemical, although this may not be the case when (inevitably) the chemical is changed. My own two plats are on impoverished, acid sandy soil. Besides bluebells, they support cow-wheat, wood anemone, wood sorrel, common spotted orchid, broad-leaved helleborine, wood sorrel, barren strawberry and primrose.

Natural mosaics

Old orchards can score highly as places of value to a mind-boggling variety of beetles, bees and bugs, as well as spiders, snails and woodlice, and scores of other invertebrates, according to Roger Key, senior invertebrate biologist with English Nature. Here, he explains how each piece of the orchard jigsaw enhances its attraction to wild life, from a bug or beetle's point of view.

Why are old orchards so hospitable to life? Part of the answer is that a traditional orchard is effectively a combination of different habitats – a wood standing within flowery meadows enclosed by a hedge, which itself may have more and different flowers. In this happy combination an orchard becomes an entity that is much more than the sum of its parts.

Indeed, most insects and their relations abhor uniformity in the environment. Only diverse, patchwork habitats can satisfy the conflicting demands that youth and maturity hold for them – almost as though they were two species rolled into one. Consider, for instance, the life history of longhorn beetles such as the stag beetle. These impressive-looking insects specialise, as bees do, in feeding on nectar and pollen. As adults, they target wild plants that bloom in open grassy spaces such as orchard margins. They enjoy warm sheltered spots with plenty of flowers.

But the grub of a longhorn beetle is completely different. It requires cool, moist, decaying wood, ideally in contact with the soil. So if you want longhorn beetles in your orchard, these two very different sorts of habitat need to be close to each other. And when this happens, it's not just longhorn beetles that benefit. The invertebrate fauna in general tends to be much richer than it is when either of the two habitats exist in isolation from one another. The micro-habitat mosaic is as important as the larger mosaic: a tussock within short grassland could harbour bush crickets – which will leap into the short grass for their prey, perhaps a grasshopper of some sort – then quickly return to the tussock before being seen by a predator such as a jackdaw. In this sense, a varied orchard with patches of nettles and grass tussocks as well as hedges and grassland may be exceptionally good for invertebrate diversity.

When old orchards are dotted about the countryside, connected by unimproved meadows and hedges or strips of woodland, the orchard ecosystem grows even richer. Populations of plants and animals need to be able to move between islands of favourable habitat, but some invertebrates, such as the woodland snails readily found in orchards, don't naturally travel about easily. They rely on 'corridors' of hospitable habitat that join good patches together. Some of the main orchard areas – the Marches, the south-west and the Lake District, for instance – have good mixed habitats and connectivity within their landscapes.

Grasslands: If an orchard's grasslands are highly grazed, shaded, neglected or all three at once, the grassland invertebrate fauna may be poor. But get it right, and the result can be superb. Butterflies include shade-tolerant species such as the orange tip or the speckled wood, a typical orchard butterfly that feeds in grass and likes the kind of dappled sunshine often found between fruit trees, especially plums and pears. Nettle patches along walls or hedges, or areas where prunings have been heaped up and allowed to decay attract laying butterflies such as peacock and small tortoiseshell as well as moths – notably the small magpie and mother of pearl moth.

Cockchafer beetles thrive in orchards. They remain common in the pastures of western Britain, but in some eastern counties cockchafers are found only in old orchards because good grassland has been lost elsewhere. The cockchafer in turn provides food for bats. A number of click beetles, such as the metallic green-bronze *Ctenicera plectinicornis*, are also typical of western hay meadows and orchard grasslands.

Flowery grasslands attract predators such as the soldier beetles. The grassland or the hedge bottom will harbour bee and wasp populations. Bumblebees and solitary bees in particular are very important in orchards in that many are more efficient as pollinators than domestic hive bees. A good hedge bottom with tussocky grassland for bumblebees will aid the pollination of fruit blossom. Solitary bee and wasp species can be found in bare sandy or chalky soil, especially on banks, or in the mortar of old walls, and are also good pollinators.

Orchard walls: A walled orchard presents a whole new habitat for many invertebrates. Invertebrates need external sources of heat, so walls, gates or exposed tree trunks – areas that catch the sun and have no covering vegetation – can be 10 to 15° C warmer than the surrounding area. Basking is an essential part of invertebrate existence.

While many orchards grow on neutral clay or sometimes acid sandy soils, calcareous chalky soils also support orchards and are attractive to snails and other molluscs, which need calcium carbonate to make their shells. Britain's only terrestrial periwinkle, which loves limestone and chalk grasslands, may also be found on walls.

Those appealing beetles known as glowworms may depend on an orchard's wall to provide an adequate source of the snails they feed on. Some spiders also like walls; the woodlouse spider, for instance, feeds on the pill woodlice that live in the crevices in old mortar. Like snails, the pill woodlouse also needs the wall's calcium carbonate.

Orchard hedges: A surrounding hedgerow can significantly boost the biodiversity of the orchard it encloses by providing shelter, diverse species of plants and even a suntrap with a diverse range of plants within and beneath it. Hedgerows around single-fruit orchards extend the nectar season. Hawthorn, for instance, is one of the best nectar plants and can extend the nectar season of early-flowering plum and cherry orchards. Unfortunately,

Let the wild life take their tithe and watch as a rich ecological community develops. Blackbirds are one of the orchard's most discerning devotees. Photo: R. Wilmshurst (RSPB Images).

Primroses, beneath the unfurling canopy of Kentish cobnut leaves, colourfully herald a new season in an old plat near Plaxtol, Kent. Photo: Meg Game.

hawthorn can be a carrier of fireblight and so is not recommended for pear and apple orchards. Bramble in the hedge provides both a good nectar source later in the year (July) once most other nectar sources have finished, as well as being a main food plant for many invertebrates such as the buff arches moth. The hedge can also support leaf-eating insects not present among the orchard trees. For example, if the hedge contains buckthorn it may attract the bright yellow brimstone butterfly.

The fruit: Birds, particularly thrushes, are well known for their love of fallen fruit, but windfall fruits also attract a variety of invertebrates including butterflies and sap-feeding beetles such as the red-spotted *Glischrochilus hortensus* which feeds in holes that have been pecked in the fruit by birds. Wasps, which are beneficial biological control agents for most of the year, love fallen apples but tend to become inebriated and aggressive after feeding on fermenting fruit. Hornets, which are much scarcer and much less aggressive than wasps, also feed on windfalls.

The flowers: Fruit blossom is a valuable source of nectar for bees and other insects. A variety of benign beetles feed on the pollen of plants in the rose family – which includes most fruit trees – and can be found in unsprayed orchards. One pest species, the blossom weevil *Anthonomus pomorum*, is particularly targeted for spraying by growers. Unfortunately, there are about seven other harmless species of *Anthonomus* associated with fruit blossom which suffer from sprays aimed at *A. pomorum* and these are now Nationally Scarce or Red Data Book species.

The leaves: Apples rank among the top ten trees in their importance to plant-feeding invertebrates, according to ecologist Richard Southwood at Oxford University. A wide variety of invertebrates live or feed among the foliage of apple in particular, or as part of a wider predilection for plants in the rose family. The caterpillars of the eyed hawkmoths, commonly associated with willow, also feed on apple, pear and cherry. The adults are well camouflaged against apple bark until, disturbed, they display their bright-pink eyespots. Many predators living among the orchard foliage – such as lacewings, small soldier beetles and hoverfly larvae – help to control pests such as aphids and plant hoppers. Unfortunately, chemical pest controls kill predators as well as pests.

The black-veined white butterfly, was particularly associated with orchards in Britain until its extinction in the 1920s. In the plum and apple orchards at Craycombe in the Vale of Evesham, this butterfly had its last viable population in Britain. Now orchards themselves need friends if they are not to follow the black-veined white into oblivion.

Not all an orchard tree's foliage is its own. Mistletoe, whose favoured host is apple, has four invertebrate species associated with it – a moth and three bugs. Ivy, where it grows on fruit trees, is of enormous benefit to wild life. A late nectar source for many insects, it also provides evergreen shelter for overwintering adults. Some species, such as the nocturnal thick-legged flower beetles *Oncomera femorata*, are uniquely attracted to ivy blossom.

The bark: The bark of fruit trees offers lots of structural texture for invertebrates. Apple bark consists of plates gently held on at the middle, with plenty of nooks and crannies to scuttle around under. Pear bark has many chequerboard-type cracks that attract species such as tree-climbing ground beetles *Dromius* spp – my own garden orchard harbours five species of this one genus. The nocturnal darkling beetle *Cylindrinotus laevioctostriatus* is another highly specialised invertebrate, which lives in the tussocks at the base of apple tree during the day and emerges at night to graze the green *Pleurococcus* algae off the surface of the bark. Ladybirds, so important in aphid control, overwinter under loose bark.

One bark-dwelling beetle has distinctly eccentric dietary preferences. Called *Ctesias serra*, it is a 'wild' relative of the larder beetle. But far from living in a larder, it exists solely on the sucked-out remains of the insects that a bark-dwelling spider has already caught and consumed. And not just any old bark will do: this beetle can live only on really ancient trees with loose, thick bark.

Dead wood: Even dead wood is a vital habitat to many creatures; try to resist the temptation to tidy it away. Benignly neglected old orchards offer much to invertebrates. All trees eventually decay internally; it is a natural part of their biology and usually of no harm to the living tree. Internal decay fungi are present throughout a tree's life, but they only start to decay the wood when it is exposed as in a pruning wound or snapped twig. Early colonists of this area are bark beetles, of which fruit trees have their own species, *Scolytus mali*, which eventually loosen up the bark and allow other species, such as the cardinal beetles *Pyrochroa serraticornis* to follow.

On trees where the wood is exposed, various wild equivalents of the woodworm beetle bore into the dry timber, leaving various sized small holes. Once the beetles have finished with these, they are used by solitary wasps as nursery holes, in which they stock up prey items such as a plant hoppers or aphids as food for their grubs, and then cover the hole with mud. ▸ However, raiders such as ruby-tailed wasps *Chrysididae* may enter the hole before the solitary wasp has sealed it, then kill the egg, lay its own and fly off, all before the solitary wasp returns to cap it off. A whole community exists simply in the

---

The very rare noble chafer beetle lives in a few old orchards in southern England.

Orchard walls can be vital hotspots for basking invertebrates. Photo: James Ravilious.

holes left by the bark beetles. Decay will eventually get into the heart of the timber. Rot holes offer nesting opportunities for hornets as well as birds and bats. Wet rot-holes, or 'rot-pools', constitute a separate habitat for species of, for example, hoverflies. Particular bumblebee-mimicking hoverflies live only on exposed rot-holes in tree roots.

Once decaying wood starts to become soft, it offers habitats for the larvae of many wood-feeding insects and their predators. As they decay, apple trees often provide white-rotted timber, where both the cellulose and lignin decay away equally, leaving a soft, spongy textured material. Various longhorn beetles – the stag beetle *Lucanus cervus*, the rhinoceros beetle *Sinodendron cylidricum* and the lesser stag beetle *Dorcus paralellipipedus* – all particularly love white-rotted timber. The 'Great Stag Hunt' beetle survey – launched for the People's Trust for Endangered Species in 1997 by Environment Minister Michael Meacher – revealed that of all the trees in Britain, the apple comes third as the best place to find a stag beetle.

The fungi responsible for all this beneficial decay are themselves a vital resource for many creatures. The fungal fruiting bodies, for instance, support a wide variety insect species, including highly attractive false ladybirds *Endomychus coccineus*, with different species living on the bracket fungi, the gill fungi and the pore fungi. And the mushrooms and toadstools in the underlying grasslands may be vital to the trees, forming intimate associations with their roots known as mycorrhiza.

Eventually the wood in the heart of the tree is broken down into wood mould, which is then particularly attractive to the rarer species. Unfortunately, many trees, once they reach this stage of decay, will be removed by the orchard owner who is probably unaware that the wood mould may attract rose chafer beetles *Cetonia aurata* or the very rare noble chafer *Gnorimus nobilis*. The noble chafer now has an incredibly reduced distribution – restricted to the orchards around the Wyre Forest, on the Cotswold fringes of Worcestershire and Gloucestershire, in the New Forest and in Oxfordshire. In continental Europe the noble chafer is largely associated with oak, but in Britain it is almost exclusive linked to ancient fruit trees. In the New Forest, its distribution appears to mirror the distribution of crab apple. And it's not just the noble chafer itself that is significant. Its presence signals a very rich dead-wood invertebrate fauna, which may extend to several hundred species of beetles, flies, bees, wasps, spiders, molluscs, centipedes, millepedes, false scorpions and more. Biodiversity indeed!

Inspiration

MENTION POETRY, plays or pastimes, and few of us will immediately think of orchards – words such as picking, pruning or planting are far more likely to come to mind. But the linguistic reflex that instantly consigns orchards to the horticultural realm misleads us. In operas and oil paintings, cartoons and computers, orchards and their fruit continue to play a vital inspirational role.

In stories that reverberate through civilisation after civilisation, the apple is frequently a lure: from Eve to Snow White, women in particular are tempted by that shiny red skin. Deceived by appearances, the innocent heroines succumb – though it is often the reddest patch on an apple that hides a maggot.

Today, apples as whimsical emblems of temptation and lost innocence pop up on book spines as well as in advertising. They feature in political cartoons, on stamps and as corporate logos – this book has been produced on an Apple Macintosh computer. Apples appear in county, district, borough or parish council emblems, on pub signs, street names and in cosmetics. Everywhere we look, we are likely to find the apple, orchard or other fruit used as a symbol, ripe with multiple meanings.

Time and again, apples and orchards have bridged the cultural gulf between the everyday customs and traditions and high art. The apple's rich symbolism extends undiminished right the way through from classical Greek and Roman literature to contemporary fine art, as Michael Cassin, former Education Officer at the National Gallery of Scotland, argues in this short extract from his essay, *Forbidden Fruit*:

Barn and yard, Burrow Hill Cider, Kingsbury Episcopi, Somerset. Photo: James Ravilious.

But perhaps the apple's most famous appearances occur in the two traditions which still exert so strong an influence on the culture in which we live: those of the Classical and Judaeo-Christian past. In the Old Testament, apart from in the story of the Fall, apples are most commonly symbols of health; simply to inhale the scent of an apple could help the sick on the road to recovery. And it is from this tradition that our most prized possession became known as 'the apple of our eye' (Deuteronomy: XXXii, 10)....

In Classical legends the first and most idyllic of the four ages of the world is the Golden Age, of which there is a painting in the National Gallery of Scotland, by Il Poppi, which shows splendidly nude figures draped in relaxation, or pursuing a number of delightful activities while little putti pass apples around for everyone to eat. Images like this, and representations of the Garden of the Hesperides, probably provide the sources for pictures of the Garden of Eden.

The Hesperides were languidly beautiful nymphs who lazed about, guarding, with a serpent called Ladon, a tree which produced golden apples. One of the labours Hercules undertook for Eurystheus was to procure some of the nymphs' golden apples. The golden fruit could not survive for long away from its native soil and Athene eventually took the apples back to the garden. But their journeys were by no means over. When Peleus married the nymph Thetis all the gods of Olympus were invited to the wedding except for Eris, Goddess of Discord … She appeared at the wedding feast in a fit of pique and flung down one of the Hesperides' golden apples inscribed with the words "For the Fairest".... In 15th- and 16th-century Northern European paintings of the Madonna and Child, for example, Jesus, as the second Adam, often holds an apple in acknowledgement of the fact that His life and death counteract the sin of the first Adam. … like any other fruit, apples can become infected by worms and can wither in time. From the 17th century onwards they sometimes appear in paintings with a Christian message, such as the 'Vanitas' still lives, as a reference to the transience of human life and the futility of worldly aspirations.

In the 19th and 20th centuries, painters who were not remotely concerned with apples as symbols continued to include them in their paintings for their shape and colour alone. But the most famous apple painter of the 20th century must be René Magritte, whose work includes images in which familiar objects appear in unfamiliar circumstances: monstrously huge apples which fill ordinary domestic interiors, for example. Magritte consistently denied any symbolic interpretation of his paintings, but post-Freud, it is impossible not to see in them references to the world of dreams and the unconscious.

Commercial art too had early beginnings linked to orchards, particularly in Canada and Tasmania, in the guise of decorative labels pasted onto apple crates destined for export. With recent consumer demands for traceability in food products, perhaps now is the time for growers to create a new form of Britart – distinctive fruit labels in the great tradition.

The crate label art of Canada is celebrated in Kelowna at the heart of Canada's main apple-growing region in the Okanagan Valley. There, the British Columbia Orchard Industry Museum exhibits a wealth of documents, paintings and photographs of apples, orchards and packing factories. One of the stars of its collection of orchard artefacts is its impressive array of apple crate labels.

Crate label art is a 'peculiar phenomenon', says the museum's curator, Wayne Wilson. 'Its imagery is varied, its colours are rich, its design elements are distinctive.' In short, the labels are 'saturated with meaning'. They made use of the iconography of the 'wild west', illustrated the intrepid hunter or showed picturesque scenes contrasting a rugged mountainous backdrop with the neat rows of orchards. Less traditional images incorporated references to the exotic, while other labels featured

Youth orchestra at Apple Day, Home Cottage Farm, Buckinghamshire. Photo: Reproduced with permission from The Uxbridge Gazette.

simple bold logos. A further range seemed designed to find favour in Britain, then the largest export market for Canadian fruit: consumers could choose The Thistle, John Bull or The Lion brands, their labels bedecked with Union Jacks. On the other side of the world, crate label art was also developing alongside the Tasmanian apple industry. The Huon Valley was the heart of the region's apple industry until the 1970s, when the government's 'tree-pull' programme encouraged orchardists to take out their uneconomic orchards. By the mid 1980s, despite new orchards being planted, 90 per cent of small growers had given up, and the industry was dominated by three main growers. Based on recorded interviews, Catherine Watson's book *Full and Plenty* tells the story of the growth and decline of the apple industry in the Huon Valley and with it the crate label art.

Musicians too have found inspiration among the trees and produce. The Andrews Sisters told us 'Don't sit under the apple tree with anyone else but me' and the Yetties exhort us to 'Drink up the Cider' while scores of other singers have pledged 'I'll be with you in apple blossom time'. The beauty of orchards and evocative nature of apples makes them prime candidates for immortalising in song.

New songs have been created in schools on Apple Day and for celebrations in Community Orchards. English singer-songwriter Steve Ashley was inspired by Common Ground's *Orchards: a guide to local conservation* and our *Apple Day* poster to write his orchard song, 'Say Goodbye'. Recorded with bass player Danny Thompson and Fairport

Convention's Chris Leslie, the song is featured on the album *Everyday Lives*. Another 20th-century musician and writer attracted by the lure of the apple was Ian Dury; his *Apples: The Musical* was first performed at the Royal Court in 1989, with evocative reminders of cockney barrow boys selling fruit.

In Blantyre Prison, Sussex, in April 1999, Glyndebourne Opera created a piece of music theatre about the prison orchard, with help from the Women's Institute and a local high school. Consider commissioning a composer to create music inspired by your orchard – perhaps it could be performed on recorders, made in the traditional way from pear wood. In 2000 the Dorset Youth Jazz Orchestra enjoyed such a fantastic response at the festival 'Jazz sous les Pommiers' (Jazz under the apple trees) in Normandy, that they were invited back to to tour the region. Pommiers refers to Normandy as a whole, rather than an orchard venue, but performance among the harvest fruit was one of many excitements at the 1999 Apple Day at Home Cottage Farm near Iver, Buckinghamshire (see caption).

From the writings of Pliny in 77AD to Charles Dickens in 1894, through classical mythology and medieval prose to contemporary literature, orchards have been celebrated for their beauty and bounty. They are potent symbols of the rural idyll exemplified in the Kent cherry orchards of the Larkin novels by H E Bates, or in the cider apple orchards of Gloucestershire described by Laurie Lee in *Cider with Rosie*. In Stroud, not far from Lee's own roots in Slad, the Riff Raff poets celebrate Apple Day with readings of their orchard-inspired compositions.

Storytellers such as Hugh Lupton, Michael Dacre, Ben Heggarty and Pomme Clayton have many tales to tell of orchards as secret trysting places, magic gardens and sacred groves. In Somerset, the Apple Tree Man is still guardian of many an orchard, where on sunny days beneath shady trees visitors can claim to have come under the influence of Lazy Lawrence, the spirit of indolence. Far to the north in the western Highlands, a tale is still told about the hero who, wanting to pass from Islay to Ireland, threw 16 apples into the sea and was able to cross the water as he stepped from one to the other.

Shakespeare, always at ease with botanical allusions, turns to fruit to suggest romantic love in *Romeo and Juliet*. During the preparations for the feast to celebrate Juliet's marriage to Paris, the nurse informs Lady Capulet that 'They call for dates and quinces in the pastry'. As tokens of love, quinces have been traditional fare at weddings since Roman times, a custom ripe for revival.

Shakespearean tradition is continued each year by the Lion's Part Theatre Company who, on Apple Day, perform the October Plenty celebrations outside Shakespeare's Globe Theatre on the South Bank of the Thames. At New Year they also wassail both the theatre and the apple trees they have planted nearby, reviving the orchards which grew alongside the river in Shakespeare's time.

Anton Chekhov was also aware of the symbolic nature of the orchard as evinced by his play *The Cherry Orchard* which tells of the Gaev family's refusal to sell their orchard despite facing bankruptcy. The orchard's fate is symbolic of the fate of all the play's characters.

Contemporary playwrights know too that apples are always more than just a delicious fruit. Stephen Poliakoff's play *Talk of the City*, set in the 1930s, features a conversation between Robbie, the mercurial master of ceremonies of a popular radio variety show, and his producer, Clive. Clive suggests that they work together on a subversive new form of radio broadcast that would link documentary with entertainment. The subject he chooses for this broadcast is English apples. Today's wordsmiths have also made good use of long-established forms of entertainment both to dramatise the parlous state

'The Magic Apple Tree' by Samuel Palmer reflects the inspiration he drew from the orchard landscape around his home in Shoreham, Kent. Reproduced by permission of the Fitzwilliam Museum, Cambridge.

Ron Haselden's Tree Dressing Day in his orchard. Photo: Ron Haselden.

of Britain's old orchards and to celebrate their importance to local distinctiveness. James Crowden, the first Apple Day Poet Laureate, wrote a poem in honour of Apple Day which formed part of Common Ground's press release in 1999. This extract describes the wonderfully diverse celebrations, all over the country:

So to start in the north and working down:
In Cumbria, at Acorn Bank, they dance the apple from the walled garden,
Pipped to the post, The Lemon Square or across the Pennines at Rothbury,
Orchard House, Cragside, National Trust, Northumberland.
At Walbottle Community Orchard, Tyne and Wear, apple bobbing,
Longest peel in Geordie land, treasure hunt and chocolate apples,
At the Riverside Country Park, Newburn. Hornsea Herring at Hull...
And then in the east of the country on the right hand side:
In Lincolnshire, the Life Museum in Lincoln and at Woolsthorpe Manor,
Sir Isaac Newton himself, demonstrating the gravity of the situation
With juggling and jollification at Waddingham Brandy Wharf Cider Centre...

Drawing on the traditional form of mummers plays, Eddie Upton of Folk South West recently devised *The Somerset Apple Play*. The characters – based on apple varieties ranging from old Pearmain, bold Worcester, brave Bramley and proud Pippin to Golden Delicious and Granny Smith – tell a tale of the decline in popularity of the old varieties, as bold Worcester cries:
...My flesh is clad in rosy red.
Countless generations on me fed.
But though my taste is crisp and pure
For many now I've lost allure,
And in chain stores now throughout the land
Cursed foreign fruits in my place stand...

The drama finishes with the characters calling out the names of Somerset varieties of apples and a wassail song. First performed at the Brewhouse Theatre in Taunton on Apple Day in 1993, the play has since spawned local variations on the theme.

Over the centuries poets have written of the changing seasons and changing orchard landscapes. Some, such as Michael Hamburger, have their own orchards and are passionate about fruit growing. Simon Fletcher wrote his collection *The Cherry Trees of Wyre* in response the Worcestershire landscape in which he grew up. In schools everywhere, but especially those which celebrate Apple Day or have their own orchards, hundreds of children have written poetry and prose inspired by the orchard and its fruit.

Apple people

At least since the Romans linked the apple goddess Pomona with fruitfulness and fertility, orchards have frequently been the province of women. From Catherine de Medici in the 16th century, who favoured the planting of fruit trees in the garden of the Palace des Tuileries, to the farmer's wife who looks after the farm orchard, women have been a force for good when it comes to orchards and their fruits. Often they leave little trace of their influence, though women are frequently celebrated in the names of apples. The apple variety known as the Lady Sudeley was renamed by the nurseryman, Bunyard, after the Sudeley estate, his best customer for the tree. The apple was also said to be as colourful as the dresses Lady Sudeley wore at court.

The Lady Henniker was raised from cider pomace on the Henniker's estate in Suffolk. Duchess's Favourite was

Pomona, made by Morris and Co., c 1885 (tapestry) by Sir Edward Burne-Jones (1833-98). Harris Museum and Art Gallery, Preston, Lancashire, UK/Bridgeman Art Library.

so named because it was admired by the Duchess of York, and Annie Elizabeth was named after the daughter of the nurseryman who introduced the apple.

The names of other apples reveal the identity of the women who raised them: Bess Pool, daughter of a village innkeeper in Leicestershire, Mrs Peasgood of Grantham, Lincolnshire, who as a child raised the Peasgood's Nonsuch from a pip, and Mrs Thomas Smith of Ryde, New South Wales, who discovered that the pip she had thrown out of the window had grown into the apple we now know as Granny Smith.

More often, women have been the unsung heroines of new varieties. Bramley's Seedling, for instance, was raised from seed by Mary Anne Brailsford in Southwell, Nottinghamshire. But when it was recognised as a worthwhile variety by the nurseryman Henry Merryweather, it was named after the local butcher, Mr Bramley, in whose garden it was then growing.

A woman's help was also needed in the development of the Discovery. Mr Dummer, a farm worker from Essex, had raised seedlings from pips of the Worcester Pearmain, but having only one arm he needed his wife's help in planting them. Unfortunately, she slipped and broke her ankle and the tree remained covered in sacks to prevent frost damage until both were able to finish the planting.

Women cooks, food writers and chefs have frequently championed the apple. The tarte Tatin was named after Madame Tatin, the French cook whose 'mistake' resulted in this delicious dessert. Jane Grigson and her daughter Sophie write passionately about the fruit. Women illustrators, horticulturalists and gardeners too are keen to pass on their knowledge of fruit growing. Rosanne Sanders' beautifully illustrated book, *The English Apple*, was timely and influential. Joan Morgan was the first woman to be a member of the RHS Fruit and Vegetable Committee and a Founder Trustee of the Brogdale Horticultural Trust. June Small, a Somerset fruit grower, has celebrated the orchards of the county by producing an Apple Map, and she actively promotes local fruit and other produce. The prime movers in many campaigns for orchards or research into local apple varieties are women. Trudy Turrell has enthusiastically and inventively extended policy and practice on orchards from within South Hams District Council. Claire Peasnall led the campaign in Lincolnshire to save Cross O'Cliff orchard from development. After years of battle with bureaucracy, she and her allies triumphed and now manage the orchard for the community. Pauline Buttery almost single-handedly initiated the planting of three Community Orchards in Leicestershire, while Sheila Leitch is the driving force behind the Marcher Apple Network along the border of Wales and England. Catherine Lloyd is championing orchards in Fife and Margaret Miller, headteacher of Gartmore School in Stirling, is encouraging the next generation to appreciate orchards and teaching the practicalities of their care. All over the country, countless other women are working to create and conserve orchards in their place. They weave new strength

When wintering birds gathered
Under an apple tree
To feed on fallen fruit.
Visiting fieldfare mixed
With blackbird, missel thrush,
Chaffinch, hedge-sparrow, robin,
Blue-tit, drawn down to earth
For a dole of sustenance
Disdained while berries clung,
Worm and snail stirred.

Bullfinch, long missed, flew in
Before buds could swell.
Wren, rare goldcrest braved
Marauding magpie, gull.

Hard weather mingled them all,
Hunger, but starved not one
Nor left one killed in battle.

From *Late* by Michael Hamburger, 1997

into that enduring thread of history that celebrates orchards as good places.

Other apple icons through out history include William Tell, a Swiss who challenged the authority of Austria in the 14th century and is renowned for shooting an apple from the head of his son. Equally famous is John Chapman, who became known as Johnny Appleseed when he created America's first apple nursery and helped to spread orchards all over the nation. He is often depicted striding through the countryside scattering apple pips along the way.

Isaac Newton (1642-1727) was born into a sheep-farming family in rural Lincolnshire. His encounter with an apple is probably the best known of all scientific stories. Dr William Stukeley, who knew Newton well in his old age, recalls:

After dinner, the weather being warm, we went into the garden and drank tea, under the shade of some apple trees, only he and myself. Amidst other discourse, he told me he was just in the same situation as when, formerly, the notion of gravitation came into his mind, it was occasioned by the fall of an apple, as he sat in a contemplative mood. Why should that apple always descend perpendicularly to the ground, thought he to himself? Why should it not go sideways or upwards, but constantly to the earth's centre? Assuredly, the reason is that the earth draws it.

Newton's work on gravitation was begun at Woolsthorpe in 1665-7, and so the story has always been rooted in the orchard that is now part of a National Trust property. What was believed to be the original tree – a Flower of Kent – blew down in 1820. But a gnarled old apple tree that lives on in front of Woolsthorpe Manor may have grown from its remains.

Alas, not everyone believes Newton really was inspired by a falling apple – indeed, even the apple tree at Woolsthorpe has been a source of controversy. The tree has recently found its defender in Richard Keesing of the department of physics at the University of York. He argues that that the tree still growing at Woolsthorpe Manor is of the same stock as the original tree that grew there in Newton's day. Dr Keesing visited Major H B Turnor, the last private owner of the Manor whose family had owned the property from the time of Newton, and discovered in the family archives a drawing of the apple tree made 150 years earlier. Today, in that very spot, an old, prostrate tree that could be a regeneration of Newton's original apple tree still survives.

Attempts to analyse the DNA taken from a piece of wood described as coming from the original tree have so far been unsuccessful. So at the moment no one can be sure which of the trees currently being grown around the world as Newton's tree are descendants of the original. But as scientific developments continue apace, we may not have long to wait. The story of the apple tree inspired Newton's friends to commemorate his discovery by planting apple trees in the grounds of their houses. In the early 1700s, William Dawson, who had studied with Newton, planted an arbour for his mentor at Lancliffe Hall in north Yorkshire, of which two fruit trees remained in the late 1800s. University physics departments might like to plant a Flower of Kent tree outside their

Is this really how Isaac Newton had the idea of gravity knocked out of him at Woolsthorpe?

The Apple Tree Man and the Orchard Scrumpers game board made for Common Ground by Jim Partridge. The tactics are similer to Nine Mens Morris but you can eat any 'counters' you win.

laboratories in celebration of Newton's achievements and to remind students of the connections between science and nature.

Arts and crafts in orchards

Orchards are special places that have, for centuries, inspired a breadth of expression across craft traditions and fine, folk and applied art. Today, they continue to form a recurrent motif in the work of many contemporary visual artists. In 1988, Common Ground commissioned photographer James Ravilious to spend a year documenting the orchard life of the west country. This was his home territory, the place where he immersed himself in everyday life for the 28 years prior to his death in 1999. No one could have better captured the subject. His hundreds of images let us share in blossom time and harvest, in planting and even grubbing out. He was there for the winter Wassail at Norton Fitzwarren in Somerset and for the crowning of the May Queen at the Town Orchard in Lustleigh, Devon.

Fruit growers Wilf Lawrence, Reg Holland and Miss Betty, and the Travellers at their camp at South Petherton, are all part of the royal family of Ravilious' orchard kingdom.

Lords Derby, Duffield and Devonshire, an esteemed family of a different kind, along with Ribston Pippin, Fortune, Sunset, Czar, Hessle and Victoria are among the 24 oversize cast bronze apples, cherries, plums and pears in artist Mark Dion's recent 'Tasting Garden', at the Storey Institute in Lancaster. They sit elegantly on simple concrete bases, while beside them grow still-diminutive trees of the same species. The reddening colour and slim form of just-set fruit contrasts with the full perfect shapes of the bronze giants that sit beside them.

In Lancaster, Dion has neither made art for an orchard nor depicted one. Rather the orchard itself is a part of an artwork that was created for Art Trans-Pennine in 1998, with support from the Henry Moore Foundation, Tate Liverpool and maintenance provided by Lancaster City Council. In the 1930s the land was the kitchen garden of a nearby house, and a mature cherry and a few damsons are possibly reminders of this time. Two years ago, however, it was a knotweed jungle that had to be cleared before the new orchard was laid out.

The orchard plan follows a series of winding paths in the form of a branching tree, such as might be derived from a medieval illumination; simultaneously a tree of history, of fertility, of knowledge and of life. The end of each branch swells as if about to bud, and it is here that bronze fruit and real tree have been left to take root in the soil and in the imagination.

As the classically inspired bronze fruit, without blemish or deformity, glint in the sunshine, we might easily imagine we have stumbled into the Hesperides' back yard, fetched up on the shore of some Cumbrian Avalon or found one of God's early versions of Eden. The branching evolutionary trail from that first Biblical tree, aided and abetted by human intervention, has led us to thousands of varieties found in Britain alone. Those picked for Dion's 'Tasting Garden' were carefully selected to grow well in the particular climate of north-west England. Many varieties have been lost forever, and three paths in Dion's orchard end in small engraved stones on the ground, bearing the names of extinct fruit varieties.

The orchard is hidden from the sound and bustle of the nearby road by a high retaining wall. It is not advertised or sign-posted. In a few years time when the trees have matured, this will be a delightful and secret garden. Sitting on the grass beside a youthful Lord Derby, local people can already cast off the stress of a bad morning in the office and those with a little imagination dream of a not too distant future of high leafy canopies heavy with ripening fruit.

Not all artists today appear quite so optimistic and perhaps feel that Eden is for the next world rather than this one. Anya Gallaccio touches on the subject, with a newly planted 'orchard' as part of a wider project about apples and the way our society lives with nature. 'Falling from Grace' began as an installation at Roman Kurzmeyer's Gallery in Basel, exhibited for three months from January until March 2000. Hundreds of Ida Red apples were suspended like a curtain, with the fruit hanging on a series of knotted ropes. As this 'screen' of firm bright red and yellow-green changed to a soft pulpy brown translucence, the aroma shifted from sweet scent to that of the over ripe. Everything, the artist seems to suggest, has its own time, its own birth and death.

These Ida Reds were purchased in bulk from the local grocer, but of course they were neither grown nor developed nearby. Gallaccio highlights the way in which we treat fruit as a product to be shipped around the world, and orchards as factory floors or science labs for breeding new species. Visitors to her show felt that food was being wasted, but remained ignorant of agricultural policies that continue to lead to the dumping of thousands of tonnes of perfectly good fruit each year. At the end of the exhibition, the pips from each apple were gathered together and planted within a circle one metre in diameter. As they seeded and began to grow, they were thinned and replanted in an outer circle, and these in turn thinned and allowed to ripple outward. Eventually, a circular orchard of irregularly spaced trees will grow; pippins which will undo the hard work of the Idaho Agricultural Experimental Station where these baby boomer apples were developed in the 1950s. In our relationship with nature we have fallen from grace, but this new orchard suggests at least an awareness of a problem.

Back in the 1940s, however, and in spite of impending war, the idea of heaven on earth was still very real to sculptor Eric Gill. A mature orchard stood to the front of his home and studio at Pigotts, in High Wycombe and perhaps inspired the memorable Adam and Eve Garden Roller. With its frank depictions of our most famous ancestors carved into its Portland stone ends, it evokes an earthly paradise of love and sex. This was also a simple garden tool that was meant to be used and this duality fits perfectly with Gill's ethos. He wrote in his autobiography in 1940, 'I am reuniting what should never have been separated: the artist as a man of imagination and the artist as a workman'.

Gill would have approved, when in 1992, Common Ground asked sculptor and blacksmith Richard Farrington to make three metal seats, cum tree guards, which form the letters C O X for a new Community Orchard of mainly Cox's Orange Pippins at Colnbrook, a parcel of land near Heathrow Airport. Common Ground, with the Colne Valley Park Groundwork Trust and 40 local school children, joined forces to plant this orchard in memory of Richard Cox. In 1825 in a garden not far from the new orchard, Cox

Two apple trees grow in my garden,
Five hundred in my head,
Two trees confer dawn's colour on the town air
Giving it, if only for a season,
The appearance, though not the heart, of Eden.
But the hundreds in my head,
Blow triumphantly on my boyhood hill,
Massed, orchards of them,
Transmuting Severn's skies
To every shade of pink,
Taming the primroses at their feet,
And so full of song, the hill
Is one continuous fire of trembling sound.
Blenheim's at peace with Cox, Beauty of Bath
Passes time of spring with stout James Grieve,
Laxton's superb, Edmund's Russet is neat,
Ribston's Pippin wears an everlasting face;
They are huge with the promise of fruit.
My nameless trees have no proud harvestings,
They go like two old cripples into age,
Their true identity is long remembrance,
They have their blackbirds still.

Apple Trees by Leonard Clark.

first raised this famous apple. Most people had quite forgotten the connection between the apple, the man and the place, despite the incredible popularity of a fruit that today is worth around £90 million to the national economy. Information about the apple, Richard Cox and Colnbrook is stamped into the metal of the seats. No need for notice boards when people coming from near and far will be able to work out interesting strands of information for themselves.

This functional and locally distinctive commission was devised to inspire others to create their own art and craft works and to find new ways of passing their knowledge on. Other benches followed for Gurnard orchard on the Isle of Wight, when Farrington was again the artist, and at Ecclesfield Community orchard where the Sheffield Wildlife Trust asked artist James Thompson to create a seat. Common Ground devised an idea for an apple game board which Jim Partridge created from a single piece of oak. One day we would like him to create a seat for two, with integral game board, for playing in an orchard.

Fences, signs, sign posts, stiles, seats, tree guards, water troughs and other work-a-day, but potentially locally distinctive objects for orchards now await their own contemporary reinvention.

It is worth remembering that fruit tree wood is not suitable for such outdoor purposes, as it does not take kindly to damp conditions. However, it has many other traditional uses. Apple, cherry and pear have always been used for turning and carving as well as providing the blocks used by artists since the Renaissance for wood cuts and engraving. It is curiously satisfying to consider that a print of Adam and Eve by Cranach or Dürer might also be pulled from an apple wood block. Block makers favoured a soft pear or cherry for woodcuts which were then carved along the grain with a knife or chisel. The market still exists today, with printmakers prepared to pay up to £8 per 10 square centimetres for a piece of fruit wood. After the end of its cropping life, if not left for wild life or for aesthetic

sources) was the traditional choice for all these items, but the skills as well as the raw materials have declined in recent years. The cheap plastic products that have come to dominate in the shops might be considered another fall from grace.

Common Ground's campaigns to conserve traditional orchards, to develop Community Orchards and to promote the annual celebration of Apple Day may foster a future for some of the now almost redundant skills mentioned above. These projects have already provided a multitude of new opportunities for communities to work

reasons, the whole fruit tree would have been used for timber. Bowls were turned from the bole, less substantial branches were hollowed out into cups, smaller sections for spoons and ladles, and the tiniest branches could become pegs. Cheese and biscuit moulds, mortar and pestles, whistles, recorders, decorative chains and love tokens were all whittled in profusion as part of folk art traditions that have existed for centuries. The wood of orchard trees (no different from the wild

Richard Cox's creation, the nation's most popular apple, can be enjoyed in the place where he first raised it almost two centuries ago, on one of three new seats/treeguards in his memory conceived by Common Ground and made by Richard Farrington.

with artists and craftspeople.

Inspired by the Parish Maps Project, artist Gordon Young has included the grid pattern of his local orchards among the sluice gates, pollarded willows, hedges and wandering chickens in a pictorial 'map' of Muchelney in Somerset where he lives. Bernard Leach's grandson John, also based nearby, produced a three-handled wassail mug in 1999, which every year on Twelfth Night will be taken to these same orchards, where locals will quaff its three pints of cider as they wish their trees good health and bounty. Muchelney Abbey was also the setting on Apple Day in 1999, for James Crowden's reading of his orchard poems. In the future his poems could be letter-cut (Gill Sans perhaps) into stones, set beside the trees or the orchard entrance.

At No Man's Orchard at Chartham Hatch near Canterbury, students from Kent Institute of Art and Design carved a simple but effective wooden snake-shaped bench. Marking the parish boundary that passes through the trees, it provides not only a welcome resting place, but also the perfect 'line' for the inter-parish tug of war now held every year on Apple Day and is, as such, as much a part of the local landscape as the orchard trees themselves.

Every year on Apple Day between 1991 and 1996, Amanda Lebus's company Laughing Root was invited by South Gloucestershire District Council to create a series of multi-art form events allied to newly planted school or community orchards. *The Apple Orchard's Birthday Party* was one such event for Chipping Norton Primary School. The new trees shared a birthday cake made of leaves (ritually sprinkled around the tree bases), gingerbread birds were suspended from the branches and two wooden puppets – the 'Orchard Spirits' – bore witness to it all. Music and songs were written for a shadow play, performed in the orchard as the light began to fail; the evening ended with a real cake for the children who had taken part. Every year a different theme was chosen for a different school or community orchard. Since then, Amanda has

Having helped plant them, these young people are looking forward to growing up with the trees at Colnbrook Community Orchard.

regularly created simple rod puppets with carved and pickled apples for heads; each one based on the supposed character of a particular apple variety. Orchards are among the oldest and most beautiful of collaborations between people and nature and they clearly continue to have resonance for the contemporary creative spirit.

Calendars and customs

Songs and games – old and new – as well as traditions, divinations and superstitions have deep links with apples and orchards. Sophie Grigson, who wrote the forward to *Apple Games and Customs*, recalls what apples meant to her in her childhood:

As children, we instinctively placed a greater value on apples than that of mere sustenance. We were, quite unwittingly, slotting into an ancient pattern. Apples have played an important role in British life since time immemorial. They are the quintessential British fruit. Commonplace, to be sure, but always highly and rightly valued, at least until the latter part of this century, when big business stripped away so much of their magic. Not only did we nearly lose huge numbers of older varieties, we also nearly lost a huge chunk of our heritage....

Everyone knows that an apple a day keeps the doctor away, and most people still associate apple bobbing and toffee apples with Hallowe'en. These are familiar nationwide, but it's the local traditions that are in greatest peril of oblivion. As small orchards have been destroyed to make way for housing estates or new roads or whatever, the ceremonies connected to them for centuries have disappeared too. Wassailing and Catterning songs, for instance, were once widely spread and individual, often containing local place names and references. Now they are barely remembered, and too rarely sung.

It's not just a rural pre-occupation, either. Apple trees grow in cities too, and city-dwellers have appreciated a good apple just as much as any one else. 'Oranges and lemons' said the bells of St Clements, but did you remember that the bells of Whitechapel said 'two sticks and an apple'? Or indeed, have you ever come across this rhyme:

Upon Paul's steeple stands a tree
As full of apples as may be.
The little boys of London town
They run with hooks to pull them down;
And then they run from hedge to hedge
Until they come to London Bridge.

These kinds of traditions – rhymes, songs, rituals – provide an essential link with our history, playing us tantalising hints of the lives of our forebears. They remind us that though much may have changed, a good deal of it for the better, there are still common elements which time cannot erode. The simple pleasures in life are not so very different now – a bite of a crisp, juicy apple, apple pie with cream, a stroll through a blossoming apple orchard, the changing seasons. These are things that we can share and celebrate with the generations that came before us.

Throughout the year, orchards and apples have played an important part in the local calendar. These celebrations draw people in to rejoice in the blossom or fruit, and at the same time demonstrate the importance of the orchard and its local connections. In Kent, orchards were blessed at Youling ceremonies at Ascentiontide. On St Swithin's Day, 15 July, apples were christened, and declared fit to eat. And on various dates, depending on the locality, it was time for Crabbing the Parson – providing parishioners with the opportunity to pelt their clergy with apples.

A vital aid to divination, apples could foretell the faithfulness of a loved one or reveal the ideal marriage partner. In early September the would-be diviner searched for crab apples and arranged them, on a loft floor, to form the initials of potential marriage partners. There the crabs were to lie undisturbed until Michaelmas Day. On that fateful day, the freshest apples would spell out the initials of the most suitable partner, who would also prove loving and faithful throughout life should the fruits be in perfect order. Conversely, if all the apples were rotten, the young person would be well advised never to wed.

On Hallowe'en night a young girl would dream of her future husband if she placed an apple under her pillow. Alternatively she could peel the apple and throw the peel over her left shoulder. On landing it would form the initial of a possible spouse. A rhyme accompanied this custom:

I pare this pippin round and round again
My sweetheart's name to flourish on the plain,
I fling the unbroken paring o'er my head,
My sweetheart's letter on the ground is read.

An apple pip was also capable of divining a lover's faithfulness. If, once placed on the fire, it bursts with the heat a girl can be sure of her lover's affection, but if it burns silently it means he is false. While anxiously waiting the following rhyme is chanted:

If you love me pop and fly;
If you hate me lay and die.

In many parts of the country at New Year it was traditional for people to visit their neighbours with gifts for the coming year. These usually included a lump of coal, loaf of bread and a bottle of whisky (or other drink), but in Wales there was also a custom of dressing an apple with ears of corn, cloves, rosemary, nuts and evergreen leaves. This 'Calennig' apple was brought into the house and mounted on a stand of holly or rowan twigs and was sometimes gilded or decorated with ribbons. This is just one of many examples of presenting apples at various times of the year to wish friends and family good health and fortune. Common Ground encouraged people to reinvent this custom for Apple Day in 1994.

The snake seat at No Man's Orchard marks the parish boundary and forms the line over which the inter-parish tug of war is fought. It is made largely of apple trunks and branches.

'This is not an apple' by René Magritte.

Wassailing now and then

Perhaps the best-known orchard tradition is that of wassailing. Wassailing demonstrates the close links between orchards, music, drama, dance and song. The tradition of wassailing grew up around the idea of encouraging good health and good growth in the orchard. The word wassail comes from the Anglo Saxon *wes hal, was haile* or *wase hail*, literally to be whole, be in good health or be fortunate.

Wassailing apple orchards traditionally took place between Christmas and 17 January – Twelfth Night in the old calendar. The aim was to protect the trees from evil spirits and to ensure a plentiful crop in the coming season. The best or oldest tree, known as the Apple Tree Man, was chosen to represent the whole orchard and was fêted as its guardian. Cider was poured on the roots, pieces of toast or cake soaked in cider were laid in its fork or hung from the branches for the robins who were also considered the guardian spirits of the trees. The tips of the lowest branches were

Ceci n'est pas une pomme

drawn down and dipped in to the cider pail, as the tree was toasted with cider and songs.

The trees were then rapped and the bark sometimes torn. A huge din was made to drive away any evil spirits and wake the sleeping trees. Trays and buckets were beaten, cow or ram horns blown and latterly shot guns fired through the top-most branches. There was method behind such madness as the commotion dislodged insects from the bark, and it was believed that tearing would bring the fruit earlier. Many believed that if trees weren't wassailed there would be no fruit.

In some orchards the men showed the trees what was required of them by bowing down to the ground three times and rising up slowly, miming the actions of lifting a heavy sack of apples. Part of the ceremony in Devon orchards involved lifting a small boy up onto one of the branches where he sat crying: 'Tit, tit, more to eat', and was fed with bread, cheese and cider. The lad represented a blue tit or some other small bird regarded as guardian spirits of the trees, and it was hoped that through the performance the trees would be cared for in the coming year. While there are many similarities in wassailing ceremonies across the country, each place created its own special way of celebrating orchards. In Sussex the custom was known as Worsling and here, as in parts of Devon, parties of boys visited the orchards on New Year's Day when they encircled the apple trees and chanted:

Stand fast, bear well top,
Pray God send us a howling crop;
Every twig, apple big;
Every bough, apples enow,
Hats full, caps full,
Full quarter sacks full.

This was followed by a great noise of shouting and the tree trunks were vigorously rapped with sticks.

Wassailing has continued in some places for centuries, such as Carhampton in Somerset, while in other areas it is undergoing a

revival, as at the Brandy Wharf Cider Centre on the River Ancholme. This temple to cider in the north Lincolnshire Fens has planted its own orchard which is enthusiastically wassailed each year. Continuity of tradition, however, does not mean that customs go unchanged. In places where original wassail songs have been lost, people should not become disheartened. Composer Alan Turley was encouraged to write a new wassail song for North Somerset by the Two Hoots Biodiversity Group. It was first performed on Apple Day, 21 October 1997, in rehearsal for the wassail at the end of the year.

Nor was wassailing confined to apple orchards. In the days before Twelfth Night, the wassail bowl was taken round from house to house after dark. The bowl contained a mixture of hot ale, spices, sugar and roasted apples, sometimes with eggs and thick cream floating on it. This brew is known as Lambs Wool in Gloucestershire and was also drunk as a Cathern Bowl on St Catherine's Day (25 November). The bowl itself was traditionally made from apple wood, often elaborately carved and kept specifically for this purpose. Wassailers carried bunches of evergreen hung with apples, oranges and coloured ribbons and sang for entry at each house, where they collected alms in return for good luck wishes and a taste of the wassail brew.

Orchards feature in the customs and celebrations of many other countries. In the Dolomites in Italy, festival floats decorated entirely with apples form part of an annual procession. In France, the weather

Wassailing on Twelfth Night at a cider orchard, Norton Fitzwarren, Somerset. Photo: James Ravilious.
After the festival: May Day, Lustleigh, Devon. Photo: James Ravilious.
Overleaf: Whiteways cider orchard, Whimple, Devon. Photo: James Ravilious.

on St Eulalie's Day, 12 February, is an important moment for apples and orchards, as a local rhyme has it: 'If the sun smiles on St Eulalie's Day, it is good for apples and cider.'

Such customs highlight the need for a healthy cultural calendar. The cheese rolling in Gloucestershire, tar barrel burning in Devon and the firework spectacular in Lewes on Bonfire Night suffer from a

huge influx of visitors each year, turning what should be a joyous occasion for local people into a nightmare. We need new local customs. Apple Day is just one moment in the year when orchards can be celebrated, but every opportunity should be seized to start your own new tradition, whether it be blossom days, cherry-stone spitting competitions or mistletoe gathering. Whatever time of year, there is always a good reason to be in the orchard, celebrating its fruits.

Apple Day

APPLE DAY, 21 OCTOBER, was launched in 1990. From the start, it was intended to be both a celebration and a demonstration of the variety we are in danger of losing – not simply in apples, but richness and diversity of landscape, place and culture too. Its success has shown just how much we need local celebrations in which, year after year, everyone can be involved. In city, town and country, Apple Day events have fostered local pride, celebrated local knowledge and deepened interest in local distinctiveness.

Apple Day is now an integral part of the events calendar of many villages, local authorities, city markets and the National Trust. It is a focus for activities organised by the Women's Institute (WI), the Wildlife Trusts, museums, art galleries and many horticultural societies, as well as for schools, colleges and environmental study centres.

The first Apple Day celebrations, in the old Apple Market in London's Covent Garden, brought fruit to the market after 16 years' absence. Forty stalls were taken. Fruit growers and nurseries producing and selling a wide variety of apples and trees rubbed shoulders with juice- and cider-makers, as well as writers and illustrators with their apple books.

Representatives of the WI came laden with chutneys, jellies and pies. Mallorees School from North London demonstrated its orchard classroom, while Herts and Middx Wildlife Trust explained how it manages its orchard for wild life. Marks & Spencer helped to start a trend by offering tastings of some of the 12 'old varieties' on sale that autumn. Organic growers were cheek by jowl with beekeepers, amidst demonstrations of traditional and modern juice presses, a calvados still and a cider bar run by the Campaign for Real Ale. Experts from Brogdale identified apples and offered advice, while apple jugglers and magicians entertained the thousands of visitors – far more than we had expected – who came on the day.

For two weeks before Apple Day, in a marquee on the Piazza, Common Ground exhibited photographs of West Country Orchards we had commissioned from James Ravilious alongside a display of more than 100 different apple varieties. People were amazed at the diversity of shapes, sizes and colours. We also offered lunchtime tastings of some of the varieties on show, and many people bemoaned the lack of such choice on supermarket shelves.

We will never know just how many people came to that first celebration – it was certainly thousands and even now we meet people who effuse about it as a memorable event. Many wanted it to be repeated, but our intention was to spread the idea far and wide, encouraging people to celebrate Apple Day for themselves in their own city, village, parish, allotment or garden orchard.

And so the tradition of Apple Day began. Over the next few years, the number of events being organised around the country grew from more than 60 in 1991 to 300 by 1997 and over 600 in 1999, some attracting thousands of people. Apple Day has played a part in raising awareness of and action around the importance of orchards to our landscape and culture, and the growing interest in the traceability of food. It has been one impetus behind the developing network of

Apple Day celebrates the huge variety of domestic fruit we can grow in this country and the continuing importance of orchards as special places for people, nature, culture and landscape.

farmers' markets and is helping people everywhere to discover they are not alone in valuing orchards and local fruit varieties.

We have used the apple as a symbol of what is being lost in many aspects of our lives and shown that anyone can take positive action towards change. Over the years, Apple Day has been celebrated in a wonderful variety of ways by a diverse range of people. Doctor's surgeries, coronary support groups and the Cancer Research Campaign have taken to Apple Day as a novel way of encouraging healthy eating. Each year, alongside tasting, juicing, baking, pruning and grafting, an imaginative array of games and creative activities have flourished – ranging from simple apple printing to banner-, rag-rug and lantern-making. But invariably, year after year, the most popular event is the display of numerous varieties and the presence of an expert to aid identification.

Name your apple

Each year hundreds of people bring apples from their unknown garden trees to Apple Day events for identification. In 1991 Cornwall County Council put on a display of Cornish apples at Probus Gardens and two 'lost' varieties – Red Rollo and White Quarantine – turned up during identification. Future years saw further varieties appear, 'many of which we were unable to name because there are no written descriptions. We have to rely on anecdotal evidence some reliable/ acceptable source arriving with an apple saying "this is a so and so".' Using samples brought in by local people, the council has produced a photographic template for each variety, and is gathering a kind of rogues' gallery to support future identifications. Private gardens and small orchards are often invaluable repositories for old fruit varieties,

Thousands of people came to the celebrations at the first Apple Day in Covent Garden. Apple Day has now become firmly established in the seasonal calendar in hundreds of places in town and countryside.

as the identification services at Apple Days all over the country discover each year.

The number of people bringing in fruit from their gardens is a constant source of surprise to event organisers and demonstrates just how many old fruit trees still survive. Already, residents in many parts of the country can consult their local 'Apple Maps'. To make these maps, enthusiasts have set out to survey all the fruit trees and orchards in the locality. As unusual trees are discovered, it may be possible to take grafts to establish new trees. Some counties, such as Devon and Somerset, are also producing 'pomonas' or annotated variety lists for their area; these are added to each year as 'new' varieties are discovered on Apple Day. The Devon Orchards Initiative, which is coordinated by the Dartington North Devon Trust, has taken graftwood from these discoveries to propagate and add to the collection of county varieties, to provide trees for planting in future local Community Orchards.

Identification of apples is not without its problems, as vividly demonstrated by the Apple Day at Ranworth Trees, in Norfolk in 1995. Shortly after the event, a letter from a local apple enthusiast, Jim Holmes, appeared in the *Eastern Daily Press* stating that the Dr Harvey apple on sale there was a fake. He claimed that older people throughout Norfolk and Suffolk supported his campaign to prove that this was not the true Dr Harvey. The letter started a chain of reactions that came to a climax in a discussion on Radio Norfolk between Jim Holmes, Neil Thomas of Ranworth Trees, David Pennell of Brogdale and another local apple expert, Gerald Fayers.

David Pennell explained how the confusion may have arisen. He discussed the problems in identifying old apple varieties particularly those, like Dr Harvey, which have been in existence for centuries. He also described the ways in which different growing conditions, soils and climate can bring about subtle changes in the characteristics of the apple. The programme ended on a positive note, however, with both David Pennell and Neil Thomas vowing to try to track down the true identity of Dr Harvey with the help of anyone listening who might already be growing putative Dr Harvey apples. The news to date on the fate of Dr Harvey is that several examples of the 'real' tree have been discovered. New trees are being propagated from grafts for both Ranworth Trees and the Brogdale collection.

As the desire to have fruit identified grows, the skilled individuals able to perform this task are put under increasing pressure. Experts are booked months, sometimes years, in advance for Apple Day and are often so inundated on the day that it may take them at least another day to work through the samples. There is a desperate need for more fruit identifiers, but with possibly 6,000 British variety names and hundreds more cider apples on the books, it is not a skill that is easily learnt. John Edgely of Pershore College, Worcestershire, is organising fruit identification workshops in a number of places and has a chart which aids the identification of plums from their stones. Harry Baker of RHS renown and many others work at Apple Days across the country to spread their enthusiasm for and knowledge of apples and other fruit.

But where experts are unavailable, people often find great enjoyment in trying to work out the name of their apple themselves with the aid of reference books. If still defeated, some resolute enthusiasts take the strong-minded decision to name it themselves, with ample justification, for if the tree had grown from a pip it would indeed be a new variety.

Maps and surveys

On Apple Day 1993 we published the *Apple Map of Britain,* beautifully illustrated by Kate Charlesworth. Around the poster's border is our first attempt at a county gazetteer, giving the names of hundreds of local apple varieties. We hoped that this publication would inspire community groups to create more detailed maps showing the local apples, orchards and associated customs. In many towns, villages and counties, people have been encouraged to use Apple Day to annotate a local map with the location of fruit trees and orchards they know. The new maps can then be compared with older maps to establish what has been lost and to encourage replanting.

In 1995, June Small of Charlton Orchards was inspired to begin an apple map of Somerset. She enlisted the help of Somerset County Council, and many local people offered information, photographs and researched local orchard customs and connections. The finished result is a wonderful collage of photographs, drawings and information. It has been displayed at subsequent Apple Days and other events including the Bath and West Show, and has led to the development of the booklet *Apple Varieties of Somerset: a guide to the origins of Somerset's apples.* This guide is constantly being updated as June and her husband Robin travel the southwest around Apple Day each year identifying garden fruit and talking passionately about apples. Once they have tracked down local varieties, groups in many counties have begun to create 'mother' nurseries, often with grafts taken from trees discovered at Apple Day – as in Cheshire, Gloucestershire, Devon and Hertfordshire. Trees from these nurseries can then be used to stock new Community Orchards.

Apple games

Apple Day 1994 saw the launch of *Apple Games and Customs*. This diminutive book explores the games, divinations, cures, superstitions, stories, songs and sayings connected with apples. Some are old, gone but not forgotten, others equally ancient are still continued. Yet others are new, invented specially for Apple Day, and fast becoming part of the local tradition.

New traditions have to start somewhere. The success of Apple Day builds on a long history of calendar customs and the desperate need we all feel for meaningful local celebration.

The publication of the book saw a flurry of apple bobbing and other games organised on Apple Day including longest peel competitions (Newcastle registered 2.1 metres), pin the maggot on the apple and many more. In Hertfordshire, a Beaver group had to find apples buried in buckets filled with straw. In Coventry, paper apples, each containing a number, were attached to a tree branch. Visitors picked an apple, to claim the prize linked to its number. On the Isle of Wight, children pretended to be pigs and searched for windfall apples and 'green gold' – bottles of apple juice. In Nottinghamshire, a game of skittles was set up at Norwood Park, with giant wooden pears as the pins and a hanging apple ball.

We promoted the idea of apple-giving on Apple Day. Once, it was customary to give apples at certain times of the year as a token of friendship and to wish good health, and we wanted to resurrect this custom. We discovered that many fruit growers already offered a mail-order service, and some were willing to promote special Apple Day boxes to be sent as gifts. The Eynsford Women's Institute in Kent created special labels for Apple Day gifts and students at both Nene and Skelmersdale Colleges of Art designed Apple Day gift packs.

A wealth of wild life

The wild life of orchards has been an important part of Apple Day since the first event when we invited Herts & Middx Wildlife Trust to Covent Garden. On Apple Day 1995 we launched Orchards Observances, inviting people to keep a diary of the wild life in their own or nearby orchards over the year. As the year progressed, 'observers' sent in regular lists of birds, butterflies and mammals recorded and more lyrical accounts as well.

Lynn Fomison from Ropley, Hampshire, who took an active part in Orchards Observances, has continued to demonstrate the value of orchards to wild life, and vice versa, with walks on Apple Day through her wild life garden and orchard. The following extract comes from her description of the year in the orchard:

May ... Cascades of white blossom on the wild cherry and the air full of the hum of bees. The fruit – it's not just the blackbirds who feast on the cherries, the stones are seized upon by nuthatches and the field mice who live in the long grass.

My orchard will be a really special place come July and August. I will be there every day enjoying the sheets of wild flowers growing amid the trees – scabious, knapweed, marjoram, hemp agrimony, wild basil and the odd teasel too. All special flowers because they are so loved by butterflies. One year, wasps wrecked our Early Rivers Plum crop, all the fruit was holed and eaten. But there was a bonus, the shriveled plums hanging on the tree were a popular source of sugar to butterflies, especially commas!

In Autumn I would be feeling ratty about the grey squirrels stealing the hazel nuts and the walnuts. Funny though the sound of the nuthatch chipping away at a nut wedged into a bark crevice is one that I welcome.

January and there is plenty to see. Last year's hogweed stems poke from the grass like old bones. The last few seeds are providing some food for the tits. Even a wild area like this cannot provide enough food in winter for a hungry bird population. In summer the brown seed heads of dock look so dominant, but now I am pleased those brown spires are there. I just heard the low piping call of a bullfinch feeding on the seed heads. The bird has a bad reputation for stripping fruit buds. However, I feel that they only turn to buds if natural food is short and even if they were to damage some buds it is small price to pay for having such lovely birds as constant visitors.

The trees have never been sprayed with winter wash so the trunks support an interesting range of mosses and lichens. These knarled trunks are also well loved by treecreepers, they search for insects in the crevices of the bark and in hard weather I push fat, cheese and chopped nuts into the bark, which encourages them to stay with us through spring and summer so ridding the garden of pests. I am content to enjoy the birds and the apple I am munching.'

Lynn invariably has queues of visitors to her Apple Day event, but whether this is because of the diverse wild life living in her orchard or the wonderful array of delicious apple cakes she produces each year for the occasion is open to question.

Schools and education

Schools have taken up the challenge of organising a day's lessons around the apple or, better still, the school orchard, should the school be fortunate enough. While some have focused their efforts on the kitchen, creating simple apple dishes and comparing the flavour and texture of different varieties, others have looked at the artistic and cultural side of apples and orchards, creating drawings, paintings, poetry, prose, songs, stories and performances. The chemical properties of the apple have been investigated in the laboratory and the biology of the apple tree and ecology of the orchard can be studied amongst the trees themselves.

Line bobbing at Blondin Orchard, London and wooden fruit skittles at Norwood Park, Southwell. Games are a hugely popular element of many Apple Day events. New ones continue to appear.

Local authorities in many counties such as Yorkshire, Devon, Lincolnshire and Kent have supported schools' activities by providing special Apple Day school meals or supplying fruit trees to be planted in the grounds. Other organisations have also been drawn in. In 1994 Nottingham Permaculture Association invited 16 schools and youth centres in the city to join them in celebrating Apple Day. Each school was given ideas for organising its own celebrations to be linked to a city-wide display and were offered fruit trees for planting in the school grounds later in the year. In the same year, the South Wales Wholesale Fruit Association organised an Apple Day poster competition for schools in five counties, which concluded with an exhibition of the designs in Cardiff Central Library.

Among the many that celebrate Apple Day each year, Gartmore School in Stirling has been at the forefront of experiment, helping the idea to spread farther afield. Having planted its own orchard and celebrated Apple Day annually, headteacher Margaret Miller went on to create an Apple Day Schools Starter Pack, full of ideas for other teachers to develop with their own pupils. This initiative proved so successful that ideas from it were used in the Learning Through Landscapes/Common Ground *School Orchard Pack*, which gives information and advice to schools on how to create a school orchard and how it can be used as an outdoor classroom. In addition, Margaret and her pupils began giving talks to other teachers and children. In 1996 they also took a stall at the Apple Day at Earthward, the permaculture centre in Roxburghshire, to talk about their project. More recently, they were invited to

contribute to a Royal Scottish Forest Society project at Cashel and, of course, planted apple trees.

Horticultural and agricultural colleges around the country, most notably Pershore in Worcestershire and Kingston Maurward in Dorset, have opened their doors to visitors and offered the services of their experts to identify unknown garden varieties and give advice on care of fruit trees, pests and diseases. Community Orchards have also seized the chance to make use of expert knowledge and skills and organised pruning and grafting demonstrations in the orchard, so that everyone can gain a rudimentary knowledge of these techniques.

Individual experts are often in attendance on Apple Day, running workshops on orchard care and beekeeping as well as helping with identification. One such is Paul Hand of Bees and Trees who is particularly active in the National Forest where he is helping a number of groups set up Community Orchards.

It is not only horticultural knowledge that is passed on. Cooks such as Sophie Grigson are happy to demonstrate their culinary skills by creating a variety of apple dishes, while cider- and juice-makers take their mobile presses to countless places to show how the drinks are made. They are usually inundated with willing helpers to operate the crushers and presses as well as sample the finished product.

More formal training courses are organised around Apple Day by organisations such as the Green Wood Trust in Shropshire, Ragman's Lane Farm in Gloucestershire, the British Trust for Conservation Volunteers and Pershore College, Worcestershire.

Apple Day offers an opportunity for horticulturalists, gardeners and fruit growers to pass on their knowledge to others in an informal setting and perhaps inspire others to follow in their footsteps.

Recipes, cooking and restaurants

The Apple Source Book: particular recipes for diverse apples is a collection of recipes demanding named varieties of apple. The book sprang from Common Ground's challenge to cooks, food writers, restaurateurs, gardeners and growers to celebrate Apple Day in 1991. Smiths of Covent Garden hosted a launch party for the book and amongst a huge display of apples and regional cheeses, recipes from the book came to life. Food writer Michael Barry created his apple pancakes, while chef Fergus Henderson made apple and cheese tartlets from the recipe by Christine and Craig Pillans, using local apples and the corresponding regional cheeses, such as Ribston Pippin and Wensleydale, and Annie Elizabeth and Red Leicester.

The Apple Day Poster lists 592 varieties of British apples around its border. It was printed in 1990, and illustrated by Dovrat Ben-Nahum.

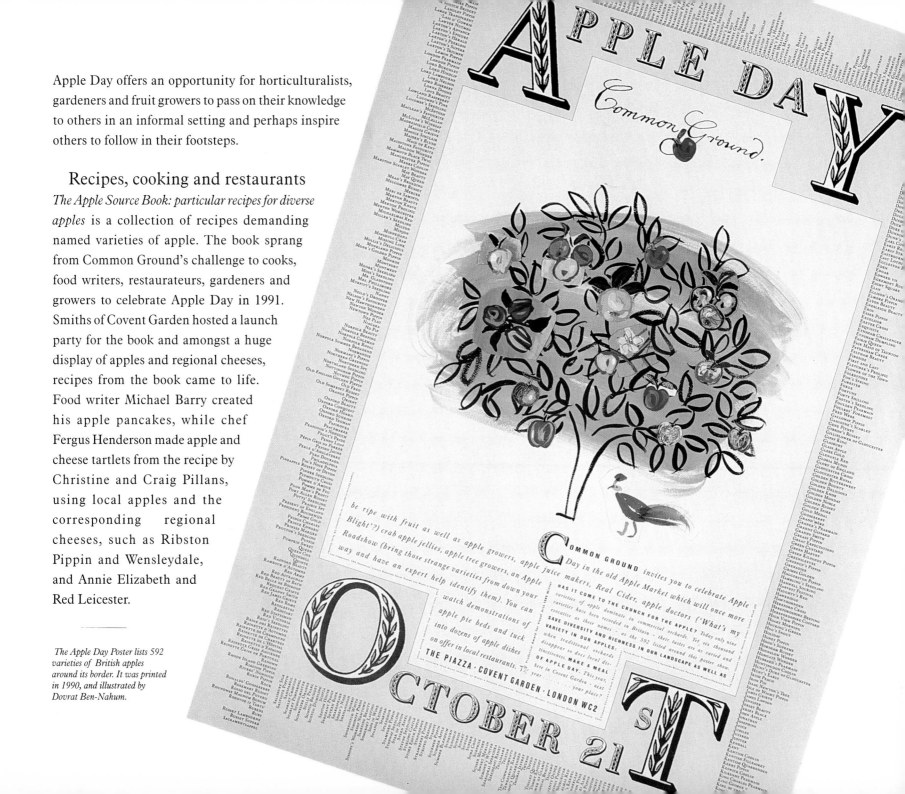

The book has since inspired other groups to produce their own county or village collections of apple recipes from local people – some with illustrations by local school children – and the opportunity to make, taste and sell the finished products at Apple Day events.

Chef Fergus Henderson with apple and cheese tarts to launch the Apple Source Book. Photo: Jeff Pick.

The Women's Institute was represented at the first Apple Day. More than 10 years on, WI groups around the country provide apple cakes, pies and preserves for many local events, in addition to organising their own Apple Day markets offering not just apple produce but other appley items as well. *The Apple Source Book* has also encouraged caterers, restaurateurs, cafés and workplace canteens to celebrate Apple Day with special menus, using particular varieties.

The catering department at the Houses of Parliament began celebrating Apple Day in 1991, members eating their way through a tonne of apples and an undisclosed quantity of cider. Celebrations have continued each year when the Houses are sitting, with MPs having the chance to sample a range of ciders and apple dishes. Apple Day has also been an opportunity for questions to be raised in the House. In 1993 Nicholas Soames, then Parliamentary Secretary to MAFF, in reply to a question on support for English apple production, said: 'traditional English apples have never been more popular ... it is right that consumers should be reminded of the outstanding quality of English apples'. The Parliamentary Secretary added that 'the House catering authorities did a marvellous job on Apple Day'.

In 1999, the restaurant Chez Lindsey in Richmond in Surrey created The Apple Carte, a special menu for Apple Day. All the recipes were made using Surrey apple varieties such as Claygate Pearmain, Cockle Pippin, Margil and Cox's Orange Pippin. As a Breton restaurant, it had already made liberal use of apples and cider in its cooking. Although authentically French most of the time, chef Lindsey Wotton willingly adapted her recipes to include local Surrey varieties. The menu was a sell out, perhaps aided by the Anglo-French agricultural dispute – this time, a French restaurant was helping British growers.

In addition to the special menu, the restaurant also organised a schools' morning that involved children from one school pushing a laden apple cart from Freshers greengrocers, who provided a lot of the fruit, over Richmond Bridge to the restaurant. The Apple Afternoon was open to all children to play apple games and sample apple pancakes, while parents could leave their children playing upstairs as they enjoyed a quiet meal in the restaurant. An apple-saying competition was organised for all visitors with prizes of cider and apple trees and an apple tree was donated to the Russell (formerly Orchard) school who had pushed the cart.

In 1995, a number of London restaurants devised special Apple Day menus that were well received by their customers. These included The Chop House at Butlers Wharf where Apple Day was a part of its celebration of the Best of British Food; Rowley Leigh at Kensington Place and David McHugh of the Pierre Victoire restaurant in Notting Hill proclaimed Apple Day 'a big success'. Chef Martin Lam of Ransomes Dock in Battersea gave a report on the special menu he had created to a meeting of the Academie Culinaire, bringing Apple Day to the attention of the member chefs and restaurateurs. The dishes he concocted featuring named varieties of apples just might continue to appear in restaurants across the country. The National Trust has produced special menus for Apple Day in many of its restaurants and tearooms, often using fruit from the property's walled gardens and orchards in regional specialities. In 1999, Oxburgh Hall in Norfolk celebrated its wonderful quinces, linking the gardens and kitchens with talks on both the growing and cooking of this unusual fruit.

Farmers' markets

Bath City Council ran its first Apple Day in 1995 and by 1997 they had decided to hold three trial farmers' markets, during September and October, one continuing the celebration of Apple Day. The markets were so successful that by 1999 they were a going concern in Bath and had spread rapidly across the country. As Deborah Morris of Bath & North East Somerset Local Agenda 21 Team writes:

If you went to the Bath on 16 October, you'd have seen a lot of apples – in all manner of shapes, sizes and autumn hues. Farmers' Glory, Captain Kidd, Cheddar Cross, D'Arcy Spice, Tower of Glamis, Hoary Morning – many old and largely forgotten varieties, laid out in a splendid display for all to admire. They were a feast for the eyes and certainly gave a sense of the amazing variety of this homely fruit.

If you were there, you might also have had a go at apple pressing, or tasted locally made single-variety apple juice – or attempted to do better than 160 cm in the Longest Peel Contest.

We also heard that 'Charles Ross' had sold out that day. This very large, smooth, round apple is evenly shaped with a polished appearance. Its superb flavour is rather like that of a Cox, and its crisp, juicy flesh holds its shape well when cut into rings and sautéed in butter with a sprinkling of sage. When golden and sizzling, the apple rings are plonked on the top of real pork sausages. Ours came from Sandridge Farm, but sausages from Pigs' Folly would have been just as good. Apple Charlotte with Bramley's Seedlings, winter salad of Egremont Russets and 'Saddles' of Charles Ross on pork sausage 'horsebacks' went down rather heartily, and demonstrated the various flavours and properties of different apple varieties when subjected to the kitchen stove.

All of these activities were in support of Apple Day. Getting back to the market, it's well known that Bath Farmers' Market started a shopping revolution in the UK, and as a result of its enormous appeal – fresh produce direct from the people who grew, bred, bottled, brewed or baked it – there are now nearly 100 Farmers' Markets operating in other towns and cities across the country. But perhaps less known is the fact that the Bath Farmers' Market grew out of Apple Day in Bath & North East Somerset!

Literature and performance

In holding the first Apple Day in Covent Garden, we were able to ensure that resident street performers, musicians, jugglers and acrobats were on hand to entertain the throngs. Other Apple Day events have been based specifically around the cultural associations of the apple and orchards, involving local theatre groups, poets and musicians in special performances at arts centres and theatres.

For instance, in 1993 people

attending the Apple Day at the Brewhouse Theatre in Taunton were invited to take part in Eddie Upton's *The Somerset Apple Play*. After a brief rehearsal these fledgling actors gave two performances for fellow visitors.

The play has since travelled to Stratford on Avon where the Shakespeare's Morris Men performed their version as part of the Apple Day at Shakespeare's Birthplace Trust, which celebrates both Warwickshire fruit and the bard's fruitful associations. Other local versions of the play are performed at events around the country. The children of Onny School in Shropshire wrote and performed their new play, *Hercules and the Apples*, for Apple Day 1997. Another dramatic celebration of orchards, *The Apple Orchard's Birthday Party*, was devised by the puppet theatre Laughing Root and has entertained children in many schools on Apple Day.

A more traditional mummers play, *Gammer Gurton's Needle*, is performed by the Lions Part Theatre Company as a part of its October Plenty event in celebration of Apple Day. The play is performed outside Shakespeare's Globe Theatre on the Bankside, along the south bank of the Thames in London, and is followed by the procession of the Corn Queen, who generously offers her harvest of apples and cider to the

Identity parade: 100 Devon varieties on display, Apple Day in Eggesford Garden Centre, 1997.

The Apple Source Book: particular recipes for diverse apples. You can make an apple pie every day for 16 years and not use the same variety twice.

audience. Next comes the planting and wassailing of an apple tree and finally singing, dancing and storytelling. In 1999 the Lions Part joined with the Southwark Festival and Borough Market for Apple Day to take their performance around the streets of Southwark and into the market place.

In the Gloucestershire town of Stroud, the Riff Raff poets celebrate Apple Day each year with an evening of poetry and song. Folk musician Johnny Coppin has put together an evening's entertainment, *A Slice of Apple*, based entirely on songs, stories and poetry about apples and orchards, which is performed at Apple Day celebrations each year. In 1994 and 1997 Apple Day in Stroud celebrated one of the writers most associated with orchards, Laurie Lee. The first involved Laurie Lee himself in an evening of readings from his own work and contributions from others such as Winifred Foley. The second, after his death, was in celebration of Lee's life and work.

In 1997 the Hereford Poetry Group organised an orchard poetry competition for Apple Day. At the same time local writer Roy Palmer was compiling *Ripest Apples*, a collection of writings about apples and orchards that was published on Apple Day; pieces from it were performed during the Big Apple celebrations around Much Marcle in Herefordshire.

In 1999 Common Ground appointed James Crowden, poet and cider enthusiast, as the first Apple Day Poet Laureate. During October he appeared at several venues, performing his specially commissioned

Apple Day poem and other works on apples, cider and orchards. We hope this will encourage other groups to commission their own poet in residence for Apple Day or their Community Orchard.

Artist Mary Martin and her husband James Evans own an orchard in the Tamar Valley which often features in *The Guardian's* Country Diary column written by Mary's sister, Virginia Spiers. In 1996 they collaborated on the book *Burcombes, Queenies and Collogetts* which celebrates in words and paintings the special nature of the Tamar Valley, its orchards and Cornish varieties of apples and cherries.

While many Apple Day events have been held in just one place – orchard, garden, school or museum, for example – some communities have been brave enough to dedicate the whole village to celebrations of the apple. Staverton and Landscove in the South Hams of Devon joined forces in 1995 to organise a day of activities scattered throughout the villages. They also arranged special train and coach services. The train, The Staverton Brown, decorated with a giant apple, ferried people from the nearest towns to the celebrations on Woolston Green.

On 19 October 1996 the village of Ilmington in Warwickshire opened its doors to all comers in a village-wide celebration. Christine Wright, one of the organisers, expresses the emotions experienced by

The Apple Source Book

Common Ground

the organisers of possibly every Apple Day held before or since.

It had all seemed such a jolly idea in the summer – to involve the whole village in a celebration of THE APPLE. So many aspects of this quintessentially English fruit could be featured in this quiet village lying in its sheltered dip amongst the last of the Cotswold hills. The orchards, though depleted and ageing, still circle the activities of homes and churches, school and pubs, Manor House and village hall. What a splendid way of showing our respect for the past, our enjoyment of the present and our concern for the future!

… in fact, Apple Day was already a success. Even were the event itself to take place in a gale, with no visitors to appreciate our efforts, the preparations had brought their own satisfactions. The school had been targeting the apple for weeks, the walls were full of paintings, nature study notes from a mini-safari in a pupil's orchard and huge trees depicting the four seasons. Soon they would be joined by old maps and photographs contributed (with much reminiscing) by those who had lived in the village all their lives.

It would be a shame if no one brought any apples to be identified by our three experts. We had had such a wonderful morning organising the event in the summer house of the Manor and they were such knowledgeable, delightful men who got on so well with their talk of codlins and waxed paraffin strips and rootstocks…. And if it rained, who would eat all the cakes and pies the WI had been baking? Who would appreciate the 58 beautifully illustrated original poems dedicated to the apple? Who would drink all last year's brew that the cider-makers had been amassing to give to the spectators of their efforts for this year? Would that evening spent with the Cotswold Wardens pouring over maps (and glasses of red wine) to provide some really good walks in the hills be totally wasted? At least that afternoon spent in June's studio cutting out and painting huge apples had been a joy in itself, even if no-one ever saw the proud information they were destined to carry. Would Chilcroft Orchard have no children to welcome for games and painted faces? Who would buy the tonnes of apples, the books, the cards, the gifts?

I remember that night before Apple Day well...and I remember Apple Day itself, when the dawn revealed a bright blue sky and a golden sun – and thousands of people came to little Ilmington and drank a toast in home-brewed cider to The Apple.

The inclusiveness of Apple Day as a local celebration is reflected in the range and scale of events. In 1993, Catherine Kay invited people

into her council house garden in Moss Side, Manchester, to see her 30 small apple trees of different varieties, as well as the chickens and rabbits that feed beneath them. In her north London garden, Amanda Lebus and friends celebrated Apple Day 1999 with a ceremonial gathering of the fruit from an old garden tree accompanied by poetry to frighten away codling moth and other pests.

The National Trust has been involved with Apple Day from the very beginning. Many of its properties include orchards or walled

Town and country: Banners announce Apple Day outside the Elephant and Castle shopping centre in London and Sulgrave Manor in rural Northamptonshire.

Preparing apples for juicing, at the Staverton and Landscove Apple Day 1995 in Devon.

gardens that would have provided the house with fruit in their heyday. As interest in orchards has increased so the Trust has focused more attention on renovation and replanting of their orchards. In some areas, such as Cornwall and Cumbria, these orchards have become hosts for collections of local varieties. They also demonstrate the wide variety of ways in which apples have been cultivated or used at different

periods of history. Those Trust properties without orchards actively celebrate Apple Day with special menus in their tea rooms and restaurants, displays of fruit around the house and activities for children.

Many other large houses and country estates regularly celebrate Apple Day. Exuberant events have been organised every year since 1991 at Sulgrave Manor in Oxfordshire, once home to George Washington. Residents from the surrounding village are involved, as well as local growers, cider makers, craftspeople, artists and performers. Over the years, they have experimented with a diverse range of activities and participants, but keep coming back to the delight people find in apples and all things connected with them.

House of commoners

The 'Big House', once the seat of power in the community, has in some places been handed to the people as a communal asset. Entry to Sulgrave Manor is free to members of the village, while the houses and estates of Cockington Court in Devon and Oakwell Hall in Yorkshire are now country parks with open access to all. Richard Aspinall, a ranger at Oakwell Hall, describes their orchard and Apple Day celebrations:

Oakwell Hall in West Yorkshire is a 16th-century mansion set among 40 hectares of woodland, pasture, hedgerows, ponds and streams. It's a beautiful place ideal for a family wander, a lazy amble of an afternoon or a snooze under an old oak.

The walled garden, behind the Tudor stonework of the Hall, replete with lady's mantle, hellebore, germander, lavender and rambling rose, plays host to our fan-trained cordons on the southern wall. At only four years old, the ebullient branches bear rich fruit. We have Cornish Aromatic, Devonshire Quarrenden and Autumn Pearmain to name but a few. The apples are often scrumped by the local kids who seem marvellously resistant to indigestion. I've had to chase them out many times, but my anger is half hearted – I too went scrumping and had I not done, well I possibly wouldn't be doing what I'm doing now.

The working garden houses our orchard – with its 15 old varieties sheltering under

the wrinkled boughs of an old Grenadier apple and a couple of tired old pears – dreaming of past glories, yet still proud in their lichen-encrusted dotage. Planting an orchard is such a rare privilege (and planned hard work) and reflects, I hope, a pattern spreading across the land as Community Orchards spring up and old trees are once more cared for. Apple Day for us is the most wonderful day of the autumn, just when the wet weather is getting us down it's time to remember the balmier days of summer with apples. All those sweet flavours forged with summer sun and mellowed through early autumn seem to contain the essence of summer, distilled and compacted. Apple Day is the celebration of this seasonal bounty – we open our doors and the public come. They come from across Yorkshire eager to enter into the simple wonder of the apple. The myths, the stories and the folklore of the apple linger on. They are re-created and re-interpreted over time, yet still lose none of their magic.

There is something special about the apple, something that continues to amaze us, yet its workaday nature contrasts with its rich associations of wisdom and forbidden pleasures. Maybe this dichotomy, this splendid paradox, is what Apple Day reaches within us. Apple Day is not just a celebration of the orchard, it is a celebration of our relationship with the land. The apple is a symbol of nature and the nation's heritage. Long may Apple Day continue. It reminds us who we are, where we've been and how truly lucky we are.

APPLE-PIE

& I SCREAM!

POETS & MUSIC

Celebration of *APPLE DAY.*

(Oct. 21st.) – Created by persons

alive to Local Diversity – who

began *COMMON GROUND*

Music & Song: Richard Valentine.
Bob Bray. Phil Palmer.
Becky – Violin. David
Stringer – Cello. &
The Tickle Fishermen

★ *Poets:* Roger Berry. Stuart
Butler. Ms. Pat West.
& *Special Guests –*

COMMON-GROUND
APPLE DAY

MON. 21st! OCT. 8 ~ PM

Pay on Door & £2!50

Advance Tickets:

LATE:NIGHT
CAFE

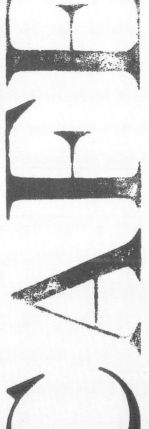

STROUD

21.10.96

HANDSET LETTER PRESS

Produce

NO WASTE from an orchard they say: the fruit can be eaten raw or cooked, pressed into juice or fermented into cider, fed to pigs or left for wild life, mulched as a fertiliser or nurtured as the source of new varieties. Making, trading, buying and selling distinctive products from orchards can form a vibrant part of any local economy, today just as much as in times past.

Cities, towns and villages have always been the centre of local trading – our wide main streets and market squares are evidence of this. Yet while the advent of the supermarket has fostered an exodus from these public spaces, the home-grown apple has helped to fuel a revival. Increasingly, all over Britain, you can shop in farmers' markets – and buy fresh local food direct from the grower or producer.

Bath pioneered the idea of direct selling in farmers' markets around Apple Day in 1997. Growers with a wealth of apple varieties ripened in local orchards had at last found an appreciative audience, as had other producers too. The markets proved so successful that the city council published a guide to organising them to encourage other local authorities to develop the idea. In 2000 there are now more than 100 regular farmers' markets across the country. Statistics from the National Farmers' Union survey carried out in May 2000 estimated that annual turnover is around £65 million and that this could top £100 million by the spring of 2001. The number of farmers' markets is steadily rising as small-scale food producers recognise the advantages of selling directly to people, avoiding the middleman, and reducing transport costs and wasteful packaging. A National

The first Apple Day at Covent Garden was an opportunity to eat and drink a huge range of orchard produce.

Association of Farmers' Markets has now been established to coordinate the growing number of markets countrywide.

Even wholesale markets that usually operate in the early hours of the morning are waking up to the potential of opening during the day to retail customers. Borough Market in south London held a specialist food market in 1998 which proved to be hugely successful. Inspired by this they began to organise monthly markets throughout the year including an Apple Day in October 1999, where juice- and cider-makers rubbed shoulders with cheese merchants, pork butchers and bakers who created apple breads, cakes and Colchester Lobo apple dumplings. The market now opens regularly each Saturday with larger markets once a month.

It is so easy to succumb to the lure of shopping exclusively at the out-of-town supermarket – free parking, one visit, cash machine, dry cleaner. The flip side can be long queues, oppressive buildings, mild Cheddar rather than single Gloucester, chemical fizz rather than Kingston Black cider. Many local producers are happy to welcome visitors to their farms, workshops or orchards, which are often in beautiful landscapes. Visits can give shoppers an opportunity to learn more about the products and the production crafts. Local food is an integral part of local distinctiveness. Jellied eels in London, shrimps in Morecambe, Blenheim Orange apples in Oxford. Supermarkets are not able to cope with such localised purchasing, so individual consumers must celebrate these gems by direct contact with producers.

Buying local cider, fruit juice and seasonal fruit will help to keep the knowledge of their production alive at a time when our taste buds are in need of excitement and our children need help linking fruit with trees not with cellophane packets. Small cider- or perry-makers or farm shops selling, for example, Shropshire damsons, often grow fruit in their own old orchards. Increasing demand for the product reinforces the reasons for keeping the orchards in good shape. As well as the opportunity for more variety, seasonal variation and freshness that has not been artificially sustained, local produce can also be consumed in the happy knowledge that it has not been shipped from half way around the world.

The Soil Association too seeks to encourage consumers to support local growers and producers, through its Local Food Links initiative. Meanwhile, local authorities such as Mid Bedfordshire, Malvern Hills, West Dorset and those covering north and east Dorset are encouraging the consumption of locally produced food and have compiled directories that list growers, suppliers and small retailers. Somerset County Council, for example, has produced a list of cider-makers who are happy to buy bagged apples from people with orchards of unused fruit.

In the South Hams, the capital of Devon's cider-making tradition, orchard owners are joining forces within Orchard Link, an initiative funded with help from a three-year European Union rural development grant. Founders Cathy Fitzroy and Trudy Turrell used the grant to set up a limited company which collects bagged fruit from traditional orchards from a network of members. The bags are delivered to cider producers who buy the apples at an agreed price, and the money is redistributed to the growers. People can

Stall at the Pershore Plum Festival. Juicing apples at Bath Apple Day farmers' market. Both annual celebrations attract ever more visitors.

also drop off fruit they have gathered themselves at one of two collection points. The money earned from the Orchards Link scheme acts as an incentive for owners to maintain their orchards, while the fruit itself helps to sustain the local cider economy and generates jobs. Although it's been hard work, the scheme has been an inspiration to many other groups and its original south Devon focus is widening as other local authorities in the county plan to set up allied collection services. Anyone can join Orchards Link and members receive a quarterly newsletter. 'They welcome the support and seasonal advice,' says Trudy.

Picking and storing the fruit: First comes the harvest. Apples are ready to be picked when their stalks part readily from the branch, they should never be pulled with force or broken from the branch, nor should the stalk be removed. To pick an apple, lift it on the palm of your hand and gently lift or twist the stalk, if it is ripe it will come away easily from the branch. Fruit for storing should not be over-ripe, bruised or blemished, so careful handling of some varieties is needed. Early varieties are best eaten straight from the tree, while many late varieties improve with keeping.

According to Dorothy Hartley in *The Land of England*, the domestic storage of fruit has changed little through the centuries. Authorities ancient and modern agree that fruit in store should be checked regularly for signs of mould and any rotten fruit removed immediately as 'one bad apple can spoil the whole barrel'.

Almost two thousand years ago Pliny offered the following advice in his *Natural History*:

In regard to keeping fruit it is universally recommended

that fruit-lofts should be constructed in a cool and dry place, with boarded floors and windows facing north that are left open on a fine day, and with glazed windows to keep out south winds, the draught from a north-east wind also spoiling the appearance of the fruit by making it shrivelled; that apples should be gathered after the autumn equinox, and not before the 16th day of the moon nor later than the 28th, nor on a rainy day, nor till an hour after sunrise; that windfalls should be kept separate; that the fruit should have a bed of close-packed straw or of chaff underneath, and should be placed far apart so that the spaces between the rows may admit a uniform draught.

Those without access to Pliny's ideal apple-storage facilities might follow Jane Grigson's advice; in her *Fruit Book* she recommends wrapping apples loosely in newspaper and standing them on slatted wooden trays with air circulating around them. All the same, she finds that the erratic climate in Britain makes fruit storage problematic … 'no wonder we developed a passion for dried fruit to fill that third of the year between the last of the apples and the first gooseberries'.

Cold storage, from domestic freezers to the large controlled atmosphere stores used commercially, is a tempting solution, but there are still benefits to be gained from the more traditional methods of preserving fruit. Drying is probably the simplest method and provides you with an extra ingredient. 'Dried fruit is very different in taste and texture, being a concentration of sweetness and flavour even after it has been soaked and cooked,' Jane Grigson contends. Plums, apples, pears and apricots all dry well. Grigson recommends an airy steady temperature between 50-60°C such as a plate-warming oven or a warm airing cupboard; gas and electric ovens can be too hot even on the lowest setting. Fruit should first be dried cut-side-up and the pieces should not touch while drying. Apples are usually sliced and dried in rings, but in the past they were cored, hung on strings and dried whole like giant necklaces. Other fruits depending on their size are either halved or dried whole.

The Norfolk Beefing apple seems to have been created specifically for drying since, although it cooks well, it has a tough skin and rather dry flesh. When baked very slowly at the lowest oven setting for 24 hours, it takes on a new persona, the flesh becomes thick and tastes of raisins and cinnamon. The tough skin of the apple allows the flesh to baked in its own juices without bursting. Traditionally, Norfolk Biffins, as they became known once baked, were put into the bread ovens after the bread had been removed and an iron plate placed on top to press the air out. Until the early 1900s, Biffins were packed in boxes and dispatched by Norwich bakers to London. The diary of Parson Woodforde is full of references to his 'Beefans' apple trees, which benefited many poor parishioners.

TRADITIONAL ORCHARDS: WELL WORTH PRESERVING

Bottling is perhaps more suitable for soft fruits such as plums, damsons or cherries. Fruit for this purpose should be firm but not over-ripe, the stalks removed and the fruit packed into preserving jars with layers of sugar, the final layer of sugar being thick enough to completely cover the fruit. Once filled the jars are baked in the oven until ready. The cooking time will vary according to the fruit, between 40 and 50 minutes for cherries or plums, between 30 and 40 minutes for apples which will be cooked further before serving and up to 70 minutes for pears. After cooking the lids should be sealed as tightly as possible to secure the vacuum, leave to cool and test the seals to ensure the fruit is preserved correctly.

Fruit can be bottled without the addition of sugar, but this may not be to everyone's taste. Jane Grigson writes: '...I confess that I dislike bottling wholeheartedly. Something to do with the horrible bottled plums of wartime: all that labour for something so disagreeable (I seem to remember that they were put down without sugar).'

Fruit cuisine

Apples are nothing if not versatile: throughout the world they are vital ingredients in sweet pies, tarts and cakes as well as savoury dishes, from soups and sauces to salads and stews, as Duncan Mackay of the New Road Cyderists describes in *Apples, Berkshire, Cider*:

Apples have been part of the human diet for tens of thousands of years and in all cultures where the apple is known it has produced interesting eating ideas. The Cherokee Native Americans of the Great Plains were especially fond of campfire-baked apples called SU-GA-TA. The Austrians have strudel, the Danes and Italians have apple cake, the Americans Brown Betty. The fabulous French *Tarte aux Pommes* from Brittany and Normandy uses sweet dessert apples and sharper cooking apples to spectacular effect. The Dutch and Chinese like apple fritters but in Britain we like pies made from Bramleys. In Germany, apples were used as an ingredient in the traditional *Himmel und Erde* (Heaven and Earth) – boiled apples and potatoes with bacon. The Dutch add haricot beans to create *Hette Bliksen*. In Poland, *Bigos* is lamb, beef and sauerkraut with apple, and vies with the savoury stuffed apples *Dolmehsib*, of Iran. For Christmas Eve in Sweden you will be served braised cabbage and apples, and on Walpurgis Night or Hallowe'en you need witches cream (apple snow) to spot any witches in the dark.

The soft, sweetness of cooked fruit has a great affinity with crisp pastry in a tart or the moist sponginess of a pudding that is made even more sublime by the addition of cream or custard. As can be expected, every place has its own local variation on the apple pie or plum pudding, the crumble, charlotte, tansy, fool or flan.

In Yorkshire, where 'apple pie without cheese is like a kiss without a squeeze', the cheese would of course be Wensleydale or another local variety. In some places, a pie will have only a top crust where in others the crust will be top and bottom. Wilfra Tarts are a double crust pie, decorated with three pastry leaves, filled with sweetened apple and a layer of cheese. They are made for a procession for St Wilfred the patron of Ripon Cathedral, North Yorkshire, held on the Saturday before the first Monday in August. The content of the tarts has changed over time, but the apple and cheese filling is the current favourite.

In Bedfordshire they have the Clanger, an oblong baked pasty with a suet crust, filled with savoury and sweet ingredients at opposite ends. Most often it includes pork with apple, the idea being that it was a meal in one, easily transportable and eaten while working. Similar recipes are found in other parts of the country. In France the great mistake which became tarte Tatin is cooked with the crust on top then inverted when serving. Whichever type of fruit dessert you make, there is an ideal variety for the recipe, as Joan Morgan in Common Ground's *The Apple Source Book* describes:

It was in Victorian England that the notion of a culinary variety, one specifically grown for the kitchens and often especially valued for a particular dish became firmly entrenched in our culture. Definite opinions were then held as to which were the best varieties for making apple sauce, apple dumplings, jelly or pies and particularly which were the best plainly baked.

Summer codlins were ideal and provided the first baked apples of the new season. Keswick Codlin and Early Victoria will quickly rise up like a frothy souffle, and need no embellishments except perhaps a little sugar and a dribble of cream, but they were too juicy and insubstantial for pies and charlottes.

One had to wait for the autumn ripening apples, such as Golden Noble, which is sharper, keeps a little of its form when cooked and so filled the pie with soft, golden fruit. It has a distinct flavour that can stand on its own, and the purists did not permit any distraction from cloves or lemon peel in a pie.

For apple sauce Eckinville Seedling was prized for its smooth, savoury quality and the cider apple, Foxwelp with a rough, piquant flavour also made a fine accompaniment to the Michaelmas goose, or roast leg of pork. In a more delicate style there was juicy Hawthornden and the Reverend W Wilks. These were followed by the large and angular Warner's King, suitable for most uses but not Apple Charlotte, which called for an apple that would make a stiff puree. Blenheim Orange was requested by the cooks. This is usually thought of as a dessert apple, but picked early it cooks well and will make a firm sauce for the moulded Charlotte.

Then came the late-maturing apples, which were not picked until October and kept until the spring. The Victorian favourite was Dumelow's Seedling, which was sold in the markets as Wellington and is still to be found in old orchards. It has a translucent quality, good for pies and makes delicious creamy brisk baked apples or sauce. Dumelow's was overtaken at the beginning of this century by the larger and heavier cropping Bramley's Seedling, which at first was favoured for dumplings but soon became recommended for every kind of dish. Alas, Bramleys are now picked as early as August, but these 'thinnings' are immature, sour and starchy compared with the robust flavour of fruit left to develop properly on the tree. Not all late varieties are as strong. Many, like Annie Elizabeth, of the Midlands, are mild; it needs no sugar and was claimed to be the best of all for making a dish of stewed apples, because 'the quarters never break'....

Apples also vary in flavour from year to year, and depending on where they are grown, says Joan Morgan. Grow a variety on its home ground and you can probably taste the difference.

Many Scottish and northern varieties of high culinary repute often lack acidity in southern gardens and are rather bland. Lord Derby, for instance, which arose in Cheshire, remains green and sharp until Christmas in the north, but in Kent is at its best in September and soon loses its acidity and appeal. On the other hand, James Grieve is a valued eating apple in southern gardens, but if deprived of sun is sharp and in the north regarded as a cooking apple.

The way in which an apple cooks also depends to an extent upon when it is used and how it is stored. Windfalls and early picked fruit will be sharper and cook more easily than those harvested in their proper season. Kept in a

frost-proof garden shed or some other dark, cool equivalent of the old-fashioned fruit store, the apple's acidity will fall and the sugar level rise. The fruit will cook more firmly and taste sweeter. Before the inventions of the refrigerated and controlled atmosphere storage, varieties that remained sharp through the winter without any trouble were highly valued.

That apples matured and sweetened over the winter in the barn or store, however, meant that many, like Annie Elizabeth were dual purpose. Another was Forge from Sussex, which is still grown in its home territory of East Grinstead. A brisk cooking apple in September, it is sweet and quite perfumed by Christmas, and even a Bramley becomes a sharp eating apple by March.

In its prime, a good English cooker nevertheless possesses plenty of bite and savoury character so that it can offset the richness of pork or game. Cooking itself ameliorates sharpness and if apple is to contrast with buttery pastry and zing through the sugar and cream, it needs to have plenty of flavour and piquancy to begin with. Bramley's Seedling greatest virtue must surely be that no matter how much sugar, cinnamon, lemon peel or cloves a recipe demands, it will still emerge tasting strongly of apple. Delicate, mild-flavoured cooking apples are easily swamped and best used in very simple ways. Similarly if one uses a dessert apple, such as a Cox, in a recipe it will be more interesting if cooked early and sharp....

Newton Wonder, which is grown in hundreds of gardens, is not as acidic and aggressive as Bramley; it is good used raw in vegetable salads, where the crisp, sharp, fruity taste is not overwhelmed by the vinaigrette dressing. A large Newton Wonder is just right for baked red cabbage, it can add plenty of flavour grated into stir-fried cabbage, and chopped apple greatly improves the bread and herb stuffing for the Christmas turkey.

Fresh fruit salads, on the other hand, ask for the best dessert apples, those with intensely aromatic rich flavours – a ripe Cox's Orange Pippin, Sunset, Holstein, Ribston Pippin and Orleans Reinette in the autumn – and well ripened they will have plenty of colour. Later in the season there is Ashmead's Kernel with its sweet sharp taste reminiscent of fruit drops and the robust Suntan and Tydeman's Late Orange. Plenty of interest can be provided in August and September by Discovery, Miller's Seedling, bright red Worcester Pearmain, which if really ripe is very sweet and tastes of strawberries, and Ellison's Orange with its lovely aniseed flavour.

Become familiar again with the diversity of flavours that English apples can offer. If you have the chance, experiment with different varieties and explore ways best suited to their particular qualities.

D'Arcy Spice

George Neal

Golden Noble

Howgate Wonder

Keswick Codlin

Ribston Pippin

Stirling Castle

Sweet Alford

Tom Putt

Tower of Glamis

Worcester Pearmain

Yarlington Mill

Particular recipes have also developed in other places around other fruit. In Kent, once famous for its cherry orchards, we find ripe stoned cherries cooked in batter and served sprinkled with sugar – in France this is called *clafoutis*. Kent also offers cherry huffkins – flat oval cakes, a kind of tea bread, with a hole in the middle that is filled with hot stoned cherries after baking – as well as cherry ale and cherry brandy. In Cumbria, in the Lyth Valley, the damsons that grow in hedgerows and small orchards are made into beer at the Masons Arms, Cartmel Fell, as well as ice cream, wine, pickled damsons and, of course, tarts, pies and cakes and damson 'cheese'. You can buy these delicacies at the Westmorland Damson Association's annual Damson Day in April.

In the west country, recipes abound for cider cakes, cider gravy and peas cooked in cider. Apples are also a frequent addition to savoury pies, especially Squab Pie, found in Somerset, Devon and Cornwall, which mixes pigeon with apple. Recipes including fruit are also associated with celebration, such as Barnstaple Fair Pears, these spiced cooked pears were served in restaurants and private houses during the annual fair where visitors could also buy apple pie doused with hot spiced ale before serving.

Another delicacy of festivals and fairs since medieval times is the toffee apple, when they were made with honey and beeswax. They are now most commonly seen in greengrocers and supermarkets around Hallowe'en and Guy Fawkes Night, but can easily be made at home, to be consumed round the bonfire. In Cornwall, the Kea plums that grow along the shoreline, seemingly unaffected by the salt spray, are made into jam and sold as a regional speciality. Similarly in Shropshire discerning B&Bs serve Shropshire Prune jam in preference to marmalade at the breakfast table.

Every Apple Day, recipes for apple cake, buns, scones and muffins flood in, all with subtle differences. In Devon apple cake is made with apple purée, cinnamon and raisins, in Dorset with chopped cooking apple and currants, and in Somerset the chopped apple is combined with cinnamon and mixed spice. In Cornwall the cake may resemble the French tarte Tatin and in Cambridgeshire it is closer to German streusel. In more northern counties where there is a tradition of gingerbread making, apples or pears are frequently combined in these recipes, while in other places the apple is grated and combined with nuts. In cider-making counties such as Herefordshire, Worcestershire, Suffolk and Gloucestershire, the apple is replaced by cider and mixed with spices and dried fruit that has been soaked in the liquid overnight. This splendid diversity has inspired much cake- as well as apple-tasting on Apple Days throughout the country, as well as cake-making competitions and a growing number of local apple cookery books.

Glance at a menu in a restaurant in almost any part of the world and you will find at least one dish containing fruit, sweet and savoury, from cherry soup in Hungary, herring and apple salad in Sweden, spareribs with plums in China, sauerkraut with apple in Germany, poires belle Helene in France, quince cheese in Spain, Portugal and Brazil, followed by cherry brandy, apricot schnapps, calvados or damson gin.

The best cooks flavour a joint of meat with the flavour of the food the animal ate, according to Dorothy Hartley in *Food in England*. Mutton from the Midlands raised in orchards would be served with fruit sauces, for instance, while the combination of pork and apple may well have arisen with the Gloucester Old Spot pig.

This breed is able to thrive on the by-products of two of Gloucestershire's most important industries, cheese production and orchards, as the pigs feasted on whey and windfall fruit. Its local name is the orchard pig and local folklore has it that the spots are the bruises caused by falling fruit, perhaps reflecting the pigs' penchant for rocking the trees to rain down more fruit. It is unlikely that the pig was kept in the orchard all year round. Pigs can cause damage to roots

through their foraging, and in a confined area or on clay soil quickly turn a grassy area into a quagmire. The pigs were probably allowed in the orchard only after harvesting to clear unused fruit from the ground. While Gloucester Old Spots are highly prized for the flavour and texture of their meat, they are now considered a rare breed and are still being kept in traditional ways.

The growth of the orchards in Cambridgeshire, particularly around Histon and Wisbech, was encouraged by, and in turn encouraged, the jam-making industry. John Chivers established his factory at Histon in 1873. In Essex, the Tiptree Heath factory of Wilkins & Sons and Elsenham Quality Foods at Elsenham Court also developed at the end of the 19th century. Sugar was cheaper in England than elsewhere in Europe and jam provided a market for surplus and poor-quality fruit. Apples contain pectin, which helps jam to set, and formed a cheap ingredient for the mixed-fruit jam that became a staple part of the working-class diet.

Wilkins of Tiptree is still supporting the orchards of Essex and Cambridgeshire and is the one major grower of the Cambridge Gage. This variety is considered to have such a good flavour that it is the only variety of greengage used in its jams. Wilkins and Elsenham were also among the few commercial producers of medlar jelly, which can be served with game, lamb and other meats that go well with tart fruit jellies. Less common fruits such as medlar and quince are often popular with jam makers, and preserves from these fruits are frequently found on local market stalls and at WI gatherings.

Jellies made with fruit juice have long been popular in Britain and may well have their origins in the recipes such as quince paste from Renaissance Spain and Portugal. This was made from fruit juice, boiled until concentrated enough to form solid confections that could be stored for long periods in boxes and cut into slices for use. Other

Bill Hammond building a 'mock', a Devonshire device that holds the apple pulp during pressing, at Rashleigh Mill, Devon. Photo: James Ravilious.

types of jellies, developed during the 19th century, have since evolved into either the fruit jellies, gums and pastilles now sold as children's sweets or the jellies made at home or by jam companies. Many of the orchards in Yorkshire and the north of England supplied fruit to the factories of Joseph Rowntree and Terry's of York for use as pectin in the making of fruit jellies and other confectionery. The creation of chemical pectin saw the swift demise of many northern orchards.

Apples, plums, damsons and sometimes cherries are also popular ingredients for chutney makers. Visit an Apple Day event and you will find jars of fruity preserves created by local producers especially for the day, such as the Sweet Cider Jelly made by Dorset Delights for Apple Day at Kingston Maurward in Dorchester, or the Cherry Chutney made by Academy Fruit, for the Borough Market Apple Day in 1999. Community Orchards also provide an ideal opportunity for people to try their hand at making jams and chutneys, as well as fruit-filled cakes, pies, tarts and scones. Kentish Town City Farm, north London, with the help of local people, collected apples from the orchard at the nearby La Sainte Union School to create a wide range of preserves including Kashmir Chutney.

Fruits are often pickled as a means of preserving and enhancing their flavour. Pickled damsons have been associated with Westmorland for at least 150 years and are made with damsons cooked with vinegar, sugar and spices. The kernels from the stones are sometimes added to give an almond-like flavour. Pickled apples have long been a Cornish delicacy, in particular the variety Sweet Larks, which although difficult to find, is still growing in old orchards and gardens around the county. One recipe began 'take a stone of Sweet Larks ...' The vinegar with which such pickles are made may also be a product of the orchard, cider vinegar being highly regarded by cooks for its delicate fruity flavour which enhances salad dressings and sauces.

Apple juice has found a new market in recent years as manufacturers have capitalised on a growing interest in apple varieties.

Instead of blends, juice makers such as James White are producing single-variety apple juices, demonstrating the distinctive characteristics of different varieties and offering people the choice to suit their particular taste. Such products can also benefit orchards themselves; James White has donated an amount from the sales of each bottle of apple juice to support the renovations to the walled garden and orchard at Wimpole Hall in Cambridgeshire, owned by the National Trust.

In Germany, the Naturschutzbund, a charity dedicated to the conservation of wild birds, has pioneered a national fruit-juice marketing scheme taking fruit from traditional orchards. The project began in an attempt to help conserve little owls, following research which linked the decline of this species with the demise of old orchards. Fruit from standard orchards is more expensive to collect, but this scheme has reduced the retail premium to a few pence per litre.

Apple juice is easy to make and is an ideal way to use surplus fruit. On many Apple Day events, juice pressing has become a popular centrepiece. For the past three years, Scarthin Books in Cromford in Derbyshire has set up a press outside the bookshop on Apple Day and invited local people to bring along bags-full of fruit for pressing, with the resulting juice bottled and taken home.

Good wood, mistletoe and more

Fruit and nut trees are a source of beautiful timber. Walnut often appears on the dashboards of more expensive cars and has long been prized for furniture making. Tall cherry trees give good lengths of timber that are chosen for cabinet making as they will polish into attractive reddish tones. The wood from plum and damson trees also has a highly coloured heartwood, usually red and purple, and is frequently selected by wood turners. Pear is the hardest and most finely grained of fruit-tree woods and is used by wood engravers as an alternative to box, and its fine grain also makes it a favourite of woodturners. Pear is also used for woodwind instruments, especially recorders, as it takes stain well and can easily pass for ebony. Along with apple it is also chosen for marquetry and inlays. Fruit wood has been used for cogwheels and wooden screws. Mill wheel cogs need to be close-grained and hard-wearing and most fruit woods fit this description. 'The cogs need to wear away rather than splinter,' says Peter Loosmore at Sturminster Newton watermill, which includes some apple cogs in its wheels. Local abundance may have determined which type of fruit wood prevailed. Apple wood is relatively plentiful in north Dorset compared with cherry or pear.

Crab apple can often be found in the heads of golf clubs, while depending on the way the trees are managed the thinnings from hazel nut plats can be used for heatherings for binding layed hedges. The Nuttery in Northamptonshire, owned by the Woodland Trust, provides

Walnut trunks near Boxted, Essex. The beautifully-grained wood is highly prized as a furniture veneer.
Boxed and tissue-wrapped, these wooden apples look like the real thing, St Remy, France.

a harvest of nuts from trees that are grown as a coppice for timber, two products for the effort of one.

Even the stones or pips can be used once the fruit has been eaten. Cherry stones are used in some parts of Europe as hot water bottles – they are put into a bag and slowly heated in the oven, retaining their heat for hours. Plum stones that are removed during pulping have been used to clean the lights on airport runways. At the famously 'green' 2000 Sydney Olympics, the athletes enjoyed their meals served on plates made of crushed apple pulp, as part of a major recycling and composting system and in an effort to minimise the use of plastic.

Orchard trees may be host to crops of mistletoe and can provide shelter for daffodils in the spring or soft fruits in the summer. Hay crops can be cut in the traditional way in summer for animal feed. Orchards can also provide grazing for livestock, but bear in mind animals can damage trees. Find out what the practice has been in the past. In Kent cobnut plats the local short-necked Southdown sheep can't browse the fruit buds. Before you decide to hire the orchard out for grazing, consider what you want to use the orchard for. If you wish to cultivate a good ground flora to encourage wild life, perhaps grazing is not the best option.

To produce fruit, orchard blossom needs to be pollinated. Cherries rely on the wind, but apples and pears need the help of insects to set fruit. So orchards can be good homes for beehives, and the honey can generate extra income. Pupils from Mallorees School in north London brought samples of the honey made by their school orchard bees to the first Apple Day in London's Covent Garden in 1990.

Fermented fruits

Wherever fruit is grown, some form of alcoholic drink is sure to follow. In Britain we have cider in the West Country, perry in Herefordshire and Worcestershire, damson beer in Cumbria and cherry brandy in Kent. In other parts of Europe we find calvados from the cider orchards of Normandy, kirsch, the cherry brandy from France, Germany and Denmark and an assortment of fruit beers from Belgium. Throughout the world, fruits are steeped in alcohol to infuse the liquid with the flavour of the fruit – producing sloe or damson gin, pear and plum liqueurs.

Cider has a long history. The methods and traditions involved in its production are as varied and deep-rooted as the orchards in which the cider fruit grows. The practices and experiences of one cider maker may contradict or complement another, because the knowledge of cider making is as much about culture as it is about chemistry. As a rough guide, cider making in England and Wales can be divided by a line between the Wash and the Solent. To the east of the line, ciders are traditionally made from the blended juices of locally grown culinary or dessert apples. The sunnier climate of the east benefits the growth and ripening of table fruit, which relies partly on its appetising appearance. Early varieties or those with short shelf lives are, as they always have been in the past, sent quickly to the London and other regional city markets while lower quality fruit goes to the juice or cider mill.

To the west of the imaginary line, special cider apples have been cultivated over centuries through selective breeding to produce fruits with varying acidity, tannins or sugars that can be blended to give the desired taste. Accordingly, these characteristics define cider apples as sharps, bittersharps, sweets or bittersweets. Cider apples do not need to be visually pleasing, though many are. Nor are they carefully (and therefore expensively) hand-picked – they are harvested from the orchard floor after fruit fall. The wetter western climate also offers the orchard owner an opportunity to cultivate hay or graze stock beneath the trees while the crop ripens.

Perry, which is made from pear juice, is similarly a blend of juices. The stronghold of perry remains the West Midland counties of Gloucestershire, Herefordshire and Worcestershire as well as Monmouthshire, although some growers like to perpetuate the local claim that the best perry comes from pears grown within sight of May Hill, on the Herefordshire-Gloucestershire border. Here the old red sandstone soils are said to support the largest of perry pear trees though even wild crab apples struggle to find nourishment within them. The region as a whole has a history of pear cultivation, many varieties of which were originally destined for the table or the oven. Changing tastes have left some, such as Brown Bess, too sour for modern palates but they make good perry.

The huge variety of orchard fruit grown in Britain over the years is significantly bolstered by the cider apples and perry pears, some of which are so suited to local climate and soil that they do not grow successfully away from these conditions. Many also have fantastic names that reflect their origin and the people who raised them, or which lay claims to their qualities either as fruit or as cider: Yarlington Mill, Collington Big Bitters, Brown Snout or Slack Ma Girdle, which is a Devon cider apple named perhaps as a warning against overindulgence (or an encouragement for it).

Varieties have distinct qualities that may wax and wane in popular demand. In the 17th century, Lord Scudamore, French ambassador to Charles I and master of a Herefordshire ancestral seat, did his utmost to plant the entire county with Redstreak apples, the cider of which he had tasted in France. The prices paid for Redstreak apples were huge, and its cider was claimed to surpass the taste of continental wines. Today, a revival in the production of bottle-fermented ciders is proving lucrative for growers of the Kingston Black who can expect to earn almost twice as much per tonne as growers of more common or unreliable varieties. This Somerset variety is dark maroon and very susceptible to canker, scab and low cropping, so its high price must reflect the grower's trouble.

The importance of soil is fundamental. Yarlington Mill, a quality vintage variety with high-yielding trees, was found growing from a wall by a watermill in Yarlington near Cadbury, Somerset. It does well in its home county and the limestones in parts of the West Midlands. A Cornish grower, recognising its qualities, was nevertheless disappointed in his attempts to grow a few acres of Yarlingtons in his local soils – they did not crop well. Local geology is also responsible for the way we produce cider. James Crowden, the poet and cider-maker, in his book, *Cider – the forgotten miracle*, outlines the familiar but localised granite horse-drawn mills (even more familiar perhaps to continental visitors, for they may be modelled on olive presses): 'These troughs are almost unknown in Somerset today, they are more of a Devon, Hereford and Gloucester phenomenon. It may well be that most of Somerset's stone is limestone in one form or another and will react with cider, in fact the apple juice will probably dissolve it away in time and taint the cider.'

Perhaps this is why Somerset mills and presses are constructed of wood – oak for the strength of the framework with elm and ash, damp-proof and flexible woods – for the parts of the press that come into contact with the flowing juice.

Local variation even directs the ways in which apple pulp, or pomace, is piled up in the press. Pulping or milling the fruit first ensures an easier release of the locked-in juices under pressure. The subsequent need to restrain the pulp as it is squeezed in the press led to the development of the 'hair', which piled on top of one another

Whiteways cider orchards, Whimple, Devon. Photo: James Ravilious.

are collectively called a 'cheese'. As its name suggests, the hair was originally made from horsehair (now more commonly nylon) and provides a tough, woven mat upon which the pomace can be placed, with the mat wrapped up and over the sides to form a flat parcel. Another hair is made on top of the first until a cheese about a metre high is created. This conglomeration is then subjected to pressure and the juices expressed. Instead of horsehair, some cider-makers, particularly in Devon, use long barley straw to make a sort of thatch, called a mock, to contain the milled fruit.

Cider and perry, away from the chemical processes of the bulk producers, strongly reinforce the sense that local fruit is the sum of many local parts both 'natural', as in geology and climate, and 'cultural' reflected in grafting traditions or cider production. Orchards represent the best in our close relations with nature – trees and land worked gently to our advantage within the confines of local conditions.

There are 100 varieties of

Farmhouse cider remains a common product in the west country, where it inspires fierce competition at local agricultural shows. Photo: James Ravilious.

perry pear in Gloucestershire alone which are 'worthy of note' and each parish would have had its own suite to blend together according to tried-and-tested method. Each apple and pear variety in turn has its own strains of unique wild yeasts, so that the fruit presses of Somerset or Norfolk may hold latent yeasts among their wooden timbers making the cider from each producer a little different from his or her neighbour.

Farm cider orchards are a distinctive feature of the Somerset Levels, where they often exist on the drier slopes above willow beds, which provide another traditional Levels crop. Somerset County Council, in common with a number of other local authorities, offer grants to restore and restock traditional orchards in recognition of the continuing importance of orchards in the local landscape and the county's economy. Most farms in Somerset would once have included an orchard,

153

often small and undergrazed, probably by sheep.

The changing methods of fruit-growing and cider-making have diluted the richness of orcharding culture and the difference between regional tradition. Round wicker- or hazel-picking baskets, with canvas funnels for emptying, are now usually metal. Kentish pickers wore trousers with huge pockets sewn into the buttocks into which fruit could be dropped. These apple bottoms are not common now. In cider orchards, trees are mechanically shaken after which the fruit is vacuumed up into hoppers. It gets the job done quickly and as soon as the fruit is ripe, but turns the orchard into a monoculture and has led to the replacement of valuable old standards with bush plantations. Big British cider firms even resort to importing apple-juice concentrate from France, or from as far away as Eastern Europe or China, where it is cheaper. This concentrate is then watered down and chemically reliable yeast strains added to ensure a standardised product.

Cider and perry traditions are still evolving and being renewed. A number of groups are working to retain the richness of cider and perry culture, as well finding new ways of making old orchards pay and remain productive in the light of the often devastating effects of big cider business. The superior taste and quality of traditional cider has to some extent encouraged a demand-led replanting of the trees of the great cider varieties such as Yarlington Mill and the troublesome but delicious (and therefore very expensive) Kingston Black, even by larger firms.

The aptly named company 'Bramley and Gage' makes fruit liqueurs using the fruits from local orchards and gardens. It has created liqueurs from Dittisham plums, Bramley apples and quince, as well as damson gin, sloe gin and Slider – in which the sloes used in sloe gin are reserved and infused with Devon cider. This process apparently took place in farmhouse kitchens for centuries, but has never been given a name, until now. The liqueurs are made using fresh fruit that is pressed then pasteurised; cane sugar and cane spirit is added and the liqueur left to clarify. The Dittisham plums that grow in the village of Dittisham, Devon, are legendary. In fact there are many legends relating to how they arrived in the area. Most agree that they came by sea when a ship's captain dumped the cargo of plums he had been unable to sell on the villagers who were only too happy to take them home. The stones were planted and the resulting orchards became famous for the quality of their fruit.

Cider brandy has been the source of much controversy in recent years as one of the major producers in England, Julian Temperley, has battled with the European Union over the right to give his drink this name. Somerset Royal Cider Brandy is made by distilling the fermented juice of cider apples and the resulting spirit aged for a varying number of years.

King Offa, cider brandy made by the Museum of Cider in Hereford, is distilled twice and the spirit matured for five years in oak casks. The Somerset Royal Cider Brandy Company also produce apple aperitif, apple *eau de vie* as well as single variety and blended ciders and have breathed new life into Somerset's orchards.

Fruit wines are another popular product of the orchard, and

we have probably all been encouraged to try a friend's or relative's latest batch of damson, plum or elderflower wine. There are several companies around the country making fruit wines commercially particularly elderflower – the popularity of which, in addition to the number of producers making elderflower cordial, has led to the need to plant more elderflower orchards. Cordial is also made from elderberries, but seems to be less popular than elderflower. Some apple juice producers have created blends of apple and elderflower to expand their market.

Fruit has always been just part of the potential harvest of orchard produce, which varies from place to place. The widening of financial support for standard orchards needs to be seen not merely as an answer to the decline of traditional orchards, but as a breathing space while we explore old and new ways of feeding ourselves from them. Keeping local orchards as an active contribution to the local economy will provide new opportunities to continue the development of recipes such as Leek and Cockpit Quiche or Devonshire Rabbit.

This need not hark back to old days of junket and dripping. Many orchards are being kept in good shape by cider-makers without their own trees. The New Road Cyderists in Twyford, for example, buy or beg fruit from as many of their neighbours as they can for their annual pressing. On a larger scale, the award-winning Three Counties Cider Association owes its name to the fact that, for more than 20 years it has been collecting its juice fruit from the orchards of Middlesex, Hertfordshire and Buckinghamshire.

Hay crops sold to horse owners from the orchards of Melrose Farm in Worcestershire, and from Nunnington Hall National Trust in Yorkshire, are today more of a by-product of floral conservation than fodder production.

Just a few decades ago it would have been financial nonsense to plant a Kent cherry orchard without soft fruit or sheep grazing beneath to provide an income before the cherries cropped well up to a dozen years later. We should not be sentimental about the felling of a

---

The organic fruit at No Man's orchard is harvested for distribution in local veg-box schemes.

Window display of apple products for Apple Day 1990, Crabtree & Evelyn, Covent Garden.

walnut tree, if the profits from it are reinvested in the orchard and contribute to increasing the supply of renewable domestic timber.

Fruit for the community

No Man's Orchard, the Community Orchard near Canterbury, is owned by the two parish councils (Harbledown and Chartham Hatch), which its 4 hectares straddle. The orchard contains many old apple

trees including Bramley, Howgate Wonder and Golden Delicious. While local people (and wild life) have open access to the orchard and its fruit, the not inconsiderable surplus is used in local 'box schemes' so generating an income to help with the maintenance of the orchard. New cider varieties have recently been planted in anticipation of the future production of 'Charbledown' cider. In 2000 No Man's Orchard was awarded organic accreditation by the Soil Association. Lustleigh Orchard in Devon raises funds for its care from sales of part of the apple crop, by selling mistletoe and by allowing

155

local farmers to graze sheep.

Cider-makers are often pleased to take the fruit; Stoke Gabriel Community Orchard in Devon, for instance, sells its fruit to the local cider press. Even in areas where cider making is less common there are often amateur ciderists who would be grateful for just some of the crop. You could also try making your own cider.

In Shropshire the recently formed Shropshire Apple Trust have discovered the potential of a community apple press. It provides an excellent way of using surplus fruit as well as a means of generating a feeling of community among local people not least through the physical work of operating a large apple press by hand and seeing apples being turned into 'the most delicious apple juice in the world'. Michael Pooley, one of the founders of the Trust, writes:

Relics of cidermaking equipment are common enough across Britain. Large stone troughs and wheels, or the metal superstructures of old presses, to many people they are no more than gently dozing reminders of a bygone age. But the fact that they have been put there is also an expression of pride in an important activity that went on in the life of the community for hundreds of years. Far from being obsolete, much of this type of equipment still has a great potential today in terms of its practical and community value.

There is a strong case to be made for every community, neighbourhood, parish, village, having (or having easy access to) a manually operated large apple press and scratting mill. Manually operated equipment has many advantages: it is robust, almost maintenance free, requires no independent power supply, and, above all, encourages group participation in use.

But there is more to it than this. Not only are we missing a wonderful opportunity to do something useful with the neglected fruit, and at the same time protect many old and rare varieties (there may even be retailing opportunities for what is, after all, likely to be premium organic, additive-free juice and cider) but to do it at a community level in a thoroughly enjoyable way. It is this latter point that is as crucial as any of the practical considerations. Wherever the apple grows, apple culture is already a part of people's lives. In Britain almost without exception, the fruit is used and appreciated by all social classes, ages and ethnic groups. For this

reason Apple Day usually finds an immediate resonance, drawing people to them from all walks of life. Such events are growing in number and scope each year and rightly carry their own particular emphases and purposes according to local needs. However, the great majority still make no attempt to practically offer the means on site of turning the (largely wasted) harvest of apples that people have in their back gardens and orchards into delicious apple juice for drinking or fermentation to cider and other products. Whilst people get informed about apples, get their own varieties identified, are able to purchase new rootstock, learn about orcharding techniques, cidermaking and so forth, they can also be physically involved in an enterprise that draws them closer together through participation. It is this practical, physical involvement in helping to build community capacity that is particularly compelling.

Though the equipment is only reasonably efficient compared to the modern hydraulic press and powered milling machines, it should be a cause to celebrate the fact that making the juice this way is labour intensive. The physical labour in juice extraction and cidermaking is satisfying because it is shared, varied, and directed to splendid products. Judged by how much juice is obtained from the time and energy put in, the process is very inefficient. But it is wonderfully efficient in terms of how much sharing takes place, the wit and humour and gossip generated – as refreshing of the spirit as the juice and cider themselves are destined to be. In short, it is an activity and an occasion full of rich social and recreational possibilities. It is an opportunity for children, for the old and young not only to meet, but to *do* together, and to draw in often socially excluded minorities.

Having and using this equipment to process their apples is like putting the heart back into an important annual community event. Perhaps it has something to do with actually being able to make more than just mental connections with our history? Certainly it has something to do with the scale and nature of the equipment itself. A traditional apple press has a very distinctive physical presence. Often seven or eight feet tall, six feet wide, with massive oak timbers, the whole weighing perhaps as much as a ton, they are imposing pieces of equipment and yet 'human' at the same time. They are simple in design and deeply satisfying to use.

Anyone who has ever operated it will vouch for the enormous sense of pleasure that comes about by first milling apples, building up a 'cheese' of layers of apple

---

Washing fruit for the Shropshire Apple Trust Community Press. Photo: Janet Price.
Detail of Somerset Apple Map coordinated by June Small.

pulp and then, as you turn a couple of hefty screws, squeezing the pulp under a great baulk of timber, watching juice pouring out of the press. It has something to do with actually physically feeling your own energy and power being transferred, transforming apples into juice.

In March 1999 Shropshire Apple Trust was set up by a group of enthusiasts as an organisation whose long term aims would be nothing less than the promotion of apple culture in all its ramifications within in the county. Based in the Ironbridge Gorge, the group set themselves three initial projects. Firstly, to build a traditional twinscrew cider press using green oak and salvage metalwork; to do the same with a salvage scratting mill. Secondly, to organise a large community Apple Day where these rebuilt pieces of equipment would provide a central focus of activity for the day around which all the other apple and craft demonstrations would be set. Thirdly, that there would be built a modern strengthened trailer for both the press and scratter so that other communities in time would, if they wished, be able to conveniently access the equipment for their own locally organised Apple Days. The Trust applied for some grant support through the 'Millennium Festival Awards for All' and were fortunate enough to get £4,700. There are many other sources of possible funding, much of it Lottery-based, for these types of community project.

roadside collection system. Most importantly of all, there has to be something in it for the apple contributors. Apples came by the dustbin load, box, sack, or humble carrier bag, and people were offered a share of the juice using a ticket system on an approximate *pro rata* basis. For those who wanted to preserve the juice or ferment it to cider there were free instruction sheets. There was a pig roast and bar with traditional cider, umpteen demonstrations, including plenty open to the public to try. Children were also catered for *gratis,* including apple bobbing, apple prints, games, help with the large pressing and their own small scale presses and scratting mills with which to make (and drink!) juice.

I still have an abiding memory of the day: a picture of industry with people surrounded by piles of apples, shovelling them into a water tank for washing, of two men nearby, arms flying, operating the scratting mill, of other people hurrying hither and thither with buckets of apples, of someone else pouring samples of juice out of a big jug at a table for people to taste and 'ooh' and 'ah' over. And at the centre of all this was the working twin-screw press that a few volunteers with a good idea had built, its ironwork nearly pristine, its timbers still relatively clean and unweathered. Someone is shovelling milled apple pulp into the wooden frame, spreading it out by hand, folding over the press cloth.

The Apple Day event itself proved a huge success, with advance publicity of the 'Millennium Community Apple Press' turning out to be a terrific crowd-puller. Eight hundred people attended admission-free and the press easily made over 200 gallons of apple juice on the day. In the week prior to the event Trust members had organised a personal collection system for larger sources of the fruit, but most apples were brought by the general public on the day. Obviously, there are prerequisites to getting people to spend the time gathering their bounty. The organising body needs to maximise publicity, and if necessary have some means of offering help such as making available sacks, or bags, or even a modest garden/

Then the screws' winged collars are being turned, first by hand then with long ash poles, bringing down the top block onto the cheese, and out of the chute apple juice is cataracting into its container below. Someone's two-year-old daughter is leaning over the container, holding her cup below the lip, entranced with its filling, its overflowing. Again and again she empties it, fills it. She's centre stage. The cameras are popping. It is a very happy occasion, lots of smiles and laughter, sweat and noise, a genuine community event. It's what every community needs. And we know we are doing right because we even have glorious warm October sun on our backs!

Passing on Knowledge

ASK FOR ADVICE about pruning plums, making cider or baking pears, and answers will vary from place to place. This rattlebag of tips, cautions and rules of thumb, amassed over generations, deserves to be savoured, even cherished. It is hard-won knowledge, a legacy of the lives and labours of people in particular places at particular times. Common Ground seeks to foster old and generate new orchard insights that can help to make localities even richer, more diverse, more interesting. Standardisation can take the heart out of a place and all the enticement out of an orchard.

Our lives are more mobile; we have shallower roots in the places where we live. We sometimes expect to find the same opportunities available everywhere. It is easy for the distinctions between places to become blurred, as our connections with them erode.

After the Second World War, many orchards were grubbed up in the effort to maximise agricultural production. Old orchards became bush plantations, easier to pick and maintain, or were turned into wheat fields or grazing land. Traditional orcharding was launched on a steady downward trajectory – deposed from its status as everyday work, it lumbered into obsolescence, and now risks ending up as so much 'history'.

As the traditional orchards disappeared, so local knowledge and wisdom about them started to melt away. Today, the cumulative loss has stopped us in our tracks. We no longer have confidence in our own abilities or knowledge and look to experts – historians, horticulturalists, conservationists – to tell us what to do next. These specialists can help us to learn or relearn valuable skills – techniques

---

Taking a break from cidermaking at Burrow Hill Cider, Somerset. Photo: James Ravilious.

such as sensible pruning, for instance, or how to recognise signs of disease. But always, expertise needs to be interwoven with local knowledge and devotion to the genius of the place. Orcharding is in danger of becoming a science with little room for local detail. Our challenge is to let new developments inform the best of the wisdom we have inherited, in order to put the pleasure and the particularity back into orchards.

People caring for Community Orchards, for example, must not be persuaded (albeit in good faith) into spraying against aphids if the desire is to grow untreated fruit. The owners of old orchards should challenge those grant agreements that stipulate grazing as a blanket perception of 'tradition', but which in practice may ruin this particular orchard's flora. Schools have been offered well-meaning advice from enthusiasts to plant local cider apples in their grounds, despite the fact that any ambition of a delicious harvest will be met by inedible fruits of limited use to pupils.

Huge leaps have been made in commercial fruit production. We can produce spotless, beautiful apples, pears and plums, of consistant size, colour and quality from less land, and with fewer workers. We have, wisely, stopped spraying orchards with nicotine and instead use computers to tell us exactly when to spray which chemical for best effect on particular pest species at a certain stage in their life cycle. Some domestic apples are now easily available almost all year, and when we can't provide them, we can import them from the southern hemisphere. Researchers are spending much time and money on developing a strain of the popular Braeburn, a southern hemisphere variety, to be grown in Britain, while consigning the thousands of other varieties that grow happily here to a fruit museum.

squeeze fruit. Sheila Leitch of the Marcher Apple Network, and a regular identifier at Herefordshire Apple Days, admits that if DNA testing could successfully provide a more accurate analysis of an apple's pedigree, it might avoid confusion and false naming but it could also take all the fun and the challenge out of it.

Kevin Croucher of Thornhayes Nursery in Devon sells not far off 200 varieties of apples to growers, schools, community groups and gardeners everywhere but finds it difficult to find young people who are willing to learn the trade. New apprenticeships, like those run by the National Trust, are needed to keep orcharding knowledge and local wisdom alive and renewed.

Advances in genetically modified biotechnology may well help the chemical industry, but we have already developed – over centuries of much more benign processes such as grafting and cross pollination – varieties resistant, in their place, to scab, canker or mildew.

The handful of varieties grown commercially means that even identifying fruit has become a rare skill taught by few horticultural colleges. Apple Day events everywhere cry out for identifiers – drawn from a diminishing pool of ageing people – to sniff and taste, rub and

William Saunders, Hancocks Cider, South Moulton, Devon. Photo: James Ravilious.
Pupils plant a new orchard at Gartmore School, Stirlingshire. Photo: Margaret Miller.

New, less formal, ways of passing on knowledge can also reinvigorate the culture of orcharding, as the recent achievements of community groups in London and elsewhere admirably demonstrate.

In March 1998, Newham City Farm in east London held an orchard training day. The popular event was organised by Common Ground working with the Federation of City Farms and Community Gardens. On the day, Community Orchards enthusiasts offered insights into the ways in which they care for, cope with and use their orchards, both old and newly planted. Practical advice workshops on pruning, grafting and budding were also available.

The following winter the city farm worked with two local

primary schools to plant a small orchard of 14 apple trees, including some Essex varieties, which the farm grazes seasonally with their pigs, a non-rooting New Zealand Kune-Kune variety. People visiting and sitting in the orchard are free to eat the apples. A juice press to make best use of surplus fruit is still an ambition.

In the same year a pruning course was offered by Hackney City Farm, with help from Ron Wheeler, an experienced tutor from Capel Manor College in Enfield. Students from other city farms picked up not just the theory of pruning apples, pears and plums, but could also put theory into practice by having a go at the neglected espaliers and half standards in the farm orchard.

Beacontree Organic Growers (BOG), an association of gardeners on the London-Essex border, grow apple trees from pips on their allotments. Chairman Barry Watson, who attended the Newham City Farm course, has collaborated with the youth training department at the Ford Motor works in Dagenham to come up with modern designs modelled on traditional bee skeps made of plaster and straw. Barry's simple beehives – stacking tubes with a dome top – will house the BOG bees and are for sale (with plenty of free help and advice from Barry) to other community garden or orchard groups.

The promotion of healthy eating is high on the agenda of both local authorities and national government. School orchards are a perfect way to introduce fresh, self-grown fruit into the diets of pupils. What's more, these orchards can foster skills and spark off interests that will lead to imaginative projects throughout the school.

Gartmore School in Stirlingshire started planting an apple orchard in their school grounds in 1990. It contains Scottish varieties including Tower of Glamis, James Grieve and Gavin (planted by a pupil of the same name). Pupils and parents celebrate Apple Day each year, enjoying a variety of games, classroom activities, tasting and cooking. Pupils also learn how to care for their trees and share this knowledge with younger children as they pass through the school.

This ensures continuity in tree care and the development of new skills.

In 1999 Gartmore pupils took their expertise beyond the school gates. Five pupils visited another local school and prepared a presentation on apple horticulture, with overheads and display materials. They spoke to 60 younger pupils and their teachers and are also advising on tree selection and will help with maintenance and pruning when the time comes.

Gartmore School's proposal for a Millennium Project also reflects their love of apples. Pupils hope to plant an orchard of Scottish varieties in the Forest for the Millennium at Cashel in the Queen Elizabeth Forest Park near Loch Lomond. The proposal has been submitted to funders with details of the provenance of over 30 varieties of Scottish apples. The school has also produced an Apple Day Starter Pack, which other schools can buy.

In 1997 Common Ground and the school-grounds charity Learning Through Landscapes (LTL) published *The Schools Orchards Pack*. Linked to the primary school curriculum it explores how wide use can be made of school grounds, orchards or fruits to cross fertilise learning in many different subjects.

The grounds of La Sainte Union convent school in Dartmouth Park in north London contain an orchard of around 60 apple and pear trees. It once supplied the nuns with table fruit, but in recent years has been neglected. No longer valued for its fruit, the orchard

and its border of cordons fell into decline. Orchard jobs such as pruning and grass cutting were incorporated within the other school grounds maintenance tasks and became a drain on the school's limited budget.

Enter Nancy O'Brien, Head of Media, with a keen interest in getting the orchard back into shape. Following initial meetings with Common Ground and discussions with her Year 8 tutor group, Nancy successfully applied for a Camden Council Agenda 21 grant and a BTCV Natural Pioneer Millennium Award, together totalling more than £5,000. The money was used partly to train Nancy in tree care and orchard restoration techniques which she continues to convey to her group in fortnightly lunchtime training sessions and quarterly Conservation Saturdays, to which parents are invited. The class is also planning to undertake an oral history project interviewing local people about their memories of local orchards.

Activities linked to curriculum subjects including English, history and biology have transformed the orchard into an aid to learning. The girls have let the grass beneath the fruit trees grow to encourage wild flowers. For the first time in years, pupils are able to enjoy wandering among the spring blossom and help with picking and eating the autumn fruit. They have also created and maintain a website about the orchard (www.lsu-orchard.org). In July 2000 the school orchard was featured as an example of good practice in the Education supplement of *The Guardian* and on *London Today* on Carlton TV.

Few state schools have a Rural Sciences Department to compare with the one run at Hedingham School in Essex by Sue Trim. The school keeps free-range chickens from which pupils collect, grade and pack eggs for sale to local shops and cafés. Rabbits and guinea pigs are bred as pets in old pigsties. Crop trials of different grain varieties are complemented by experiments in potato, tomato and flower culture.

In 1997 the school embarked on a new initiative to plant more than 30 varieties of apples originating from Essex. Key Stage 3 pupils (ages 11-14) have carried out a variety of scientific experiments including food and leaf tests. Their work in the new orchard earned them a Henry Ford Conservation Award in 1999 and in the future, pupils are investigating possibilities for encouraging wild flowers in the sward, organic disease control and ongoing tree care including pruning, which respective years will pass down to their peers. The trees are still young and won't produce a heavy crop for a few years yet. However, this gives Sue enough time to research her next venture, Hedingham School Apple Juice.

As well as the new orchard, an old one containing pears, plums and apples will be restored. At the moment it is a jungle of nettles and brambles. After the brambles are cut the chickens will be brought in to clear the ground and the place will be back in business.

Ideal spots for science: Orchards, especially those near to schools, provide an ideal arena for hands-on science, where biology, botany, chemistry and physics can all be explored. The value of orchards to science teachers everywhere was vividly illustrated by an innovative popular science event – a Science Raid – held on Apple Day 1995 at Ryedale Folk Museum, north Yorkshire. Science Raids is a project run by the department of biology at the University of York which provides hands-on activities that allow people to experience science and technology for themselves.

'Getting Down to the Core' focused the attention of the Science

Raid team in a range of experiments on apples. Apples were peeled, using a machine from the museum's collection, and the flesh pressed to extract the juice. The juice was tested for pH, glucose and vitamin C content and comparison between varieties made. The team also showed that juice could be extracted and clarified using the enzyme pectinase. The serious science underlying everyday knowledge was the overriding theme of the day.

Orchards need to be culturally as well as biologically alive in order to thrive. Keeping them in good heart helps to sustain reasons for orchards to continue as places of joy in which to linger. While orchards form part of our daily round, we continue to draw inspiration from them. To experience the whiteness of a Cumbrian valley when the damsons are in blossom, or the languid promise of cider beneath a canopy of Herefordshire bitterweets, or to relax and stare at a blue sky through the leaves of the school orchard is all the more marvellous in the knowledge that such an experience is part of the enduring character of that place.

Restoration pruning at Staverton: South Hams District Council in Devon have been helping local people to celebrate Apple Day for a number of years. Every other year a different village is encouraged to host an event. A restoration pruning demonstration was part of the celebrations at Staverton in 1995. A special coach and train service was arranged to enable as many people as possible to attend in an area with limited public transport. Demonstrations of budding, pruning, grafting and harvesting have been successful and popular additions to events in dozens of places since Apple Day was launched in October 1990.

Apples for the amateur: A number of successful Apple Days in

The orchard at La Sainte Union School, London, is cared for by pupils and valued as a curriculum tool for subjects including English, art and geography.

The opportunity for communal learning in local orchards reflected a healthy thirst for knowledge at this Apple Day in Staverton, Devon.

Northamptonshire led Judy Stroud and Sue Pace to investigate the possibility of organising an orchards training course. Their ambitions were realised by the Reverend Mervyn Wilson, Rector of Bulwick, and a skilled amateur pomologist. People with old garden giants or pots full of pips, those who needed pruning advice or others who wanted simply to swap recipes signed up for a course led by Mervyn in the church hall and in his rectory orchard. The course was called *Apples for the Amateur* and was arranged and subsidised by the Workers' Educational Association (WEA) which has regional or county branches all over the country. The WEA offers support for courses from button making to biology by paying travel and course coordination expenses for tutors who set up their own courses and who can demonstrate a need for them by recruiting fee-paying students. Mervyn planned a 10-week course that cost £20 per person and attracted people from all parts of

Northamptonshire. It proved so popular that four free sessions were added, just to get everything covered. Old tricks were polished, new tips picked up and a friendly network established.

As well as practical demonstrations in tree care, which included pruning, planting and positioning, students were encouraged to taste a variety of baked apples from the orchard and to help Mervyn press apples for cider-making. The Rector's professional expertise was also drawn upon in the course in sessions on orchards in religion, history and myth.

The knowledge Mervyn imparted was built up through long experience. The amateur continues to play a vital role in maintaining and expanding our knowledge of how to care for local orchards and how to make the most of the fruit, enriching our appreciation of their rich cultural roles in our lives. Mervyn has perhaps been inspired by his profession: the Rev'd W Wilks is a large cooking apple named after the vicar of Shirley, creator of the Shirley poppy, while Tom Putt, a versatile cider apple from the west country, may have been named after the Rector of Trent in whose garden it was raised. The rediscovery of the Sykehouse Russet, an East Yorkshire dessert apple, is largely thanks to the efforts of a Sussex parson, Donald Johnson.

All over the country, colleges and orchard groups offer a variety of courses and workshops – it's worth asking around. Plenty of old orchards could benefit from a bit of tender attention, and there may be people in your area who have knowledge of fruit tree care who are willing to help. Most old apple trees will soon respond to gentle pruning, throwing out new growth and fruit buds a season or two after cutting. On the other hand, it may be more appropriate to leave the orchard more or less to its own devices if wild life conservation is the main objective. People should agree their own local priorities.

Wren's Nest orchards: Wren's Nest is a 1930s council estate of about 1,200 houses in Dudley, West Midlands. The houses are in clusters,

and wild or neglected back gardens form targets for over-the-fence rubbish dumping. In one part of the estate, Groundwork Black Country, working with Dudley Council, persuaded 15 tenants to release adjacent areas of garden wilderness for a new orchard. Following clearing by council contractors, a new south-facing orchard was planted in 1996 by trainees studying for a National Vocational Qualification in Horticulture. Its intensive stocking – 400 trees per hectare – reflect its eventual use as a commercial fruit orchard supplying the tenants' food cooperative.

Another back garden area was cleared in 1999 to create a second orchard. Groundwork's Wolverhampton Environment Centre also includes a new orchard containing about 50 apple trees. All three orchards (there is also a vineyard at Wren's Nest) are managed by the Environment Task Force and Intermediate Labour Market Trainees. A project to teach apiary design and beekeeping in the new orchards is being run in parallel.

Formal college courses: Formal qualifications on subjects including orchard restoration, tree planting, grafting and pruning are available. Horticultural colleges such as Pershore in Worcestershire or Kingston Maurwood in Dorset run full-time courses and while these will be useful to pick up grounding in best

horticultural practice, they may not be able to cater for differing uses for orchards and may emphasise current commercial practice. The Royal Horticultural Society, Brogdale Horticultural Trust and a host of National Trust properties offer day classes on or around Apple Day. *Short courses*: The Field Studies Council (FSC) has run a three-day course at Slapton Ley in South Devon since 1998. Short residential courses like the FSC's, with practical sessions in old orchards, can be fun as well as instructional. Matt Dunwell and his colleagues at Ragman's Lane Farm in Gloucestershire offer a cider-making weekend which gives instruction of orchard management, tips on cider varieties and sends students home with 40 litres of fermenting Gloucestershire juice which should be ready to enjoy by Christmas. In Somerset and Worcestershire the British Trust for Conservation Volunteers runs courses on orchard restoration, both with instructors from the cider-making trade.

Organic orchards: Interest in organic growing is increasing, and the Soil Association and the Henry Doubleday Research Association (HDRA) are good places to start for advice on organic techniques and requirements. HDRA also produces fact sheets specifically on organic fruit-growing which will be invaluable for groups or individuals getting started with, for example, the management of a Community Orchard.

Don't forget that organic growing was 'conventional' until relatively few years ago and that you may be surrounded by people who know how to do it. People can be found – ask at local gardening clubs or allotments – who know how to graft, when to harvest or what to do against mites. They'll often be willing to share this information and may even revel in a new and enthusiastic audience.

Freelance teachers or college tutors may be willing to arrange special classes at weekends in Community Orchards. Hiring them may cost anything from £30-£150 per day, but a few paying students can often cover this cost. Grants may be available and practical work can often be carried out in an orchard in need of attention. Re-rooting orchards firmly into local affection is a lasting way of enticing people back into the orchard again and again. Learning about an orchard is best done in the place. In the past we would have learnt not from a training programme but from being together in the orchard for pruning, grafting or planting as a part of what went on.

The more people you ask, the more varied the advice will be, which is part of the enjoyment. The important thing is to keep the interest in orchards active. Getting to know a place intimately is akin to peeling back the layers of history, each fragile and easily trampled, reaching back into a deep past. Your knowledge and wisdom, acquired gently in little steps, will add yet further richness to the place. People care about where they live – are experts in it – and this is the key to exciting a lasting enthusiasm for local orchards. Everyone has a role to play, so that orchards can reflect by their varied nature our diverse needs of them.

165

An Apple a Day

NUTRITIONAL STUDIES are reinforcing long-held beliefs about the benefits of fruit. The well-known saying, 'an apple a day keeps the doctor away' contains more than a germ of truth, for a diet rich in fruit can help to fend off everything from constipation to cancer. Apples – as well as onions, tea and red wine – contain flavonoids, which are good for the heart and circulation. Pears are a low-allergen food suitable as first solids for babies and for those with dietary restrictions. Nuts, particularly cobs and filberts, are energy capsules packed with protein.

Medlars, a curious and ancient fruit originally from southwest Asia, ought to be included in any new physic garden or hospital orchard. Their flowers are large and beautiful, but their fruits – which need to be half rotten before they are ripe – had a reputation for binding any looseness of the bowels. Plum leaves boiled in wine as a mouthwash has been recommended since at least the 10th century for 'a mouth troubled with eruption within'.

While Adam's apple led to his expulsion from paradise and Snow White suffered for her predilection for the red side of the apple, stories from many cultures associate apples with health and healing. In Norse mythology, for example, the gods renewed their youth by eating the golden apples guarded for them by Iduna, while in the *Arabian Nights* Prince Ahmed's Apple was a cure for every disorder. King Arthur healed his wounds at Avalon, the Isle of Apples.

Four centuries ago, cider was held to bestow longevity. As proof, a Morris dance at Hereford races in 1609 was performed by 12 men

Orchards make great places for rest and relaxation, especially after the hard work of harvest. Photo: James Ravilious.

with a total age of 1,200 years. The dangers of excessive cider consumption were thought in those days to be simply moral, rather than physical. A century and a half later, as more British sailors were being lost to scurvy than to enemy action – sometimes up to half a ship's complement – cider was found to be a highly efficacious cure. References of praise abound, and ship's surgeons report the return to duty of severely scorbutic sailors within a fortnight of being prescribed daily draughts of the drink – oranges produced results in half the time but weren't always available. The efficacy of 18th-century cider lay in its high vitamin C content, claimed by Roger French in *The History and Virtues of Cyder* to be 10 times as much as most modern pasteurised versions.

Cider aside, apples are an important potential source of vitamin C and contain traces of vitamin E. Long-lasting apple varieties were taken from Whitby by whalers to the southern oceans. Both vitamins are important antioxidants which contribute to cancer prevention, promote healthy skin and boost the immune system. The orange-coloured betacarotene, present in peaches, apricots and of course carrots, converts to vitamin A within the body and prevents one form of blindness.

Eating fruit is better than taking vitamin supplements. American research suggests that an overindulgence of vitamin supplements can be damaging, perhaps even promoting the development of cancer cells. The advice of the researchers is to stick to fresh produce for the daily dose, and apples in particular prove to be an excellent source.

The ubiquitous Golden Delicious contains between 6 and 8

milligrams of vitamin C per 100 grams of fruit – so you'd have to munch your way through six to reach the recommended daily intake, 50 milligrams for an adult. But some varieties perform much better than others when it comes to vitamin C content. The UK best-seller, Cox's Orange Pippin, weighs in at around 11mg/100g, while top performance comes in the form of the Ribston Pippin, a Yorkshire apple still widely grown, with at least 31mg/100g. Golden Noble, Sturmer Pippin and King of the Pippins are also particularly rich in the vitamin.

It may once have been common to take the teacher an apple. A better idea now could be for Yorkshire teachers to encourage the consumption of a daily Ribston, which would boost their pupils' intake of vitamin C, and complete the apple a day circle rather neatly.

An apple should be at hand if weight loss is a goal. Eaten shortly before a meal, an apple can induce a feeling of satiety yet add only 40 calories – whereas pre-prandial plums are said to whet the appetite – perhaps because they are sweeter. Fruit is also beneficial because the sugar it contains – mostly in the form of fructose – is packaged inside the fruit fibre. As a result, the sugar in the fruit is metabolised slowly, without eliciting a sudden rise in blood sugar levels that can in turn spark off an insulin surge. Pears are a bit higher in calories, often at about 70 calories per fruit and contain a bit less vitamin C – but a single pear can still provide about a fifth of our daily vitamin C requirements. Pears also contain iron, had Popeye but known.

Fruit can help to replenish stores of sodium and particularly potassium, vital to proper nerve and muscle function, but liable to be depleted during heavy exercise or illness. In a study by the Harvard

Avalon, the isle of apples. Cider orchard beneath Glastonbury Tor, Somerset. Photo: James Ravilious.
A fresh Ribston Pippin contains up to six times more vitamin C than Golden Delicious.

School of Public Health published in 1998, researchers found that men who consumed a diet high in potassium and magnesium markedly reduced their risk of suffering a stroke. Alberto Ascherio and his colleagues studied more than 40,000 healthy health professionals aged between 40 and 75. Men who enjoyed a high potassium intake, because they consumed about nine servings of fruit and vegetables each day, halved their risk of stroke compared to their peers who ate four servings per day – which would in itself be conventionally regarded as a 'good' diet. Ascherio recommends that people should increase their potassium intake by replacing low-potassium processed foods with fruits and vegetables, rather than taking supplements. In 1999 the Harvard researchers carried out a larger study of both men and women, with similar results. They went so far as to conclude that each extra serving of fruit a day could reduce your risk of stroke by 6 per cent.

Many other studies have confirmed fruits' life-enhancing qualities. A 17-year-long study started in the 1970s by the Imperial Cancer Research Fund found that people who habitually ate five items of fruit a day were likely on average to live 20 per cent longer compared to those who ate fruit less frequently. Phytochemicals in fruit also help to prevent cancers and have a beneficial effect on the heart.

More recently, the Cancer Research Campaign has advised a varied diet high in fruit fibre – apples are especially good – to help to protect against bowel cancer, which claims almost 50 lives a day in Britain and is our second biggest cancer killer. Hazelnuts contain the key ingredient in the anti-cancer drug Taxol, which has proved effective in the treatment of breast cancer.

Eating apples could even give you stronger lungs. Results of a five-year study by St George's Hospital in London reveal that the consumption of at least five apples a week is linked to a marked improvement in lung function. Of the 2,512 Caerphilly men aged between 45 and 59 who took part in the research, the apple eaters among them showed a lung capacity that was 138 millilitres higher than the others. Initially the research linked the results with a number of factors including a high intake of vitamins A, C and E as well as apples, citrus fruits and fruit juices. But after adjustments were made for factors including age, social class, smoking history, diet and exercise, the remaining links between improved lung capacity and diet were with apples, and a smaller association with vitamin E. The researchers suggest that the better lung function could reflect the influence of an antioxidant called quercitin. This phytochemical is found in hard fruits, but not soft ones such as strawberries and blackcurrants. While no antidote to cigarettes, quercitin might lessen the damage caused to lungs by smoking and pollution.

Sadly, most commercially grown apples should perhaps also carry a government health warning, in light of their repeated and regular exposure to substantial quantities of pesticides. The drive towards standardisation, coupled with the quest for 'perfect' unblemished fruit, has made non-organic growers heavily reliant on a huge chemical arsenal.

Most growers, whether plum, apple, cherry or pear, can bear witness to the extraordinarily demanding criteria attached to their supermarket supply contracts. The skin of a Cox's Orange Pippin may display russetting, but consumers often shy away, perhaps through unfamiliarity, from such perceived blemishes. Supermarkets encourage growers to produce Orange Pippins that are bigger than Mr Cox had originally envisaged with no russetting. The Cox, which accounts for the majority of our domestic crop, is notoriously vulnerable to pests. Government figures for 1996 show that this variety the most intensively treated of all orchard crops, receiving on average a total of 16 pesticide sprays containing 36 active substances.

Our increasing appetite for pears is sated with similar tactics. The average pear (according to 1996 government figures) is treated 13 times with sprays containing 24 active substances. Many growers are adamant that modern sprays are safer than old applications, which included lime, copper and nicotine – there are anecdotes of under-gardeners at Kew being sent into greenhouses to spray nicotine and having to be dragged out, unconscious, by colleagues. Nevertheless, government advice is to wash fruit before consumption and to peel fruit for children. The food and farming charity Sustain claims that chloremquat, a growth regulator, left residues in 30 per cent of domestic and 48 per cent of imported pears, despite the fact that the chemical is not licensed for fruit application in the United Kingdom. And despite efforts to target sprays precisely, there is no doubt that drift does occur in many commercial orchards, carrying chemicals into adjacent hedges, ponds or other habitats.

Modern consumerism has also eroded much of the seasonality associated with orchard fruits while bulk purchasing policies have squeezed out local diversity. Fewer people think in terms of strawberries in June and July (for Wimbledon), cherries in July, plums in August, pears and (early) apples in September. This has had some convenient consequences: thanks to modern cold storage technology, *home-made* Bramley apple pies can be 'exceedingly good' all year round (Bramley apple week, a promotional invention, is in April). And there is a certain security in the notion that a traveller keen on New Zealand Gala can find fruits of uniform size, quality and price in almost every supermarket from Paisley to Plymouth.

The apparent imperative of the market to conquer domestic seasonality means that fruit needs to be imported. This does British growers no favours, particularly if fruits are coming from the south. French cherries will hit our counters several weeks early, with the result that consumers may be sick of them by the time the domestic crop is available. There are global environmental consequences, too, attached to importing fruit from the other side of the planet. All the 'food miles' these well-travelled fruits notch up extract a heavy price on the environment, through the fossil fuels consumed in transit, the packaging waste and even the loss of countryside to road building.

People can suffer directly too. Orchard workers in developing countries such as Chile, who harvest apples destined for the UK market, suffer from their exposure to organophosphate pesticides, according to the World Health Organization.

There are cultural implications, as well, in the ways fruit is grown, marketed and sold, for orchards are part of a much wider food picture. As we become distanced not just from the raw ingredients of the seasons but also from the regionally diverse and ever-evolving cuisines, our expectations of food change. Intensive agriculture, without the need to point accusatory fingers, has given us not just super-efficient production levels but also the well-publicised crises of BSE, listeria and salmonella. One result could be a suspicion of untested, unpasteurised, unsterilised produce, such that we disdain even fruit. Could there be a logic in the preference among younger people for a bag of reliably sterile, air-tight crisps over a scabby russet?

Where food is concerned, we send all the wrong messages to our children, according to nutritionist Joachim Westenhofer, professor at the University of Applied Sciences in Hamburg. Speaking at a conference on child nutrition in Rome in 2000, he argued: 'It is a basic problem that food considered not nutritionally valuable is offered to children as reward. Children learn from this that chocolate and ice-cream are very valuable.' Such a reward system can create a lifelong aversion to healthy foods, fruit included, reports Rachel Shabi, writing in *The Guardian* (10 May 2000).

Yet children can make healthy food choices. When Westenhofer offered kindergarten pupils a breakfast buffet with fruit, vegetables and cereal laid out against junk food, the children reached for fruit, not fizzy drinks and crisps. 'If you offer a variety of foods, and give them opportunities to taste new foods, they develop good eating habits,' he claims. He recommends visits to farms and orchards in particular,

so that the child can establish the connection between soil and sustenance, alongside the celebration of the seasonality of food – the first strawberries, for example, then the first plums, next pears and apples to follow.

Positive health products from orchards may even come from under as well as in the trees. Research in 1997 showed that galanthamine, a compound derived from daffodil bulbs, may be successful in slowing down or even arresting the effects of Alzheimer's disease. Some areas, such as Norfolk, have traditionally grown daffodils as spring crops beneath apples. The development of galanthamine-based drugs could yet revitalise this association.

Healing orchards

A famous study in the US, published by Roger Ulrich in *Science* in 1984, reported that hospital patients who could see a tree from their sickbed recovered more rapidly after surgery than did those who looked out on a treeless urban scene. 'A fascinating body of evidence is now accumulating to show that short-term, daily and casual contact with "nearby nature" such as street trees plays an important role in reducing stress,' concludes Tony Kendle of the department of horticulture and landscape at the University of Reading.

Yet the link between orchards and recuperation is long established. The Isle of Avalon may be hard to pin down on a map, but more concrete examples remain. For instance, an early Victorian workhouse at Southwell in Nottinghamshire, now owned by the National Trust, contained an orchard within its 4-hectare garden. Residents were encouraged to walk through the grounds during rest hours for exercise and fresh air. The fruit was a vital seasonal supplement to what must have been a meagre diet.

Evidence is growing of the multifaceted benefits that can follow from regular walking and working in orchards – digging, pruning, picking or mowing. Regular exercise of even a modest nature can reduce high blood pressure and halve the risk of coronary heart disease, which remains the leading cause of death for both men and women in Britain. By some reckonings, tending an orchard for 45 minutes can use as many calories as 30 minutes of aerobics. Weeding for an hour uses 300 calories, the same as walking or moderate bicycling.

Newham City Farm in east London is situated next to King George Park where health walkers are sent for laps as part of the local Council's exercise prescription scheme. In spring, the farm's new orchard may be an attractive place to rest as the spent striders breathe in the scent of the blossom.

In 1997 the British Trust for Conservation Volunteers launched  its Green Gym initiative in Oxfordshire. Since 1959 this practical conservation charity has encouraged people to carry out tasks to improve their local environment. The Green Gym explicitly links the physical exercise involved in BTCV work to the real health benefits that could accrue to people for whom the exercise bike or the badminton court hold no appeal. People with mental health problems or feelings of isolation have also enjoyed the regular social contact as well as the exercise. Warm-up and cool-down exercises are led by experienced Green Gym coordinators, and local health practitioners are happy to prescribe Green Gym for their patients.

The link between outdoor work and healing has deep roots. Many of the former asylums built around London over the past century were entirely self-sufficient, with patients responsible not just for the construction of their own beds from estate timber, but also for tending the hospital dairy, walled gardens and orchard. There is evidence that regular exercise can lessen a sense of anxiety and depression through the release of endorphins. These are the brain's natural morphine, sometimes called a 'runners' high' – though the inducement of 'orchard highs' will hopefully involve less pounding of joints as well as cheaper footwear. So walking, working and just being with others in a Community Orchard can be of mental and physical benefit to a wide range of people. The beauty of the place, the physical exercise and the social contact can all merge together to result in an increase in confidence, stamina and hope. For jail inmates or elderly people in care, for instance, looking after an orchard can build self esteem as individuals are empowered to interact positively with their environment and effect changes.

Hospitals such as Claybury in Essex as well as Shenley, Napsbury, Cell Barns, Hill End and Harperbury – which are all clustered around St Albans in Hertfordshire – retain all or part of their old orchards even though only Harperbury is still a hospital. The other four old Hertfordshire hospitals along with Claybury are gone – with the hospital buildings largely demolished for housing. But these places have retained much of their open space as part of planning agreements set out when the hospitals were wound up in the 1980s. At Shenley and Highfield – the new housing estate and park formed from Cell Barns and Hill End – the orchards have been restored after a decade of neglect.

At Shenley, three-metre-high brambles obscured almost 400 semi-dwarfing apple trees laid out in the 1940s by the celebrated Stanley Lord, an RHS fruit judge. This orchard, along with the walled garden cordons and espaliers, is now managed by the Shenley Park Trust. There is free access to the orchard by all villagers, who enjoy seasonal flowers beneath the trees including cowslips, vetches and scabious. At Highfield, regular pruning training days enable interested

Digging in the compost is not the only physical activity to be enjoyed in the Community Orchard. Apple Day in No Man's Orchard, Kent, is the occasion for an annual inter-parish tug-of-war.

locals to learn restoration pruning from a professional horticulturalist. By (re-)learning these practical skills, locals will pay a greater interest in the future of the orchard, find they have a ready supply of unsprayed fruit of unfamiliar varieties and do some exercise to boot.

When the Littlemore Psychiatric Hospital, Oxford, went the same way in the 1980s, patients who were dab hands found they were welcome at the Elder Stubbs allotments a few miles away in Cowley. Several plots are worked by people with mental health problems. A small orchard with open access, seating and a sculpture is regularly harvested, and a new orchard of 1.2 hectares was planted in 1999.

New healing orchards include the one planted in the grounds of the Coalville Community Hospital in Leicestershire in the National Forest. The trees will eventually bear cider fruit – which could make scrumping a once-only adventure – as well as some traditional Leicestershire varieties including the cookers Annie Elizabeth and Dumelow's Seedling. The blossom will add beauty and scent to the otherwise grassed but featureless grounds. At Newton Grange old people's home in Stocksbridge near Sheffield, local school children and Duke of Edinburgh Award volunteers have planted and maintain apple, pear and plum trees as well as soft fruit and rhubarb. The blossom will be welcomed by the home's residents, as well as the fruit and regular contact with the teenagers. Unexpectedly, some of the older residents remember a time when this part of the Don valley was a fruit farm where as children they collected blackcurrants for a penny a basket. The farm was bought by the industrialist Samuel Fox who built homes for his steel works employees. He provided each garden with an apple tree.

The Townsend House Surgery in Devon has put on a display for Apple Day for several years. For some weeks before 21 October visitors to the surgery ask, 'what are you doing for Apple Day this year?' When the day arrived they have been treated to displays of apples and healthy eating, people brought in apples from their gardens to add to the display and stories abounded about apples and orchards. The staff too enjoyed apple cakes and the practice is now considering planting apple trees in the grounds around the surgery.

In Fife, community worker Ann Lolley is using the restoration of the old orchard in her Scottish National Trust-owned house, as well as other Scottish orchards as the basis for a new CD-ROM called the Therapeutic Orchard. Her aim is to suggest and explore ways in which orchards can offer positive mental and physical health benefits.

Rivers Nursery Community Orchard in Sawbridgeworth, on the Hertfordshire/Essex border, is the remnant of a business established by the Rivers family in the 17th century, making it the oldest surviving commercial nursery in England. The celebrated Thomas Rivers, born in the village in 1798, introduced many fruit varieties including River's Early cherry, widely planted in the Kentish cherry orchards, and our most-loved pear, the Conference, which was commercially raised here. When the nursery closed down in the 1980s, much of the land was bought for the construction of the Thomas Rivers Medical Centre, a private hospital, and a number of retirement homes. The remaining orchard of apples, plums and cherries has been patiently restored by the Friends of Rivers Orchard who are keen that patients or residents should enjoy walking and lingering among the trees, where cowslips and orchids grow. Benches have been provided. The seasonal calendar includes Apple Day, wassailing and spring-time dawn chorus walks followed by breakfast in the orchard.

The examples in this chapter explore some of the ways in which orchards can foster the mental and physical health of a wide variety of people. New orchard initiatives reinforce a long tradition and show how this can continue. Orchards and the work they demand, both physical and social, offer a positive and healthy way of bringing people together within their communities, so breaking down isolation. We ought to make more room for orchards in our lives.

Everyday Tasks

A WEALTH OF MANUALS, growers' diaries, guides and advisory works spanning two millennia give expert guidance on how to look after orchards. But it is worth bearing in mind that in most cases, these experts have focused on orchards designed for the production of the biggest, best or most fruit. This is not our aim – we hope to encourage the manifold use and enjoyment which orchards can offer. Priorities can and should differ. Here we explore new ways of making the most of orchards everywhere, as they are invited back into our communities and sustained there with a dynamic knowledge and growing affection.

Think local: is there any wisdom in battling against nature (and spending a fortune on sprays) when many varieties have arisen or been nurtured to enjoy the local conditions? Endemic varieties are often more at home in local soils, attuned to rainfall and prevailing wind and can be resistant to bacterial infection.

Planting or conserving local fruit varieties reinforces local distinctiveness and will add further enticement for local involvement in the orchard and consumption of its harvest. Might a resident of Colchester love the chance to munch on a Mile End Russet before resorting to a Gala? Stirling Castle, from Causey Head, grows well in colder climes and is intolerant of sprays – making it a good bet for a northern organic orchard. Many Cornish apples and cherries are able to cope with the wet western climate that might otherwise cause canker in upcountry varieties.

Communal gathering of the harvest. In cider orchards the fruit is collected from the ground, rather than hand-picked from the trees. Photo: James Ravilious.

The appendices offer information on where to find horticultural books, courses and advice. What follows is mostly encouragement, bolstered by the experience of enterprising orchardists in town, city and country.

Pruning: Depending on who you ask, pruning is either a hallowed art, the domain of wizened ancients who have become initiated into its secrets by word of mouth passed down through the generations, or it is a suck-it-and-see sort of task, easily picked up by anyone competent with the secateurs. Other people dispute the need to prune at all, maintaining that the tree will find its own balance. Fruit trees need a lot or a little looking after – depending on your personality and needs. Because they 'bleed' when cut, cherries and plums need less pruning than pears and apples. In fact, cherries are self-pruning – small shoots die off each year. Traditionally, hazel trees were pruned each year and kept to a height of just under two metres. But they will still produce nuts if allowed to grow tall, and can be cut back hard to a metre or so from time to time if desired, with the loss of a couple of years' harvest.

Pruning, just like coppicing or pollarding, is a technique of deliberately wounding the tree to engineer regrowth, usually of fruiting buds, or to encourage a particular growth shape. If left to their own devices, standard trees will grow a crown of criss-crossing branches and twigs. Where they touch and rub against each other in the wind, the cambium layer (the wood tissue where the growth occurs, creating the annual rings) can become exposed and vulnerable to disease or the touching branches may even fuse together. Diseased trees may bear few or damaged fruits. Because fruits grow best on the lateral

branches – that is, those that are horizontal from the tree trunk – a sprawling crown will bear less than one that is encouraged to develop fruit buds on laterals. A dense crown can also act as a sail to catch the strong winter winds that might uproot the tree, or cause it to rock on its roots, which may damage them and shorten the life of the tree. A full crown will let less air circulate through its branches and may encourage fungal infection.

Advice on pruning can be obtained from a wide range of books, but it is easier if you are shown how. The Dartington North Devon Trust, South Hams Council and the Kentish Cobnuts Association hold pruning workshops and many other groups are beginning to do so.

James Evans has worked to continue the centuries-old cherry-growing tradition in the Tamar Valley in Cornwall by collecting and planting orchards of many local varieties. His long

Misty morning tea break in a west-country commercial apple orchard. Photo: James Ravilious

New growth can be encouraged in old trees with a little pruning. Fallen trees may continue to bear fruit happily with their elbows on the ground. Orchard at Winkleigh, Devon. Photo: James Ravilious.

experience is based on traditional local techniques.

Cherries should be pruned between mid-July and mid-August, as soon as the crop has been picked. Any witches brooms may need attention. These downward hanging branch clusters are caused by traphina, a fungal infection. The brooms grow vigorously but without producing flower buds. They can be removed at this time along with any broken or diseased branches without fear of infection by the spores of silverleaf disease.

Bacterial canker, flakey sores which exude sap, can be a big problem in cherries and plums. Infected branches should be cut out as should discoloured bark from the trunk. Use resistant varieties. Silverleaf, another prunus problem, is manifested by a silver discolouration of the leaves and has to be cut out. This must be done in the summer when the spores of the fungus are not abroad.

Apple and pear pruning is best done when the sap is dormant between November and March. This reduces the risk of infection and does less damage to the tree. Some people consider that pruning late on in the winter is best because if wounds are made very shortly before the new sap rises, rapid restorative growth follows. Others like to get the job done as soon as possible in November. Vigorous watershoots – thin shoots without fruit buds, often sprouting from the upper trunk – can be removed at the end of July or beginning of August when growth has stopped. James has also developed a pruning rule of thumb for apples: if the annual growth is between about 8-23 centimetres (3-9 inches) prune lightly; if growth is more, then leave the tree alone; if less, prune to stimulate new growth but also check for root damage and consider feeding.

Tools for the job: Four tools will be very useful for maintaining fruit trees: a pruning knife, secateurs, loppers and a saw. With all four, it is important to keep the blades sharp and clean. Blunt blades will make the job physically harder and will leave messy wounds – cuts should be clean and straight to minimise the area of exposure. When moving between trees, especially if some are diseased, dip your blade into some disinfectant and dry it off. This will only take a moment and will avoid the risk of transferring infection from one tree to another.

A pruning knife has a curved blade. It is useful for tidying up around the edges of larger cuts. Secateurs can tackle twigs and laterals just under two centimetres thick. Long-handled loppers can tackle high branches up to about three centimetres. Saws should be used for bigger branches up to about eight centimetres in diameter. They vary in shape and size – a single-handed Grecian saw is useful when only

one hand is free and often has a folding blade. Larger branches succumb more easily to a bow saw. If pruning in a tall tree make sure you have a companion to hold the ladder steady. Colleges and garden centres often have knife- and saw-handling courses for the beginner. As well as dealing with safety issues, these courses will show the most efficient cutting techniques.

Pruning a neglected tree: Trees remain healthy and productive for longer if they develop a reasonable amount of both vegetative regrowth and fruit buds. Problems tend to develop when this balance is not maintained. In the extremes, over-pruning produces strong upright vegetative regrowth with no fruit as the tree tries to compensate for severe wounding. On the other hand, a long-term lack of pruning produces masses of dense, ageing fruit bud clusters that allow no light into the crown. The first extreme produces timber without fruit – tolerable perhaps if you are in the apple-wood-turning business. The second produces masses of small diseased fruit on a dying tree.

A balanced tree is producing new growth from which you can choose (and retain) suitably placed shoots with which to renew the tree, as well as enough fruit bud, on young wood, to produce good, large, healthy fruit. It is worth remembering that a crop of fruit prevents the tree getting too vigorous.

Many fungal infections, most particularly scab and mildew, can be cut out to prevent spreading rather than resorting to expensive sprays that may also kill off beneficial insects and other wild life. Removing branches that grow into the middle of the tree will improve air circulation. Branches drooping near the ground will act as ladders for flightless insect pests.

If you plan to paint large cuts with a wound paint, black emulsion is as good as anything. There is a great deal of disagreement about its benefits. Most opinion is that it is not worth doing. If you disagree, then paint cuts over four centimetres in diameter, and on the same day. Similarly, experts disagree about the ability of old trees to withstand a full pruning in a single operation. The usual advice is that if the tree has not been pruned for many years, don't try and make a complete job in the first pruning. Give yourself time, try a little in the first year and see how the tree reacts. Adjust your efforts accordingly over the next two or three years.

Suckers, the thin vigorous shoots coming from the rootstock and below the graft union, should be removed. This is particularly the case with plums and cherries. Removing these suckers redirects new growth into the main body of the tree where your grafted variety will fruit. If left, suckers will eventually divert all growth energy and deprive you of your fruit.

Pruning a young tree: Young trees can be pruned to encourage particular growth shapes. For example, standard trees may need side shoots removed from the trunk to encourage the tree to grow upright, but bear in mind that climbing may be the best use for the tree as it matures. Bush forms, on the other hand, may need their leading shoots cut out. Pruning back laterals will encourage vigorous fruit bud development. If the laterals are left unchecked, they will grow longer, drawing energy away from the fruit bud into the vegetative growth. Gentle formative pruning during the early years will pay dividends when the tree is mature.

Grafting: Grafting is necessary because apples and other varieties of fruit do not grow true from seed or because the grower wishes to control the vigour of the tree. Grafting has barely changed since Roman times, although new techniques have been developed and these are best studied and practiced with the help of R J Garner's *The Grafter's Handbook*. Essentially, grafting binds together, using the tree's natural healing processes, two living sections of wood. Mostly this simply involves joining the rootstock to the scion, but in pears, particularly perry pears and in cider apples where tall straight stems are

encouraged, two grafts are made: one to join a rootstock to a stem-builder onto which the scion is then grafted.

The simplest graft is the whip and tongue method where two sloping faces are taped together, stabilised by corresponding nicks cut into the faces. In apple saplings this method leads to a swelling near the base of the trunk where the wound has healed over. In a windy orchard, tongue and groove graft on the windward side. This will steady the graft against the wind and prevent it snapping off.

In large cherries, and other trees where the union is higher up the trunk, a saddle graft is best. Here rootstock is cut into a point of two flat faces that fit into a corresponding cut into the scion. The benefit of saddle grafting is that when the tree is mature it can withstand strong winds, which might otherwise cause a high graft union to snap on the side experiencing most pressure. Saddle grafts apply uniform pressure and are responsible for the big boles at the top of cherry trunks. Cherries and plums need to be swiftly grafted. The sap in scions very quickly oxidises and as soon as the cut turns brown, it is too late to graft.

Budding: Budding is another, simple way of propagating particular fruit varieties, or even several of them, onto a selected rootstock. Like grafting, it makes use of the natural processes in the tree to heal wounds. Essentially, a dormant wood bud is carefully cut from the scion with a sliver of adjacent wood, enough to expose an arch of the cambium layer.

A corresponding arch of wood, as close as possible in size (usually about 2-5 centimetres) and shape, must be cut from the rootstock to allow the bud to be fitted in and bound up. After a few weeks the cambium layers of both the bud and the rootstock will have grown together and the wound healed over. The bud must be attached low on the rootstock so that the rising sap comes directly to it. Dormant wood buds can be budded in summer, so this technique is a very useful second chance if earlier attempts at grafting (a late winter job) fail.

Provided the bud takes successfully, any original rootstock buds can be removed by pruning the sapling down to just above the new bud. Thereafter, any new growth will be of the budded variety of fruit.

If the focus of your Community Orchard is the conservation of the rare and wonderful longhorn beetles that depend upon deadwood, you may wish to sit back and let nature take its course. Community Orchards serve a number of priorities. Most will produce fruit that is eaten or sold locally, while others may be repositories of locally unique varieties. If your orchard contains the last examples of the Knock-kneed Pearmain, regular pruning will encourage active growth and more regular crops but may reduce the eponymous character of the tree. While some pruning may well benefit tree and fruit production, very few Community Orchards need to be commercially viable and are explicitly managed to encourage a diversity of wild life to share their bounty.

Old trees with rot will support insects and fungi. Closed canopies will be good hiding places for smaller birds. Try to strike a balance between the need to produce healthy and delicious fruit and the need to create a beautiful place to be. An orchard can be a wonderful spot in which to linger, to enjoy blossom, to watch butterflies, birds and mammals, as well as floral delights in the grass and within the trees. When trees die, consider ignoring established arboricultural advice: leave them in the orchard where they will support their own complex ecosystems for many years.

What to do with your cuttings: If you are pruning old trees for the first time you may be left with lots of cuttings, and the first instinct will be to burn them. If you have pruned before Twelfth Night, use diseased

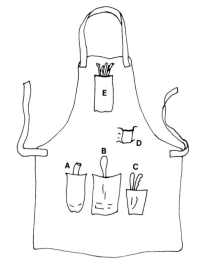

Grafters Apron
Of strong canvas or leather, reaching barely halfway down the thighs; useful when topworking and frameworking. A wad of cotton wool is placed in the bottom of the knife pouch. Knife A, hammer B, and secateurs C, firmly gripped in their pouches, protrude for ready handgrasp. Gusseted finger-and-thumb pouch for small nails D. Scion pouch well up on the chest E.

wood and some cuttings on the wassail bonfire to light up your celebrations. The pleasant smell of burning fruit wood will be a reward for your labours and will go well with the wassail cup.

If you have room you could keep some prunings back. Brushwood and larger logs could be left in piles to rot down. Small rodents such as voles and shrews will seek out grubs which colonise these piles and in turn may attract predatory birds. Insect larvae such as those of the stag beetle, the rhinoceros beetle and the very rare noble chafer live in rotting wood.

Some pieces of larger wood could be sculpted or turned into orchard seating. At No Man's Community Orchard, students from the Kent Institute of Art and Design sculpted stumps into apple shapes.

Apple wood is an attractive wood for turning. It was also traditionally used for the gears of water wheels. Pear wood, used for making recorders, makes beautiful inlays while walnut and cherry veneers are expensive. Money from the sale of fruit wood could be reinvested in the Community Orchard, perhaps to pay for a pruning course in situ.

How to learn more: Knowledge is not exclusively the preserve of the old and wise. In north London, 13-year-old pupils at La Sainte Union School learnt pruning and orchard management from their teacher. In Gartmore Primary School near Stirling, 10-year-olds care for the school ground orchard planted in 1992. Before they leave the school, the pupils pass down their knowledge to the year group coming up to take their place. At Highfield Community Orchard near St Albans, the Highfield Park Trust hire in teachers from the local horticultural college, Oaklands. The cost of the teacher is amply covered by the small fee levied on the students. Thus the college reaches out into the community, and the neglected orchard is renovated by paying enthusiasts. These in turn learn new skills while building up a pride and affection in their achievements which will lure them and their families back for blossom and fruit picking. It all makes perfect sense. Ask your neighbours to see if anyone knows how to

prune. Ask them to show members of the Community Orchard maintenance group. Organise or visit a pruning class on Apple Day.

Many traditional orchards are neglected because they are no longer economically profitable. To prevent them falling into complete dereliction, why not ask the orchard owner if knowledgeable locals can keep the orchard going for seasonal visits in spring and summer, for Apple Day celebrations on 21 October and for a share of the fruit?

Learn from your own experiences and needs. Over the years the wisdom and experimentation of horticultural dabblers has produced thousands of varieties of apples, often locally unique, as well as knowledge which can only enrich the orchards if it is passed on. By being able to enjoy, care for and use them, people will keep orchards and themselves in good heart.

Trust your convictions: Don't be brow-beaten. Old orchards, and especially Community Orchards, are rarely managed for profit. Some

Piling up prunings in a suitable corner will help to attract deadwood invertebrates and fungi.

groups have reported conflicts between the stipulations of grant givers and the objectives that they have agreed among themselves. Countryside Stewardship, a blessing to so many old orchards, has offered standardised management advice based on the one view of what orchards would have looked like in the past.

This has been an issue at West Grinstead Community Orchard, for example. A former pub orchard, it now lies behind the Little Chef café on the A272 in Sussex. No one is exactly sure how old the 0.8-hectare orchard of apples, pears and damsons is, but it's there on aerial photos from 1947. In 1997, after three decades of neglect, the West Sussex County Council Rangers Service successfully applied on behalf of the orchard owner for a Countryside Stewardship grant. The Rangers' interest in restoring the orchard was fuelled by its position adjacent to the 59-kilometre-long Downs Link that is a disused railway turned public bridleway linking the North and South Downs Way. Management at the Little Chef was happy to offer parking to visitors to the orchard, which included educational trips by brownies, cubs and local schools.

When the Rangers cleared the brambles, nettles and undergrowth, they found that a couple of the pears were dead. The Stewardship agreement stipulated that the orchard should be grazed and horses and sheep were accordingly brought in. However, the animals tended to overgraze the orchard floor, churn up the grass and nibble the tree bark. While the churning may have stimulated latent seeds into growth, it was decided not to continue grazing and the grassland is now mown once a year when the wild flowers have set seed. Apart from nettles and thistles the sward now sports early purple orchids and bluebells that have invaded the orchard from the adjacent wood. The clay soil also supports lady's smock in the spring.

In other old southern apple orchards under restoration the trees are being cut back into a goblet shape with an open canopy and a few leaders. This is a very efficient fruit-growing shape with good air circulation and enough room for picking. However, if the orchard is to become a haven for nature, a little neglect, coupled with replanting (perhaps with saplings from a local 'mother' orchard), should be tolerated by grant givers.

Have the confidence to challenge advice (which is given in good faith, but perhaps from only one perspective) and negotiate your own terms. Public grant money will be a better investment if it is used to encourage persistent local action, rather than to stifle it.

Go organic: Careful selection of hardier or disease-resistant endemic varieties will reinforce local distinctiveness and help you to cut down or cut out the chemicals, which certainly should be absent from Community Orchards. Organic methods may mean more work for dessert fruit – which could be a chance to recruit new hands to the team and widen involvement in the orchard. Fruit used for cooking, jamming or juicing doesn't need to look perfect. Certain plants, such as snowdrops and marigolds, are said to deter insect pests, if grown among the fruit trees. An organic approach will enable a greater reliance on natural predators of insect pests, and make for a more balanced orchard ecosystem.

Local groups: In some areas enthusiasts have teamed up to offer reasonably priced maintenance services. The Norfolk Apples and Orchards Project has identified and grafted an orchard of all known county varieties at the Rural Life Museum in Gressenhall. Meanwhile, the Tamar Valley Orchard Volunteers has helped busy orchard owners to draw up grant applications for schemes including Countryside Stewardship. The Volunteers also have an archive library, an office in a local community centre, and a web page. Composed of enthusiasts and small orchard owners, these groups are driven by a desire to keep local orchards productive and thriving. Both groups have a good understanding of local varieties and can lead training days or carry out tasks themselves.

Black Beauty and other beasts: As small-scale mixed farming has been marginalised into an almost impossible endeavour, farm houses and the orchards that often go with them have been sold. There is a migration back to the countryside by urban dwellers who don't depend on an income from the land but appreciate the space and property prices. Rural dwellers in search of land can often take advantage of the economic decline of standard orchards.

Using old, uneconomic orchards for horse grazing, for example, seems as natural as handing dobbin a D'Arcy Spice. There can be problems: skittish horses may gore themselves on long, overhanging branches; apple bark, so sweet and tempting in the early spring, is easily stripped by sheep, cattle and horses. Chickens have a knack of scratching up orchard grassland, transforming the ground into a dust bowl. Pigs love to root around and, according to the Worcestershire Wildlife Trust, can be as disastrous for orchard flora as the chickens.

Yet local places provided for local people in the past and history is a good guide. Chickens, which gobble up codling grubs before they become moths, need to be given enough room to roam. Low-density

Gloucester Old Spot, also known as the orchard pig, enjoys a seasonal diet of windfalls.
Let a few chickens loose in your orchard - they will seek out grubs. Photo: James Ravilious.

fowl is the key. Gloucester Old Spots – the orchard pig – can be turned out to feast on windfalls – which will flavour their pork. But don't let them live in the orchard permanently or they will soon turn the grassland into a ploughed field. Prune back long branches for horses.

Sarah Menear's north Somerset apple orchard is seasonally grazed by her horses and a local farmer's sheep. April, it seems, is the cruellest month. The grass is poor and the bark is very sappy. The sheep can do terrible damage nibbling it. Horses will also join in by mid April. Her alarm bell is the pear tree. When it bears blossom, the horses must be moved out.

Sturdy guards need to be placed around younger trees if cattle are to be grazed. The huge beasts, which don't know their own strength, use trunks, especially rough apple or pear bark, as a scratching post and can easily bring trees down.

Ask local farmers for their advice or visit areas with particular grazing or grassland cultures – the perry orchards of Herefordshire are grazed by cattle, those in Worcestershire are more commonly cut

Advanced grafting methods in an attempt to save the variety at West Grinstead.
Fertilising the apple trees at one of the regular work days at Gabriel's Orchard, Somerset.

for hay. Sheep are common in Devon cider orchards, as well as in Kent cobnut plats, where the local short-necked Southdown breed can't browse the fruit buds.

Local signatures: Many orchards will require fences, gates or stiles. Make sure these are created and maintained in the appropriate vernacular. You could consider asking a local carpenter to make an Essex gate rather than buying one 'off the shelf'. Sussex and Surrey fences could be made of chestnut post-and-rail. In Leicestershire why not carry out some research into the local vernacular and lay the hedge in the

Midland fashion, or repair the old stone wall in a style that is appropriate to Derbyshire, Gloucestershire, Yorkshire or Cumbria? If your orchard has a name, inscribe it on the gate, as they have at Broad Oak, Gabriel's and Mark's Gate Community Orchards, or make a sign like Tewin's. If the orchard has no known name, consult with local elders or parish maps for clues. Failing that, make one up which carries local meaning and make sure the Ordnance Survey is told. It may inspire great pride to see your Community Orchard marked on the latest Landranger Maps.

Young trees need to be loved into maturity. This is best done through common contact with the trees and by creating as many opportunities as possible for celebration with your neighbours in the orchard. Here are a few suggestions to keep you busy:

The Community Orchard calendar

January – Wassail your orchard on Twelfth Night to ensure a good harvest, sing wassail songs or carols (you could compose your own) and enjoy some of last season's juice or cider. Prune your cobnuts, if they need it. Start a wild life diary.

February – Prune your apple and pear trees if they need it. Look out for early signs of spring such as snowdrops and catkins. Help the cobnut pollen spread on a windy day by knocking the branches.

March – Grafting is great in early March, just as the sap begins to rise. Enjoy the crocuses and daffodils that you planted as bulbs last autumn. Water young trees.

April – The Community Orchard is a wonderful place for an Easter egg hunt. Prune off any mildew and canker on apple trees. Welcome in the spring, look out for wild flowers, and swallows returning from their winter migration.

May – Welcome in the summer on May Day. Try a dawn chorus walk to hear how much bird life you share with your city or country neighbourhood, followed by a communal breakfast under the trees. Organise a blossom walk. Check stakes and loosen tree ties where needed.

June – Do a survey of wild flowers. Have a mid-summer picnic – it will be light until after 10pm. Try a spot of weeding. Thin out apple clusters late in the month.

July – Water trees now if it has been dry. Harvest cherries towards the end of the month – if you can get there before the birds. Some branches could be netted to keep some fruit for locals. Try a cherry-stone spitting competition. Look out for the very rare noble chafer in old orchards in Oxfordshire, Worcestershire, Gloucestershire, Hampshire, Herefordshire and Kent. The People's Trust for Endangered Species offer identification cards.

August – Cut the grass after the flowers have set seed. Rake it off and remove it (add it to the compost heap ready for a winter mulch). Start to pick ripe plums. Make a plum cake. Bud any grafts that have failed.

September – Prune your plum trees if necessary. Pick early apples. The pear crop will be in full swing late this month. Watch out for butterflies feeding on windfalls. Back to school – enjoy some orchard activities within the curriculum, art, biology, English, maths and more. Pick 'wet' walnuts for pickling (test them with a darning needle – if it goes right through the soft husk, they're ready). Say goodbye to migrating swallows.

October – CELEBRATE APPLE DAY ON THE 21st (or the nearest weekend). Apple and walnut harvests are in full swing – leave windfalls for creatures to eat in the coming lean months or store them for putting out later. Include Community Orchard fruit in the Harvest Festival. Give apples as gifts.

November – Make juice and cider with your surplus fruit. Plant any new trees between now and February.

December – Medlars are delicious now after the first frost. Eat from the tree or keep them somewhere cool for weeks more – the softer the better. Celebrate *Tree Dressing Day* during the first weekend in December with tree decorations, singing or story telling. Tree Dressing is an ancient custom practised all around the world. Enjoy a Christmas apple – a pseudonym for the Blenheim Orange – of whichever variety is ready locally. Eat it with a good piece of local cheese and a glass of cider.

APPENDICES

Common Ground

COMMON GROUND offers ideas, information and inspiration to help people to learn about, enjoy and take more responsibility for their own localities.

In the spectrum of environmental organisations, Common Ground uniquely pioneers imaginative work on nature, culture and place. We link people, landscape, wild life, buildings, history and customs, as well as bridging philosophy and practice, environment and the arts.

We explore new ways of looking at the world to excite people into remembering the richness of everyday landscapes, common wild life and ordinary places, to savour the symbolisms with which we have endowed nature, to revalue our emotional engagement with places and all that they mean to us, and go on to become involved in their care.

In raising awareness and action through model projects, exhibitions, publications and events, we are attempting to create a popular culture of wanting to care: we believe that the only way in which we shall achieve a sustainable relationship with nature is by everyone taking part in the effort. *Holding your Ground: an action guide to local conservation* in 1985 established our role in informing local environmental action and cultural expression.

In reasserting the importance of liberating our subjective response to the world about us, we often work with people for whom this is everyday currency – poets, sculptors, composers, painters, writers, performers – people from all branches of the arts.

Our projects include the campaign for Local Distinctiveness; Save our Orchards; Apple Day; Community Orchards; Parish Maps; Local Flora Britannica; Rhynes, Rivers and Running Brooks and Confluence, which is helping people to create new music for the River Stour in Somerset, Wiltshire and Dorset.

Common Ground is a charity (no. 326335), formed in 1983. We seek no members and create no structures. Through collaborations we build links between organisations and disciplines, local people and professionals. We act as a catalyst and mentor; by broadcasting ideas and demonstrating by example we try to extend the constituencies for conservation and create foundations for real democracy.

Gazeteer of local varieties

THERE ARE THOUSANDS of varieties of orchard fruits, many with more than one name – Emneth Early and Early Victoria are the same apple, for example, while varieties of perry pears or plums often have very localised names that change depending on where you are. But many fruits are known to have arisen or have been raised in particular places and we believe it is worth keeping these and the knowledge which surrounds them alive and well in their place.

Seek out varieties that have originated or were widely grown in your locality in the past. This way you are more likely to choose a tree which is better suited to local soils and the prevailing weather conditions.

The following list, which is predominantly apples, is intended to help you to make a start in selecting varieties of fruit that you can grow to help to conserve cultural and genetic diversity and enhance the local distinctiveness of the place. It is not comprehensive and, being county-based, is just a general guide. The counties themselves keep changing shape and name – so please double check! We have used the early names. Many of these varieties can be obtained from specialist nurseries. Or why not graft your own from local trees?

BEDFORDSHIRE: *apples* – Beauty of Bedford, Bedfordshire Foundling, Epicure, Hambling's Seedling, Laxton's Advance, Laxton's Early Crimson, Laxton's Exquisite, Laxton's Favourite, Laxton's Fortune – cross between Cox's Orange Pippin and Wealthy, raised by the Laxton Brothers in 1904. Light green/mottled red fruit with creamy-white soft, sweetly scented flesh with a hint of banana. Laxton's Herald, Laxton's Leader, Laxton's Pearmain, Laxton's Peerless, Laxton's Rearguard, Laxton's Reward, Laxton's Royalty, Laxton's Superb – another Laxton's apple raised in 1897 from a cross between Wyken Pippin and Cox's Orange Pippin. Widely grown commercially. Fruit palish-green to purplish-red, flesh pure white, nutty, sweet, soft and juicy. Laxton's Triumph, Laxton's Victory, Lord Lambourne – the best-flavoured apple produced by the famous Laxton nurseries in Bedford in 1907. A cross between Worcester Pearmain and James Grieve. No good for damp districts. Attractive fruit – greenish-yellow flushed with broken red stripes. Sweet, juicy and delicious. Neild's Drooper, Owen Thomas, Pioneer, Queensby's Glory,

September Beauty; *cherry* – Bedford Prolific; *pears* – Beurré Bedford, Laxton's Foremost, Laxton's Satisfaction, Warden; *plums* – Black Prince, Early Laxton, Fotheringham, Laxton's Blackbird, Laxton's Blue Tit, Laxton's Bountiful, Laxton's Cropper, Laxton's Delicious, Laxton's Gage, Laxton's Goldfinch, Laxton's Prosperity, Olympia, Utility.

BERKSHIRE: *apples* – Breedon Pippin, Charles Eyre, Charles Ross – best known of Charles Ross's 30 named varieties (others being Encore & Houblon). Head gardener at Welford Park near Newbury from 1860-1908, Charles Ross bred apples on a large scale. Cross between Peasgood Nonsuch and Cox's Orange Pippin. Recommended for chalky soils. A very handsome fruit. Crisp, sweet and flavoursome. Skin yellowish-green with a light red flush of broken red stripes. Delectable, Encore – good flavoured cooker. Slices remain intact when cooked. Keeps until May. Raised by Charles Ross from Warner's King and Northern Greening. Skin bright yellowish-green with red flush. Frogmore Prolific, Guelph, Hector MacDonald, Houblon, John Standish – raised by John Standish of Ascot in about 1873. Attractive fruit with scarlet skin dotted with russets on pale green. Flesh white, juicy and firm. Little flavour. John Waterer, Miller's Seedling – once widely grown in Berkshire. Raised by James Miller, nurseryman from Newbury in 1848. Crisp, juicy, sweet and refreshing. Bruises easily. Attractive pale greenish-yellow fruit, three-quartered mottled with pink. Mrs Phillimore, Paroquet, Peacemaker, Renown, Rival – reputedly the juiciest of all the older varieties of apples. Raised by Charles Ross from Peasgood Nonsuch and Cox's Orange Pippin in the late 1800s. A very attractive apple. Pale yellowish-green flushed with brilliant scarlet with a slight bloom. Shinfield Seedling, Small's Admirable, Sunrise, Welford Park Nonsuch, Winston; *pear* – Williams' Bon Chrétien – found around 1770 in the garden of Mr Wheeler a schoolmaster at Aldermaston, grafts were sent to the nurseryman, Richard Williams after whom the pear is named. Exported to USA where it was named after the distributor, Enoch Bartlett, and provided the foundation for the American canned pear trade. The most widely grown pear in the world. *plum* – Marjorie's Seedling.

BUCKINGHAMSHIRE: *apples* – Arthur Turner – a large handsome fruit with a very attractive blossom. Better than Bramley for a small garden. Polished green skin with pinky-orange flush. Creamy-white flesh, acid and a little dry. Raised by Charles Turner of Slough and first exhibited in 1912. Ball's Pippin, Cox's Orange Pippin – planted as a pip from a Ribston Pippin x Blenheim Orange in 1825 by Richard Cox of Colnbrook and introduced by Small & Son in 1840. Now three-quarters of all dessert fruit commercially grown in this country are Cox. The original tree, which grew in Cox's garden, blew down in a gale in 1911. Difficult to grow – it is very susceptible to mildew. It likes well-drained soils and doesn't thrive north of a line from Birmingham to the Wash. Flushed orange-red on yellow-green mottled with russet. Rich intense aromatic flavour. Cox's Pomona – planted at the same time as Cox's Orange Pippin by Richard Cox. Same parents yet a very different fruit. Large, pale yellow flushed and speckled with orange-red. Good for apple pies. Creamy-white flesh. Soft and juicy. Feltham Beauty, Langley Pippin – raised by the family firm of James Veitch, a Chelsea nurserymen in the late 1800s from Cox's Orange Pippin and Gladstone. Veitch's son opened a nursery at Langley, near Slough – hence the name. Pale greenish-yellow apple with a deep crimson flush. Soft and juicy with a slight aromatic flavour. Still survives in Middlesex; *damson* – Aylesbury Prune; *plums* – Allgrove's Superb, Bullace Langley.

CAMBRIDGESHIRE: *apples* – Allington Pippin, Barnack Beauty, Chivers Delight – 'Well-known for its good nature and excellent flavour'. Raised by John Chivers at Histon in 1936. Creamy-white juicy flesh, slightly acid and sweet. Fruit attractive yellow-green, mottled with red. Emneth Early/Early Victoria – earliest of the cookers. Thought to have been raised by William Lynn of Emneth. Cross between Lord Grosvenor and Keswick Codlin. Superb flavour. Juicy, sharp but mild. Cooks to a golden froth. Good for baked apples but too insubstantial for pies. Pale yellow when ripe. Haggerstone Pippin, Histon Favourite, Hunter's Majestic, Huntingdon Codlin, Lord Peckover, Murfitt's Seedling, New Rock Pippin, Red Victoria, St Everard, Wayside; *plum* – Cambridge Gage.

CHESHIRE: *apples* – Arthur W. Barnes – raised by N F Barnes at Eaton Gardens, Chester, in 1902 from Gascoyne's Scarlet and Cox's Orange Pippin. Crisp, juicy, subacid to slightly sweet. Fruit bright red on pale green to pale yellow. Bee Bench, Burr Knot, Celia, Eccleston Pippin, Elton Beauty, Gooseberry Pippin, Lord Clyde, Lord Derby – grows well on wet, clay soils. Raised by Mr Witham, nurseryman in Stockport. First recorded in 1862. Bright green fruit, turning yellow when ripe. Slices stay intact when cooked. 'Flesh cooks to an attractive deep claret colour, and is especially delicious sweetened with brown sugar.' Millicent Barnes, Minshull Crab, Rakemaker, Rymer, Shaw's Pippin, Sure Crop, Withington Welter; *damson* – Cheshire Prune.

CORNWALL: *apples* – Ben's Red, Blackmoor Pippin, Bottlestopper, Box Apple, Breadfruit, Captain Broad, Chacewater Longstem, Colloggett Pippin, Cornish Aromatic – thought to have grown here for a long time. First recorded in 1813. Excellent quality apple, crisp, nut-like aromatic flavour. Greeny-yellow flushed with orange-red, slightly russetted. Tolerates wet climate. Cornish Gilliflower – discovered in a cottage garden near Truro in about 1800, and first described in 1813. Remarkable for its rich aromatic, honey-like flavour. 'Gilliflower' is thought to have derived from the old French word Girofle – clove-apple – as it is supposed to give off a clove-like fragrance when cut. Yellow-green streaked with red. Cornish Honeypin, Cornish Longstem, Cornish Mother, Cornish Pine, Fairfield/Millet, Glass Apple/

Snell's White, Gulval Seedling, Hocking's Green, Hocking's Yellow, Hodge's Seedling, Improved Keswick, King Byerd, Manaccan Primrose, Onion Moonstreak, Pear Apple, Pig's Nose, Pig's Snout, Plympton King, Polly/White Hair, Queenie, Red Robin, Red Rollo, Saw Pit, Scilly Pearl, Sidney Strake, Sops in Wine, Sweet Larks, Sweet Merlin, Tan Harvey, Tommy Knight, Tregonna King, Trenance Cooker, Venus Pippin; *plum* – Kea – a chance seedling found and much grown in the Kea district of Truro. Propagated from suckers taken from parent trees. Manaccan.

CUMBRIA: *apples* – Autumn Harvest, Carlisle Codlin, Forty Shilling, Greenup Pippin/Yorkshire Beauty – a very handsome fruit, discovered in the garden of a shoemaker called Greenup in Keswick at the end of the 18th century. Widely grown in the Borders 100 years ago and in Yorkshire – hence its synonym 'Yorkshire Beauty'. Flesh tender, juicy and acid. Skin white-cream with bright polished flush. Keswick Codlin – a distinctly angular and rather ugly apple found growing behind a wall at Gleaston Castle near Ulverstone, Lancs, sometime before 1793. Later introduced commercially by John Sander, nurseryman of Keswick. Widely grown in Yorkshire where it was the farmer's favourite. Pale yellow-green, large and tender. Can be used for tarts as early as July. Lemon Square, Longstart, Nelson's Favourite.

DERBYSHIRE: *apples* – Beeley Pippin, Belledge Pippin, Lamb's Seedling, New Bess Pool, Newton Wonder – prolific apple, popular until recently owing to its shiny golden-yellow skin and attractive red stripes and flush. 1,840 lbs once recorded from one tree. Sources differ as to its origin. One account says it was raised by Mr Taylor of King's Newton, Melbourne, from Dumelow's Seedling x Blenheim Orange in about 1887. Another says it was discovered growing out of a thatched roof of the Hardinge Arms, a pub in King's Newton. Traditionally used in mincemeat and in stuffings for turkey at Christmas. Good in salads as it isn't overwhelmed by the dressing. Keeps until Easter.

DEVONSHIRE: *apples* – Allspice, Barum Beauty, Beech Bearer, Beef Apple, Bickington Grey, Billy Down Pippin, Bowden's Seedling, Brown's Apple, Butterbox, Cerit, Coleman's Seedling, Crimson Costard, Dawe, Devonshire Buckland, Devonshire Court Pendu, Devon Crimson Queen, Devonshire Quarrenden – a very old variety mentioned in 1678. May take its name from Carentan, an apple-growing district in France. It was extensively grown in the west country where it tolerates the rain. Beautiful polished dark crimson flush. Distinct and refreshing flavour. Devonshire Redstreake, Devonshire Striped, Devonshire Whitesour, Docker's Devonshire, Ellis Bitter, Endsleigh Beauty, Fair Maid of Devon, Farmer's Glory, Golden Bittersweet, Hollow Core, Johnny Voun, Limberland, Listener, Lucombe's Pine, Lucombe's Seedling, Major, Michaelmas Stubbard, Morgan Sweet, No Pip, North Wood, Oaken Pin, Paignton Marigold, Peter Lock, Plympton Pippin, Ponsford, Pyne's

Pearmaine, Quench, Red Ribbed Greening, Royal Somerset, Slack Ma Girdle, Star of Devon, Stockbearer, Sweet Alford, Sweet Coppin, Tom Potter, Tremlett's Bitter, Upton Pyne, Veitch's Perfection, Whitesour, Woodbine, Woolbrook Pippin, Woolbrook Russet; *plum* – Dittisham Ploughman – grown only in the valley of the River Dart, probably originated as a chance seedling and trees are raised from suckers, not budded or grafted, good for jam or bottling. *cherries* – Dun, Large Black, Preserving, Small Black, Green Stemmed Black, Bottlers.

DORSET: *apples* – Melcombe Russet, Tyneham Apple; *plum* – Bryanston Gage – found in the gardens of Lord Portman at Bryanston, Blandford around 1800, possibly from Green Gage x Coe's Golden Drop. Similar to a very pale Green Gage, but larger.

ESSEX: *apples* – Braintree Seedling, Chelmsford Wonder, D'Arcy Spice – discovered in a garden at the Hall, Tolleshunt d'Arcy, south west of Colchester in about 1785. Cultivated by nurseryman John Harris in 1848. Well-known in East Anglia – it does best in sandy soil and dry areas. Needs a hot, dry summer to gain its richly aromatic and spicy flavour. Not a beauty, but well-worth growing. Skin yellowish-green with pale brown-grey russet. Firm, sweet, nutty and juicy. Discovery – very popular new variety. Raised by Mr Dummer in Langham in about 1949. Thought to be a cross between Worcester Pearmain and Beauty of Bath and introduced in 1963. Crimson with pale yellow russetted dots. Crisp, juicy and fairly sweet. Good in fresh fruit salad. Edith Hopwood, Excelsior, Flame, Garnet, George Cave – perhaps the best early apple often ready before the end of July. Thought to be a chance seedling nurtured by George Cave of Dovercourt in about 1923. Attractive yellowy-green fruit flushed with crimson. Crisp, juicy and slightly acid. London Pippin, Maclean's Favourite, Maldon Wonder, Monarch, Opal, Pearl, Queen – a handsome exhibition variety raised by Mr Bull, a farmer of Billericay in 1858, from pips from an apple brought at the local market. Distinctly acid, tender and very juicy. Cooks to a fluff. Pale whitish-green, flushed with flecks of red. Ruby, Seabrook's Red, Sturmer Pippin – raised by nurseryman Ezekiel Dillstone in Sturmer, near Haverhill in about 1800 from Ribston Pippin x Nonpareil. His grandson Thomas took some scion wood with him when he emigrated to Australia. It was widely grown in Tasmania and imported to the UK – 800,000 bushels arrived in 1934. It is susceptible to canker and needs a hot summer to produce its full flavour. High in vitamin C. Firm, fresh, juicy with a hint of gooseberry. Excellent with cheese. Stradbroke, Sunburn, Waltham Abbey Seedling.

GLOUCESTERSHIRE: *apples* – Ashmead's Kernel – a long-standing favourite in the gardens of west Gloucestershire. Raised by Dr Ashmead in the 1700s. One of the finest aromatic flavoured apples with a sweet-sharp taste, reminiscent of fruit drops. Yellowish-russetted flesh, firm, crisp, juicy, sugary.

Breakwell's Seedling, Bromsbury Crab, Chaxhill Red, Eden, Elmore Pippin, Forest Styre, Gilliflower of Gloucester, Gloucester Royal, Harvey, Hunt's Duke of Gloucester, Lake's Kernel, Lodgemore Nonpareil, Longney Russet, Martins Kernel, Morning Pippin, Must, Northland Pippin, Old Foxwhelp – an old cider apple – old trees can still be found in parts of Herefordshire and Gloucestershire. Large tree with upright limbs. Fruit has irregular shape and a markedly striped flush. Puckrup Pippin, Severn Bank, Tewkesbury Baron, Yellow Styre; *perry pears* – Arlingham Squash, Blakeney Red, Brandy, Brown Bess, Butt, Chaceley Green, Claret, Clusters, Gin, Knapper, Late Treacle, Lumber, Merrylegs, Staunton Squash, Taynton Squash, Teddington Green, Thorn, Thurston's Red; *plums* – Blaisdon Red, Dimmock Red, Johnnie Moor.

GREATER LONDON & MIDDLESEX: *apples* – Barchard's Seedling, Cellini, Chad's Favourite, Fearn's Pippin, Grange's Pearmain, Hounslow Wonder, London Pearmain, Merton Beauty, Merton Charm, Merton Delight, Merton Joy, Merton Knave, Merton Pearmain, Merton Pippin, Merton Prolific, Merton Reinette, Merton Russet, Merton Worcester – one of a number of apples raised during the first half of the 20th century by M B Crane at the John Innes Institute, Merton. Cox's Orange Pippin x Worcester Pearmain it has Worcester colour and light strawberry flavour, but crisper flesh and trace of aromatic quality. Mitchelson's Seedling, Morris's Russet, Reverend W Wilks – named after the vicar of Shirley, Surrey and the Secretary of the Royal Horticultural Society from 1888-1919. Raised by the Veitch nurseries of King's Road, Chelsea in 1904 from a Ribston Pippin and Peasgood Nonsuch. 'A universal winner on the show bench.' Fruits often weigh over 2lbs each. Flesh creamy-white, quite sweet and well-flavoured. Cooks to a pale yellow froth. Royal Jubilee, Scarlet Pearmain, Storey's Seedling; *pear* – Merton Pride; *plums* – Kirke's Blue, Pond's Seedling, Prince of Wales.

HAMPSHIRE & THE ISLE OF WIGHT: *apples* – Beauty of Hants – raised at Bassett, Southampton in the garden of Mrs Eyre Crabbe some time before 1850 from a Blenheim Orange. Flesh is creamy-white, fine textured and rather soft and juicy – similar in taste to a Blenheim Orange. Trees difficult to obtain. Benenden Early, Easter Orange, Hambledon Deux Ans – an old garden variety which hailed from Hambledon in the mid 18th century. Its name derives from the supposition that it 'may be preserved with care for a couple of years'. 'A large noble apple. It is richly flavoured, but rather deficient in juice.' Howgate Wonder – a fairly new variety raised in 1916 by Mr Wratton, Howgate Lane, of Bembridge, IOW. Popular for exhibitions on account of its size. Fruit a little flavourless in comparison with the Bramley and breaks up when cooked. Skin is light green flushed and striped with orange-brown. Isle of Wight Pippin, James Saunders, Jersey Beauty, King George V, Lady Thorneycroft, Lord Kitchener, Sir John Thorneycroft, Steyne's Seedling; *plums* – Angelina Burdett, Woolston Black.

HEREFORDSHIRE: *apples* – Adam's Pearmain, Ball's Bittersweet, Bringewood Pippin, Brown Snout, Cherry Pearmain, Cowarne Red, Downton Pippin, Forester, Golden Harvey, Herefordshire Beefing, King's Acre Bountiful, King's Acre Pippin – a richly flavoured high quality fruit, well worth growing despite its unattractive appearance. Introduced by King's Acre Nurseries, Hereford in 1898, a Sturmer Pippin and Ribston Pippin cross. A firm, juicy, coarse-textured fruit with a rich aromatic flavour. Good for use in salads. Dull green, slightly flushed with brownish-red. Lady's Finger of Hereford, New German, Pig's Nose Pippin, Redstreak, Stoke Edith Pippin, Strawberry Norman, Ten Commandments, Tyler's Kernel, Wormsley Pippin, Yellow Ingestrie – raised by the famous pomologist Thomas Andrew Knight of Downton Castle in about 1800, and named after the seat of the Earl of Talbot. Cross between Cox's Orange Pippin and Golden Pippin. Crisp, juicy, yellow flesh. 'A delightful little yellow apple for September'; *cherries* – Downton, Early Heart, Knight's Early Black, Waterloo; *perry pears* – Bartestree Squash, Gregg's Pitt, Holme Lacey, Holmer, Moorcroft, Pine.

HERTFORDSHIRE: *apples* – Beauty of Waltham, Brownlees' Russet – 'a favourite russet for the private gardener' well-known for its very beautiful blossom – a rich cerise-pink. Introduced by William Brownlees, a nurseryman in Hemel Hempstead in about 1848. It can withstand badly-drained soil. Green, russetted with brown-yellow ochre. Pleasantly nutty taste. Aromatic. Bushey Grove, Dawn, Edwin Beckett, Fairie Queen, Golden Reinette – 'The farmer's greatest favourite'. A beautiful apple, widely grown around London in the 1850s and 'reputed to be at its perfection in Hertfordshire'. It likes light, warm soil. 'An old deservedly esteemed table apple.' Hitchin Pippin, Hornmead Pearmain, Lane's Prince Albert – 'It is a lovely fruit which takes the highest polish of any variety.' So named by Henry Lane because he planted it out immediately after cheering the Queen and Prince Albert through Berkhamsted in 1841. The original tree was still growing in a garden in the High Street in 1936. Cross between Russet Nonpareil and Dumelow's Seedling. Bright green skin, slightly flushed with red stripes. Juicy, brisk, acid. Good for pies as it keeps its shape. New Hawthornden, Prince Edward, Rivers' Early Peach, Rivers' Nonesuch, St Martin's, Small's Admirable, Thomas Rivers, Voyager, Winter Hawthornden, Young's Pinello; *cherries* – Caroon, Alba Heart, August Heart, Hertfordshire Black, Ronald's Heart, Smoky Heart, Strawberry Heart; *pears* – Beacon, Conference – 'Raised by Rivers of Sawbridgeworth and exhibited at the National British Pear Conference of 1885 hence its name.' Most widely commercially grown pear in Britain. Fertility, Magnate, Parrot, Princess, St Luke, Summer Beurré, D'Arenburg, Verulam; *plums* – Admiral, Archduke, Autumn Compote, Bittern, Blue Prolific, Blue Rock, Curlew, Czar, Early Rivers, Early Favourite, Early Transparent Gage, Golden Transparent, Grand Duke, Heron, Late Orange, Late Transparent Gage, Monarch, Mallard, President, Primate, Stint, Sultan, Swan.

KENT: *apples* – Bascombe's Mystery, Beauty of Kent – one of the most popular cooking apples in late Victorian times because of its large size, but considered 'too ugly for present-day commercial use'! Skin pale greenish-yellow flushed, speckled and striped with red. Tender flesh, very juicy and deliciously perfumed. It cooks to pretty lemon-coloured slices. Bountiful, Bow Hill Pippin, Brenchley Pippin, Castle Major, Christmas Pearmain, Cobham, Colonel Vaughan, Diamond Jubilee, Falstaff, Faversham Creek, Fiesta, Folkestone, Foster's Seedling, Fred Webb, Gascoyne's Scarlet – originally grown for decoration owing to its attractive fruit – carmine red on milky-green. Raised by Mr. Gascoyne of Bapchild Court, Sittingbourne. One of the best varieties for chalk. Sharp, subtle, perfumed flavour. Breaks up, but not completely, when cooked. George Neal – best apple sauce variety. Raised by Mrs Reeves of Otford in 1904. Introduced by R Neal & Sons of Wandsworth in 1923. Greeny-yellow with small patches of russet. Excellent flavour crisp, juicy and acid. Golden Knob, Gooseberry Apple, Granny Giffard, Great Expectations, Greensleeves, Grenadier, Jester, Jupiter, Kent, Kentish Fillbasket, Kentish Quarrenden, Lamb Abbey Pearmain, Mabbott's Pearmain, Maid of Kent, Maidstone Favourite, Michaelmas Red, Polly Prosser, Red Devil, Robin Pippin, Rossie Pippin, Smart's Prince Arthur, South Park, St Alban's Pippin, Sunset, Suntan, Tydeman's Early, Tydeman's Late Orange, Wanstall Pippin, Warner's King – said to have originated in an orchard in Weavering Street, Maidstone and known in the 1700s as King Apple. Mr Warner, a small nurseryman of Gosforth, near Leeds, gave it to the wellknown nurseryman, Thomas Rivers of Sawbridgeworth, who renamed it Warner's King. Yellowish-green skin. Crisp, juicy. Cooks well – to a fluff; *pears* – Concorde, Michaelmas Nelis; *plums* - Black Diamond, Farleigh Damson, Kentish Bush, Orpington Prolific; *cherries* – Bloors Heart, Frogmore Early, Nutberry Black, Kentish Red (culinary).

LANCASHIRE & ISLE OF MAN: *apples* – Duke of Devonshire – 'quite indispensible for late use.' Raised in 1835 by Mr Wilson, gardener to the Duke of Devonshire at Holker Hall. Rich nutty flavour. Firm, fairly juicy and slightly acid. At its best well after Christmas. Gold Medal, Golden Spire, Harvest Festival, Hutton Square, John Huggett, Lady's Finger of Lancaster, Lange's Perfection, Lord Suffield – largest of the codlin-type cooking apples. Once grown widely as an early cooker, now superceded by Early Victoria. Raised by Thomas Thorpe, a weaver from Middleton, near Manchester. First distributed in 1836. Unsuitable for high rainfall areas. Crisp, juicy and acid. Cooks well. Breaks up completely. Frothy baker. Manks Codlin – raised by Mr Kewley of Ballanard. First fruited in 1815. Grows well in exposed situations. 'Sweet, light, fruity, keeping its shape. Delicious as a plainly baked apple – just right for 'codlins and cream'. Makes a great apple snow. Keeps until November – unusual for an early variety. Pott's Seedling, Proctor's Seedling, Roseberry, Sowman's Seedling.

LEICESTERSHIRE and RUTLAND: *apples* – Annie Elizabeth – named after Annie Elizabeth (who died aged 13 months) by her father Samuel Greatorex, who sowed a pip from a Blenheim Orange in a nearby allotment in Knighton in 1857. Harrison's Nurseries of Leicester introduced it in 1868. Best for making stewed apple because the slices never break. One of the best varieties for a small garden. Handsome ribbed fruit. Brilliant red and yellow when ripe. Barnack Orange, Belvoir Seedling, Dumelow's Seedling (Wellington) – Favourite of the Victorians. 'It has a translucent quality, good for pies and makes a delicious, creamy, brisk baked apple or sauce'. Often used for making mincemeat because of its sharp, acid flavour. Dates from the 18th century. The original tree was flourishing in 1800. Accredited to Mr. Dumelow, a farmer at Shakerstone. Thought to be a seedling from Northern Greening. Skin yellowish-green. Marriage Maker, Prince Charles, Queen Caroline, St Ailred.

LINCOLNSHIRE: *apples* – Allington Pippin, Brown's Seedling, Dewdney's Seedling, Doctor Clifford, Ellison's Orange – known for its lovely aniseed flavour when ripe. Raised by the Revd C Ellison at Bracebridge, Lincoln and by Mr Wipf, gardener at Mr Ellison's brother-in-law's home at Hartsholme Hall, from a Cox's Orange Pippin x Calville Blanc. Crisp and juicy. Good in salads and apple dumplings. Grows best in dry, well-drained soils. Grimoldby Golden, Herring's Pippin, Holland Pippin, Ingall's Pippin, Ingall's Red, Isaac Newton's Tree – one of our oldest varieties, descended from the tree, thought to be Flower of Kent, which grew in Isaac Newton's garden at Woolsthorpe Manor near Colsterworth in the 1660s and which reputedly gave Newton the idea of gravity. Also known as The Gravity Tree. Fruit 'distinctly ugly'. Pale silvery-green, greenish-yellow, flushed with red. Flesh soft, coarse-textured and subacid. Lord Burghley, Peasgood's Nonsuch – 'One of the largest and most handsome of all apples'. Raised in the 1850s in Grantham by Mrs Peasgood from a pip of a Catshead Codlin. Pale yellowish-green skin overlaid with orange and bright red stripes. Sweet, juicy and tender. Good for baking and for dumplings. Needs a warm rich, well-drained soil to flourish. Philadelphia, Sleeping Beauty, William Ingall.

MERSEYSIDE: *apple* - Florence Bennett – raised by Mrs F Bennett in the 1960s possibly from an apple core thrown onto the garden rubbish heap.

NORFOLK: *apples* – Adam's Pearmain (poss. Herefords), Admiral, Banns, Baxter's Pearmain, Beachamwell, Caroline, Dr Harvey – named after Dr Gabriel Harvey, master of Trinity Hall College, Cambridge. First mentioned in 1629. One of the most common winter apples in the Norwich market in the 1820s and used for sweetmeat. A choice fruit. Yellow with slight orange flush and light-brown russet. Crisp, juicy, subacid. Foulden Pearmain, Golden Noble – discovered in an old orchard in 1820 by Patrick Flannagan, gardener at Stowe Hall, near Downham. Handsome fruit. Rich in vitamin C. One of the best cookers. Acid, with a distinct, extremely good fruity flavour. Good for baking, apple pie and open tarts as it keeps its form when cooked. Light green-yellow. Green Roland, Harling Hero, Herbert Eastoe, Horsford Prolific, Horsham Russet, Hubbard's Pearmain, London Pearmain, Norfolk Beauty, Norfolk Beefing – raised in Norfolk and first recorded in 1807. Very popular in Norwich up to the 1950s and sold by bakers as after-dinner sweetmeats (dried slowly in bread ovens as they cooled, and then coated with melted sugar). Good for drying because they are less juicy. Skins are tough and don't burst when baked. Best eaten after Christmas and can last until May or June. Norfolk Coleman, Norfolk Royal – a very attractive exhibition variety with shiny crimson and yellow skin. Found as a chance seedling at Wright's Nurseries at North Walsham. Introduced in 1928 and once well-known in East Anglia. Crisp, juicy, sweet. Also cooks well. Norfolk Summer Broadend, Robert Blatchford, St Magdalen, Sandringham, Striped Beefing, Vicar of Beighton, White Quarantine, Winter Broadend, Winter Majetin.

NORTHAMPTONSHIRE: *apples* – Barnack Beauty – best variety on chalk. Raised at Barnack near Stamford in about 1840. Very handsome, golden, flushed with orange-red. Juicy, very crunchy, refreshing. Eady's Magnum, Lord Burghley – raised from a seedling in the gardens of the Marquis of Exeter at Burghley Park near Stamford in 1834. Bunyard considered it one of the best dessert apples. Firm, yellow, juicy with a slight pine flavour. Pale yellow flushed with red. Attractive. Thorpe's Peach.

NORTHUMBERLAND: *apple* – Mrs Lakeman's Seedling – raised in about 1900 at Stocksfield in Northumberland. Large, firm, crisp rather coarse flesh. Acid, slightly sweet. Trees difficult to obtain.

NOTTINGHAMSHIRE: *apples* – Baron Ward, Beauty of Stoke, Bess Pool – found as a seedling in a wood by a young girl – Bess Pool. She brought some fruit back home and they were admired so much that grafts were taken. Grown commercially by J R Pearson in Chilwell. First recorded in 1824. Skin milky mottled red and green. Fairly sweet and crisp. Good to eat at Christmas with cheese. Bramley's Seedling – most famous and popular cooking apple. Planted as a pip by Mary Ann Brailsford between 1809-13 in Church Street, Southwell. It still survives in the garden today. Cuttings were taken by Henry Merryweather in 1856 and sold commercially by him. Rich in vitamin C. Juicy, strong flavour. Bright green. Excellent for apple pies. Domino, Mead's Broading, Mrs Wilmot, Pickering's Seedling, Winter Quarrenden; *plums* – Bradley's Damson, Merryweather Damson.

OXFORDSHIRE: *apples* – Blenheim Orange – an old favourite. Raised in about 1740 by a tailor, George Kempster, in his garden in Manor Road, Old Woodstock, just outside Blenheim Park. It was a local landmark. People came by coach loads to marvel at the tree and to take scions from it. Known as Kempster's Pippin until 1811. Slow to come into crop. It has a distinctive nutty flavour. Excellent for making apple charlotte. Greenish-yellow streaked with red. Eynsham Challenger, Eynsham Dumpling, Farmer's Glory, Foulkes' Foremost, Hanwell Souring, Jennifer, Jennifer Wastie, Old Fred, Oxford Beauty, Oxford Conquest, Oxford Hoard, Oxford Sunrise, Oxford Yeoman, Peggy's Pride, Pheasant's Eye, Red Army, Sergeant Peggy.

SHROPSHIRE: *apples* – Bringewood Pippin, Brookes, Lady's Fingers, Moss's Seedling, Prince's Pippin, Springrove Codlin; *plum* – Shropshire Prune.

SOMERSET (& AVON): *apples* – Ashton Bitter, Ashton Brown Jersey, Backwell Red, Bailbrook Seedling, Bartletts Glory, Bath Russet, Beauty of Bath – good early eater with pale greenish-red mottled skin. Pleasantly sharp, sweet and juicy. Hails from Bailbrook, near Bath. Introduced by Mr Cooling of Bath in 1864. Beauty of Wells, Black Dabinett, Black Vallis, Bridgwater Pippin, Broadleaf Jersey, Brockhead, Burrow Hill Early, Cap of Liberty, Cheddar Cross, Chisel Jersey, Coat Jersey, Coopers Favourite, Court of Wick, Crimson King, Dabinett, Dorset, Dove, Dunnings Russet, Even Pearmain, Fair Maid of Taunton, Fill Barrell, Gatcombe, Glory of the West, Gloucester Cross, Golden Farmer, Golden Knob, Greasy Pippin, Green Pearmain, Hagloe Pippin, Harry Master's Jersey, Hereford Cross, Hoary Morning – first recorded in 1819. Large and handsome, but its evocative name is not matched by its taste. Kingston Black, Lambrook Pippin, Lambrook Seedling, Loddington, Mealy Late Blossom, Melmouth, Merchant Apple, Newport Cross, Nine Square, Pennard Bitter, Plymouth Cross, Porter's Perfection, Pyleigh, Radcliffe Nonpariel, Red Worthy, Rich's Favourite, St Ivel Pippin, Shoreditch White, Stable Jersey, Stembridge Cluster, Stembridge Jersey, Stoke Red, Taunton Cross, Taunton Golden Pippin, Taunton Nonpariel, Taylors Sweet, Tom Putt – thought to have been raised by Tom Putt, rector of Trent near Sherborne in the late 1700s. Much prized in the west country. Large, angular, red-striped. Sharp and crisp. White Close Pippin, White Jersey, Worcester Cross, Yarlington Mill, Yeovil Sour; *pears* – Beurré d'Avalon, Bristol Cross; *plums* – Frome Cross, Severn Cross, Teme Cross, Thames Cross.

STAFFORDSHIRE: *pear* – Tettenhall Dick.

SUFFOLK: *apples* – Catherine, Clopton Red, Honey Pippin, Lady Henniker – raised from a pip in cider must at Thornham Hall near Eye, in the 1840s. Introduced by John Perkins, gardener to Lord Henniker in 1873. Lovely flavour. Cooks well. Best in December/January when it has lost some of its acidity. Lord Stradbroke, St Edmund's Pippin – best flavoured of all October apples. Raised by Mr R Harvey at Bury St Edmunds and first recorded in 1875. Crisp, juicy, fresh. Bruises easily. Green, overlain with orange-brown russet; *plums* – Coe's Golden Drop – raised in 1800 by Jervaise Coe, gardener at Bury St Edmunds probably from Green Gage x White Magnum Bonum. Difficult to grow so ignored by commercial growers, but its good flavour makes it a popular garden tree. Coe's Violet.

SURREY: *apples* – Albury Park Nonsuch, Braddick's Nonpareil, Byfleet Seedling, Carswell's Honeydew, Carswell's Orange, Claygate Pearmain – found growing in a hedge near Claygate by John Braddick in the 1820s. Taken by the fruit, he sent some to a RHS meeting in 1822. One of the finest of all dessert apples. Firm, crisp, juicy, sweet and aromatic. Green-orangey-red, speckled with brown russets. Cleeve, Cockle Pippin – originated with Mr Cockle at Godstone, Redhill in about 1800 and was extensively grown in Surrey and Sussex. First-class, rich flavour, sweet and aromatic. Excellent with cheese. Orangey-yellow shaded with dull russet-brown. Colonel Yate, Comrade, Curl Tail, Duchess's Favourite, George Carpenter, Hannon Seedling, Harry Pring, High View Pippin, Joybells, King of the Pippins, Lady Isabel, May Beauty, Mitchelson's Seedling, Nanny, Palmer's Rosey, Pixie, Scarlet Crofton, Scarlet Nonpareil, Shoesmith, Surprise, Victory, Wadey's Seedling; *pear* – Onward; *plums* – Crimson Drop, Mitchelson's.

SUSSEX: *apples* – Alfriston – raised at Uckfield by Mr Shepherd in the late 18th century. Originally called Shepherd's Seedling/Pippin and renamed by Mr Brookes of Alfriston in 1819. Very popular in the last century. Large, sugary and brisk. Cooks to a tender golden-brown with a delicious pear-like flavour. Deep bright green to greenish-yellow. Aldwick Beauty, Ashdown Seedling, Crawley Beauty – discovered by the Cheals in about 1870 in a cottage garden near their nursery, now under Gatwick airport. Flavour fair. Not very juicy. Green, flushed and striped with red. Crawley Reinette, Coronation, Doctor Hogg, Duck's Bill, Eastbourne Pippin, Edmund Jupp, Egremont Russet – most commercial of all the russets. Thought to have been raised by Lord Egremont in the 1870s at Petworth. Rich nutty flavour. Crisp, firm and fairly juicy. Holds its shape well if cooked. Golden-green flushed with yellow ochre russet. First and Last, Forge – the cottager's apple in the south-east. Derived from the former iron-working area around East Grinstead and Crawley. First described in 1851. Tender, sweet, yellow and crisp. Yellow with red streaks and a red flush. Golden Bounty, Golden Pippin, Goodwood Pippin, Hawkridge, June Crewdson, Knobby Russet, Lady Hopetown, Lady Sudeley, Mannington's Pearmain, Old Middlemas, Petworth Nonpareil, Saltcote Pippin, Sussex Mother, Tinsley Quince, Wadhurst Pippin; *plum* – Victoria – chance seedling found in a garden at Alderton, Sussex. Highest class of plum for canning, bottling and jam, much sought after. A great cropper with a good flavour.

TYNE & WEAR: *apples* – Barnard's Baker, Gateshead Lemon Pippin, Hebburn Red, Teesdale Nonpareil, Woolaton Pippin.

WARWICKSHIRE: *apples* – Shakespeare, Wyken Pippin – an old variety introduced from Holland at beginning of 18th century. Believed to have come from a pip saved from an apple eaten by Lord Craven on his travels from France to the Netherlands in about 1715. Planted at Wyken near Coventry. Greenish skin dotted with russet. Delicious yellow flesh. Juicy, sweet, tender. Best between Christmas and Easter; *plum* - Warwickshire Drooper.

WILTSHIRE: *apples* – Bedwyn Beauty, Burn's Seedling, Celt, Chorister Boy, Dredge's Fame, Mary Barnett – raised by Mrs Mary Jane Barnett, Steeple Ashton, on her wedding day with a pip from a Lane's Prince Albert tree growing next to Lady Sudeley. Dual purpose apple with a savoury, brisk flavour; crisp and juicy. Roundway Magnum Bonum – a valuable and distinctive fruit. Raised by Mr Joy, gardener at Roundway Park, near Devizes. First documented 1864. Delicious pear-like flavour. Very sweet, a little juicy. Yellow-green flushed with crimson.

WORCESTERSHIRE: *apples* – Betty Geeson, Colwall Quoining, Dick's Favourite, Edward VII, Gladstone – a chance seedling originating in about 1780. First called Jackman's Seedling and re-named after the Prime Minister. Introduced by Mr Jackson of Blakedown Nursery, Kidderminster. A deep red apple on pale yellowish-green. Flesh sweet and juicy, white, tinged with green. Best eaten when picked straight from the tree. Green Purnell, Hope Cottage Seedling, King Charles' Pearmain, Lord Hindlip, May Queen, Pitmaston Nonpareil, Pitmaston Pineapple – with its distinctive pineapple flavour, thought to have derived from Golden Pippin raised either at Witley by Mr White in about 1785 or by John Williams of Pitmaston in 1825. Sandlin Duchess, Whiting Pippin, William Crump, Worcester Pearmain – a popular variety. Thought to have originated at Swan Pool near Worcester in about 1870. Raised by Mr Hale from a pip taken from a Devonshire Quarrenden and introduced by Messrs Smith of Worcester in 1873. Very sweet and juicy, crisp, attractive fruit with a red skin and white flesh, with a hint of strawberry. A good apple for sorbets; *plums* – Evesham Wonder, Pershore Yellow Egg, Purple Pershore; *pears* - Black Worcester – a hard culinary pear featured on the crest of the City and the County Cricket Club. Pitmaston Duchess; *perry pears* – Judge Amphlett, Rock.

YORKSHIRE: *apples* – Acklam Russet, Cockpit, Fillingham Pippin, Flowery Town, French Crab, Green Balsam, Greenups Pippin, Hunt House, Nursery Asses, Ribston Pippin – boasts the highest vitamin C content of any apple. Discovered in the gardens at Ribston Hall near Knaresborough, thought to have grown from a pip from Rouen and planted in about 1707. One of the most richly-flavoured apples. Crisp, juicy and aromatic. Olive-green, flushed with orange-brown & striped with scarlet. Sharleston Pippin, Syke House Russet (English Hospital Reinette), Yorkshire Greening (Yorkshire Goose Sauce); *culinary pear* – Hessle; *plums* – Winesour, Wyedale.

WALES: *apples* – Baker's Delicious – one of the most delicious of the early apples. Found in Wales and introduced by Bakers of Codsall, Wolverhampton in 1932. Firm, crisp, juicy. Yellow flushed with bright red. Breakwell's Seedling (Monmouthshire), Cummy Norman (Radnorshire), Frederick (Monmouthshire), Monmouthshire Beauty (Monmouthshire), St Cecilia (Monmouthshire); *plum* – Cox's Emperor.

SCOTLAND: *apples* – Arbroath Pippin (Angus), Beauty of Moray, Bloody Ploughman (Perthshire), Cambusnethan Pippin (Lanarkshire), Coul Blush (Ross & Cromarty), Cutler Grieve (Midlothian), Early Julyan, Galloway Pippin, Green Kilpandy Pippin, Hawthornden (Midlothian), James Grieve (Midlothian) – one of the best mid-season apples. Raised by James Grieve in Edinburgh around 1890 with Pott's Seedling as one of its parents. Commercially cultivated by Dickson's nurseries – his employers. Excellent, refreshing flavour – sweet with a nice acid balance. Soft and very juicy. Cooks well too. Very greasy skin. Bright yellow-green, speckled and striped with orange-red. Prefers the north. Lady of the Lake, Lady of Wemyss (Fife), Lass O'Gowrie (Perthshire), Lord Rosebery, Oslin (Angus), Pine Golden Pippin (Roxburghshire), Port Allen Russet, Scotch Bridget, Seaton House (Angus), Stirling Castle – raised by John Christie, nurseryman in Causewayhead. Excellent cooker for September. Tender, acid, juicy. Bright yellowish-green flushed with red. Stobo Castle (Perthshire), Thorle Pippin, Tower of Glamis (Angus) – origin uncertain. Known before 1800. Widely planted in the Carse of Gowrie and Clydesdale. Crisp, juicy firm flesh and distinctive perfume. Bright green, ripening to sulphur yellow. White Melrose (Roxburghshire); *pears* – Ayrshire Lass, Craig's Favourite, Green Pear of Yair; *plums* – Guthrie's Green Gage (Dundee), Lawson's Golden (Perthshire) Tay Bank (Dundee).

IRELAND: *apples* - Ard Cairn Russett, Ballorina Pippin, Ballyfatten, Barnhill Pippin, Bloody Butcher, Brown Crofton, Clearheart, Dockney, Dunkitt, Ecklinville Seedling – believed to be raised by Mr Logan, gardener at Ecklinville, Portaferry, near Belfast about 1800. Esteemed by the Victorians as an excellent apple for sauce as it cooks to a well flavoured soft juicy purée. Widely grown in gardens. Farrell, Gibbon's Russet, Gibby's Apple, Greasy Pippin, Green Chisel, Honey Ball, Irish Peach – possibly arose in Sligo in the early 19th century. An early apple which ideally should be eaten straight from the tree. Rich balanced flavour with a slightly perfumed, juicy flesh. Popular variety with the Victorians and Edwardians as it 'formed a beautiful dish for dessert'. Keegan's Crab, Kemp, Kerry Pippin, Martin's Seedling, Reid's Seedling, Ross Nonpareil, Sam Young, Sovereign, Striped Brandy, Striped Sax, Strippy, Summer John, Thompson's Apple, Tommy, Valentine, White Russett, Widow's Friend.

Picking up the knowledge

Horticultural courses

Brogdale Horticultural Trust, Brogdale Road, Faversham, Kent ME13 8XZ (01795 535286). Seasonal short courses and open days.

British Trust for Conservation Volunteers, 36 St Mary's Street, Wallingford, Oxfordshire OX10 0EU (01491 839766). Residential short courses and working holidays on orchard restoration in England and Hungary.

Royal Horticultural Society, PO Box 313, 80 Vincent Square, London SW1P 9PE (020 7834 4333). Seasonal short courses at associated gardens such as Wisley in Surrey or Harlow Carr in Yorkshire.

Field Studies Council, Slapton Ley, Slapton, Kingsbridge, Devon TQ7 2QP (01548 580466). Winter weekend residential course on orchard restoration.

Ragman's Lane Farm, Lower Lydbrook, Gloucestershire GL17 9PA. Residential short courses on cider and apple-juice pressing.

Pershore College, Avonbank, Pershore, Worcestershire WR10 3JP, *Cannington College*, Cannington, Bridgwater, Somerset TA5 2LS and *Kingston Maurwood College*, Dorchester, Dorset DT2 8PY offer formal training for horticultural qualifications.

More details are available from the *Institute of Horticulture*, 14-15 Belgrave Square, London SW1X 8PS.

The National Trust offers Modern Apprenticeships in gardening. Contact The National Trust, 36 Queen Anne's Gate, London SW1H 9AS (020 7222 9251).

The Workers' Educational Association can help to set up tailor-made courses from animation to zoology. Most counties have a county secretary who can offer more information. WEA Head Office, Temple House, 17 Victoria Park Square, London E2 9PB (020 8983 1515).

The Federation of City Farms and Community Gardens has affiliated gardens and farms in many towns and cities. Ask at your local farm or garden for details of setting up orchard training days, perhaps as part of Apple Day. FCF&CG Head Office, The Greenhouse, Hereford Street, Bedminster, Bristol BS3 4NA (0117 923 1800).

Who can help?

Across Britain and Ireland, hundreds people have come together to care for, protect, value, identify and enjoy local orchards and their associated fruit. Some groups are nurturing a county collection of fruit and may be able to offer courses. Here is a list, current at time of writing, of the county- or district-wide groups we know, as well as national Irish and Welsh contacts. Ask them for expert or in-depth local knowledge, or details of active parish groups or individuals. Some of the local authorities offer grants and advice.

Armagh Orchards Trust – Peader MacNiece, 65 Ardress Road, Portadown BT62 1SQ (01762 851381/852224 Fax)

Cheshire Orchards Project – John Gittins, Cheshire Landscape Trust, Fountains Buildings, Upper Northgate Street, Chester CH1 4EF (01244 376333, email: cheshire@landscapetrust.fastnet.co.uk)

Cornwall Orchards Project – Colin Hawke, Planning Directorate, Cornwall County Council, County Hall, Truro TR1 3AY (01872 322642, email:countryside@planning.cornwall.gov.uk)

Tamar Valley Orchard Volunteers – Sheila Camplin and Caroline Vulliamy, The Stoke Climsland Resource Centre, The Old School, Stoke Climsland, Callington, Cornwall PL17 8NY (01579 370493, http://web.ukonline.co.uk/sc-old-school/)

Cumbria Apple Forum – Phil Bradley, East Cumbria Countryside Project, 2c, The Old Mill, Warwick Bridge, Carlisle (01228 561601)

Westmorland Damson Association – Peter Cartmell, The Old Vicarage, Crosthwaite, Kendal, Cumbria LA8 8BP (015395 68246)

Devon Orchards Liaison Group – c/o Michael Gee, Dartington North Devon Trust, 4 Taw Vale, Barnstaple EX32 8NJ (01271 376365)

South Hams Orchard Link – Trudy Turrell, Environment Service, South Hams District Council, Follaton House, Plymouth Road, Totnes TQ9 5NE (01803 861140)

Essex Orchards Forum – Jenny Bowen, English Nature, Harbour House, Hythe Quay, Colchester, CO2 8JF (01206 796666)

Gloucestershire Orchards Project – Richard Fawcett, Senior Landscape Officer, Gloucestershire County Council, Shire Hall, Gloucester GL1 2TH (01452 425679)

Herefordshire – Fiona Lickorish/James Bisset, Herefordshire Council, Queenswood Country Park, Dinmore Hill, Leominster HR6 0PY (01568 797305)

Sth Border Counties England/Wales – Sheila Leitch, Marcher Apple Network, Wye View, Glasbury-on-Wye, Hereford HR3 5NU (01497 847354)

Hertfordshire Orchards Initiative – David Curry, 52 High Oaks, St Albans AL3 6DN (www.destiny.to/orchard, email:dscurry@netlineuk.net)

Irish Seed Savers Association – Anita Hayes, Irish Seed Savers Association, Caparroe, Scariff, Co Clare

Kentish Cobnuts Association – John Cannon, Clakkers House, Crouch, Borough Green, Kent TN15 8PY

East Kent – Jon Shelton, Kentish Stour Countryside Project, Sidelands Farm, Wye, Ashford, Kent (01233 813307)

Lincolnshire Apple Collection – The Curator, Museum of Lincolnshire Life, Burton Road, Lincoln LN1 3LY

Manchester Urban Orchards Project – The Community Projects Team, Community Technical Aid Centre, 3 Stevenson Square, Manchester M1 1DN (0161 236 5195)

Norfolk Apples and Orchards Project – Clare Stimson, Norfolk Rural Life Museum, Beech House, Gressenhall, Dereham, Norfolk NR20 4DR (01362 860563)

Central Scotland Orchards Survey – Catherine Lloyd, Greenbank House, West End, Abernethy PH2 9JL

Galloway Orchards Project – Keith Mothersson, 53 Victoria Street, Kirkpatrick Durham, Galloway DG7 3HQ

Shropshire Apple Trust – Michael Pooley, 1 Cherry Tree Hill, Coalbrookdale, Telford, Shropshire TF8 7EQ (01952 433229)

Somerset Orchards – Phil Stone/Katy Binding, Environment Dept., Somerset County Council, County Hall, Taunton TA1 4DY (01823 355617)

Bath and North East Somerset – Kären Renshaw, Ecologist, B&NES Council, Trimbridge House, Trim Street, Bath BA1 2DP

North Somerset Orchards Project – Sue Grant, Redcliff House, Brinsea Batch, Congresbury, Bristol BS49 5JP

Staffordshire Orchards Initaitive – Mike Deegan, Staffordshire Wildlife Trust, Coutts House, Sandon, Stafford ST18 0DN (01889 508534)

Wales – Hilary Miller, Forestry Policy Officer, Countryside Council for Wales, Plas Penrhos, Fordd Penrhos, Bangor, Gwynedd LL57 2LQ (01248 385648)

West Sussex (Chichester District) – Geoff Kavangh, Chichester District Council, East Pallant, Chichester PO19 1TY (01243 785166 x4399)

Worcestershire Traditional Orchards Forum – Stewart Rampling, Countryside Consultants, 1 Poole Cottage, Huddington, Droitwich WR9 7LJ

Yorkshire and Northern English Counties – Trevor Rogers, Northern Fruit Group, c/o Harlow Carr Botanical Gardens, Crag Lane, Harrogate, North Yorks HG3 1QB

Useful organisations

British Beekeepers Association, National Agricultural Centre, Stoneleigh Park, Stoneleigh, Warwickshire, CV8 2LZ (024 7669 6679)

British Independent Fruit Growers Association, Chittenden Orchards, Staplehurst, Tonbridge, Kent, TN12 0EX (01580 891756)

Butterfly Conservation, PO Box 222, Dedham, Essex, CO7 6EY (01206 322342)

Common Ground, www.commonground.org.uk

Council for the Protection of Rural England (CPRE), Warwick House, 25 Buckingham Palace Road, London, SW1W 0PP (020 7976 6433)

Countryside Agency, John Dower House, Crescent Place, Cheltenham, Gloucestershire, GL50 3RA (01242 521381. www.countryside.gov.uk)

Department for the Environment, Transport and the Regions, Eland House, Bressenden Place, London, SW1E 5DU (020 7890 3000. www.detr.gov.uk)

English Nature, Northminster House, Peterborough, PE1 1UA (01733 455000. www.english-nature.org.uk)

Farm Retail Association, PO Box 575, Southampton, SO15 7ZB (023 8036 2150)

Farming and Wildlife Advisory Group (FWAG), National Agricultural Centre, Stoneleigh Park, Stoneleigh, Warwickshire, CV8 2LZ (024 7669 6699)

Groundwork Foundation, 85/87 Cornwall St, Birmingham, B3 3BY (0121 236 8565)

Henry Doubleday Research Association, Ryton Organic Gardens, Ryton on Dunsmore, Coventry, CV8 3LG (024 7630 3517)

Learning Through Landscapes, Third Floor, Southside Offices, The Law Courts, Winchester, Hampshire, SO23 9DL (01962 846258)

National Association of Farmers' Markets, South Vaults, Green Park Station, Green Park Road, Bath, BA1 1JB (01225 787914, www.farmersmarkets.net)

National Farmers Union, Agriculture House, 164 Shaftesbury Avenue, London, WC2H 8HL (020 7331 7200)

National Federation of Women's Institutes, 104 New Kings Road, London, SW6 4LY (020 7371 9300)

The National Forest, Bath Lane, Moira, Swadlincote, Derbyshire, DE12 6BD (01283 551211)

People's Trust for Endangered Species, 15 Cloisters House, 8 Battersea Park Rd, London, SW8 4BG (020 7498 4533)

Permaculture Association, BCM Permaculture Association, London, WC1N 3XX (07041 390170, www.permaculture.org.uk)

Royal Society for the Protection of Birds, The Lodge, Sandy, Bedfordshire, SG19 2DL (01767 680551)

Soil Association, Bristol House, 40-56 Victoria St, Bristol, BS1 6BY (0117 929 0661)

Sustain, 94 White Lion St, London, N1 9PF (020 7837 1228)

The Tree Council, 51 Catherine Place, London, SW1E 6DY (020 7828 9060)

Thrive (formerly Horticultural Therapy), The Geoffrey Udall Centre, Beech Hill, Reading, RG7 2AT (0118 988 5688)

The Wildlife Trusts, The Kiln, Waterside, Mather Road, Newark, Nottinghamshire, NG24 1WT (01636 677711)

The Woodland Trust, Autumn Park, Dysart Rd, Grantham, Lincolnshire, NG31 6LL (01476 581111)

Paying for it

The grant giving arena is always changing so here we refer to long standing sources and offer suggestions for reading.

Countryside Stewardship Grants: In the early 1990s Common Ground was instrumental in persuading the Countryside Commission to include the restoration and maintenance of old orchards in their Countryside Stewardship grants covering Historic Landscapes. The scheme continues, although it is now administered by the Ministry of Agriculture (MAFF). The great strength of Stewardship grants lies in their duration – they cover a period of 10 years. Payments are made by orchard area (minimum area is a quarter of a hectare) and per tree for elements such as tree guards or pruning. A management plan must be compiled for the orchard and agreed by local staff of the Farming and Rural Conservation Agency (FRCA). Some administrative areas of the country don't include orchards in the Stewardship targets at all, while others, such as Kent, claim to have supported 1,000 hectares of old orchards in that county. The guidelines applied to orchard maintenance are standardised and so erode rather than celebrate local distinctiveness. Nor is local wisdom always upheld. It may be necessary to negotiate gently but firmly with FRCA officers to make local practice and your own priorities heard. For more details call the MAFF Helpline on 0645 335577.

Local Heritage Initiative (LHI): This grant, administered by the Countryside Agency for the Heritage Lottery, was launched in 2000 and encourages people to explore, celebrate and stand up for the small details of a place that makes it special. If this sounds familiar, then find further heart in the fact that orchards are included as an example within the Natural Heritage section. Generous grants of between £3,000-£15,000 are available to cover 60 per cent of project costs. The outstanding 40 per cent may be measured in terms of in-kind help and local voluntary labour, which could be a great leg-up for those planning for a Community Orchard. For more details contact LHI Information, The Acorn Centre, 51 High Street, Grimethorpe, Barnsley S72 7BB.

Local Nature Reserve Grants: English Nature (EN) offer grants for groups actively involved in nature conservation. A new grant was piloted in 1999 providing £250-£5,000 for works in Local Nature Reserves. Simon Richardson, the Leader of EN's Kent team, has written an Orchards Advice Note for (and available from) Common Ground called *Community Orchards as Nature Reserves*. Grants are awarded from relevant EN local offices. A list of these is available from Enquiries Service, English Nature, Northminster House, Peterborough PE1 1UA (01733 455000).

County and local grants: Once persuaded a number of local authorities have been inspired by the early steps taken by Somerset County Council in establishing a grant for local orchards. At the time of writing, grants for the restoration, maintenance or establishment of Community Orchards was available from the following county councils: Somerset, Cornwall, Herefordshire, Gloucestershire, Worcestershire, Shropshire and Kent. District councils include Chichester and Tewkesbury. Devon had a grant but this was axed during major budget cuts in 1995. There may be possibilities to revive it in future.

There are a variety of local grants independent of the council coffers but these are not always easy to find. A good place to start in rural areas is the local rural community council. Each county has a charitable RCC and most are associated to the national body Action with Communities in Rural England (ACRE tel: 01285 653477), based in Cirencester. RCCs administer their own grants and can offer information on other local sources. Grants may not specify orchards but may be able to support training, enterprising initiatives which envisage local fruit production and consumption, or which benefit the local community.

In towns and cities ask your borough council for details of grants. Often Local Agenda 21 Officers have small grants for community initiatives. The Hertfordshire Orchards Initiative and La Sainte Union have benefited from LA21 grants. Don't forget the Parish Council, who may have modest but flexible budgets.

Useful references

Countryside Grants for Voluntary Organisations – a Countryside Agency booklet detailing grants available and how to apply. Countryside Agency Publications Despatch Dept, 17/23 Albert Rd, Manchester, M19 2EQ.

Directory of Social Change, 24 Stephenson Way, London NW1 (020 7209 5151) – publish a wide range of books on fundraising, some of which are listed below. For a catalogue of publications available write to the above address.

Directory of Grant Making Trusts – guide to over 3,500 UK trusts published annually by the Charities Aid Foundation (CAF). At around £90 this is too expensive for most of us, however it should be available from your local library.

Directory of Smaller Grant Making Trusts – also published annually by CAF this directory covers over 1,000 smaller trusts, useful for small scale local fundraising.

The Environmental Funding Guide – a guide to grants for environmental activity covering all major sources including: the National Lottery, government, Europe, companies and charitable trusts, awards and competitions. 3rd edition by Susan Forrester & Dave Casson, Directory of Social Change, 1998, £16.95.

The Guide to Company Giving – 3rd edition, ed. John Smyth, Directory of Social Change, 2000, £25.

A Guide to the Major Trusts, vol 1 – Luke Fitzherbert, Dominic Addison & Faisel Rahman (eds), Directory of Social Change, 1999 £19.95. Covers the top 300 UK trusts giving a total of over £1000 million a year.

A Guide to the Major Trust, vol 2 – Sarah Harland, Louise Walker & Dave Casson (eds), Directory of Social Change, 1999, £19.95. Covers the next 700 trusts giving a total of around £140 million a year.

A Guide to the Major Trusts, vol 3 – Sarah Harland & Louise Walker (eds), Directory of Social Change, 2000, £17.95. Covers 400 UK trusts giving a total of over £24 million a year.

A Guide to the Local Trusts – four volumes covering Greater London, The South of England, the North of England and the Midlands, Directory of Social Change, 1999, £17.95 each volume.

National Council for Voluntary Organisations (NCVO), Regents Wharf, 8 All Saints Road, London, N1 9RL (020 7713 6161) – provide helpful books, pamphlets and advice on fundraising and organising events.

Commissioning arts for the orchard

Never settle for second best. Simple elegant objects that are well made will never go out of style. Irony soon wears thin, and your grandchildren may have to live with your commission sixty years on. In the past, local carpenters and blacksmiths were well-grounded in techniques and styles which were beautiful, functional and produced in a now impossible isolation that gave them a particular local character. Today, after at least a hundred years of mass production, a living contemporary equivalence for such skills is harder to find, and advice may be needed from the Regional Art Board or local Authority Arts Officer. These organisations are also possible sources of funding.

To find out more about how to commission work and organise performances, contact one of the ten Regional Arts Boards (RABs) in England, that produce information sheets on a wide range of different subjects including: carrying out a commission, organising an event or project, fees and payment for the visual arts, making proposals, carrying out a residency. All are available free from their shared web site (www.arts.org.uk). Your own local council Arts Development Officer, should also be able to help.

Before contacting the council or RAB, you should first draw up a preliminary outline of where, when, why and what the project or commission will be – it will help to clarify your thoughts and expectations. It is very important to consider the locally distinctive qualities of the orchard, the varieties of fruit and trees present and how this might influence what you wish to do. Do not be afraid to say what you want; while the artists are experts in their field, you are the experts on your own orchard, and commissioning an artist or crafts person is a two-way learning process.

Plan well in advance, as a sculptural commission, for example, could take over a year from conception to the final celebration of the installation with local people, friends and funders.

Look for artists, crafts people, poets and performers whose work deepens understanding about locality and responds to particular places; that creates a greater sense of community, is poetic, imaginative and aesthetically pleasing and that encourages discussion and stories. See examples of an artist's or performer's work in advance of any contract. Most regional art boards and local authorities will have a database that you can access.

Seek advice on the likely cost, including artists' and performers' time, assistants, materials, publicity and insurance.

Consult local people, landholders, and the statutory and voluntary bodies. Though time consuming, it is an excellent way of involving people and gradually introducing the idea, as well as ensuring that you gain all the necessary permissions.

Seek advice when drawing up a commission agreement or contract for services with an artist or performer. An evening's performance of poetry on Apple Day is obviously very different to commissioning a new orchard entrance gate, but both demand a professional agreement. Your RAB or local authority should help you. Do seek support in cash and kind from local companies and organisations, to put toward the commission costs. It is unlikely that any one grant or award will give you all the support you need. Support in kind should be included against expenditure in your budget.

Never be afraid to ask for help when you need it and to find your own solutions to the challenges and problems you may encounter.

Arts Boards

East Midlands Arts Board, Mountfields House, Epinal Way, Loughborough, LE11 0QE (01509 218292)

Eastern Arts Board, Cherry Hinton Hall, Cherry Hinton Road, Cambridge, CB1 8DW (01223 215355)

London Arts Board, Elme House, 133 Long Acre, London, WC2E 9AF (020 7240 1313)

North West Arts Board, Manchester House, 22 Bridge Street, Manchester, M3 3AB (0161 834 6644)

Northern Arts, 10 Osborne Terrace, Jesmond, Newcastle upon Tyne, NE2 1NZ (0191 281 6334)

South East Arts Board, Union House, Eridge Road, Tunbridge Wells, TN4 8HF (01892 507200)

South West Arts, Bradninch Place, Gandy Street, Exeter, Devon, EX4 3LS (01392 218188)

Southern Arts Board, 13 St Clement Street, Winchester, SO23 9DQ (01962 855099)

West Midlands Arts, 82 Granville Street, Birmingham, B1 2LH (0121 631 3121)

Yorkshire and Humberside Arts, 21 Bond Street, Dewsbury, West Yorkshire, WF13 1AX (01924 455555)

Arts Council for Northern Ireland, MacNiece House, 79 Molone Road, Belfast BT9 6AQ (01232 385200)

Arts Council for Wales, 9 Museum Place, Cardiff CF10 3NX (029 2037 6500)

Scottish Arts Council, 12 Manor Place, Edinburgh EH3 7DD (0131 226 6051)

Specialist nurseries

The following nurseries offer a wide range of varieties, including many from their own locality. Many are available on standard or half standard rootstocks, but as the less well known varieties may need to be grafted to order, which can take one or two years, please give sufficient notice of your planting requirements.

BRISTOL

Chew Valley Trees, Winford Road, Chew Magna, Bristol BS18 8HJ (01275 333752) – *10 varieties of apples on various rootstocks plus cider apples, pears, plums, cherries.*

BUCKINGHAMSHIRE

Bernwode Plants, Kingswood Lane, Ludgershall HP18 9RB (01844 237415 or 01844 238920 fax, www.bernwodeplants.co.uk) – *more than 150 varieties of apples on various rootstocks, plus pears, plums, cherries and grape vines.*

Buckingham Nurseries & Garden Centre, Tingewick Rd, Buckingham MK18 4AE (01280 813556) – *23 varieties of apple, field grown, available.*

CHESHIRE

Tony Gentil, Briarfields, Whitchurch Road, Aston, Nantwich, Cheshire, CW5 8DJ (01270 780828, email: gentil@gentil.screaming.net) – *many varieties of apples and other fruits including several from Cheshire.*

CORNWALL

Cornish Garden Nurseries, Perranarwothal, Truro, (01872 864380) – *over 50 varieties of apples including many from the west country plus pears, plums, etc. available as maidens and two year old trees.*

Duchy of Cornwall Nurseries, Penlyne, Cott Rd, Lostwithiel, PL22 0BW (01208 872668) – *20 varieties of mainly Cornish and west country apples sold as maidens.*

James MacFarlane, Trevothen Common, Coverack, Helston, TR12 6SD (01326 280594) – *particularly specialises in Cornish varieties of apples.*

DEVON

St Bridget Nurseries Ltd, Main Garden Centre, Old Rydon Lane, Exeter EX2 7JY (01392 873672) – *24 varieties of apple plus pears, cherries, plums.*

Sampford Shrubs, Sampford Peverell, Tiverton EX16 7EW (01884 821164) – *selection of top fruit particularly quinces, medlars and pears.*

Thornhayes Nursery, St Andrews Wood, Dulford, Cullompton EX15 2DF (01884 266746, www.thornhayes-nursery.co.uk) – *over 200 varieties of apple including many local types, 70 cider varieties, 30 plum, 30 pear including perry, Devon specials incl. mazzards and Tamar Valley cherries. Also offer design and advisory service.*

GLOUCESTERSHIRE

Highfield Nurseries, Whitminster, Gloucester GL2 7PL (01452 741444) – *over 30 varieties of apple, some on standard rootstocks plus family trees, pears and soft fruit.*

HAMPSHIRE

Blackmoor Wholesale Fruit Nurseries, Blackmoor, Liss GU33 6BS (01420 473576) – *75 varieties of apple (largest tree half standard) plus crab, pear, plums, cherries, nuts and soft fruit.*

Philip House, Family Trees (01329 834812) – *72 varieties of apple, 30 pears plus plums, cherries and more; also offer grafting service.*

HEREFORDSHIRE

H P Bulmer Ltd. The Cider Mills, Plough Lane, Hereford HR4 0LE (01432 352000) – *25 varieties of cider and culinary apples and perry pears. Standard, half-standard and bush.*

Paul Jasper, The Lighthouse, Bridge Street, Leominster HR6 8DU (01568 616499 fax) – *over 100 varieties of apple plus pears, plums, grapes, cherries and damsons, all bareroot.*

ISLE OF WIGHT

Deacon's Nursery, Godshill P038 3HW (01983 840750/522243) – *over 200 varieties of apple including several Scottish varieties plus some cider, pears, plums, cherries and more. Grafting stock available.*

KENT

Brogdale Orchards Ltd, Brogdale Rd, Faversham ME13 8XZ (01795 535286) – *more than 2,000 varieties of apple plus pear, cherry, plum are grown in the collection most of these can be obtained as bare root trees. Also run graft while-u-wait (March) and bud while-u-wait (August) events from stock grown at farm and will bud or graft from your own trees.*

Tim Ingram, Copton Ash Gardens, 105 Ashford Rd, Faversham ME13 8XW (01795 535919) – *77 varieties of apple, standard trees can be grafted to order plus crab, pear, plums, cherries, nuts and soft fruit.*

The Fruit Garden, Mulberry Farm, Woodnesborough, Sandwich CT13 OPT (01304 813454) – *75 varieties of apple plus pears, plums, etc. tree production fully sustainable, rotation with grazed grass leys, can bud named varieties to order.*

Keepers Nursery, Gallants Court, East Farleigh, Maidstone ME15 0LE (01622 726465, www.fruittree.co.uk) – *400 varieties of apple, 80 plus pears, plums, cherries and other fruits; also grafting and budding service.*

NORFOLK

Chris Bowers & Sons, Whispering Trees Nurseries, Wimbotsham PE34 8QB (01366 388752) – *170 varieties of apple on various rootstocks plus, pears, cider apples, plums, nuts.*

Ranworth Trees, Woodbastwick Rd, Ranworth, Norwich NR13 4SZ (01603 270755) – *full range of top fruit including 120 apples mainly Norfolk varieties, all maidens.*

SOMERSET

Cider Apple Trees, 12 Tallowood, Shepton Mallet BA4 5QN (01749 343368) – *more than 30 varieties of dessert and culinary apples and 30 varieties of cider apples available as standard or half standard trees.*

Scotts Nurseries (Merriott) Ltd, Merriott TA16 5PL (01460 72306) – *more than 200 varieties of apple including cider apples and perry pears plus plums, pears, etc.*

WORCESTERSHIRE

Frank P Matthews Ltd, Berrington Court, Tenbury Wells WR15 8TH (01584 810214) – *60 varieties of apple plus extensive range of graft wood available.*

YORKSHIRE

R V Roger Ltd, The Nurseries, Pickering Y018 7HG (01751 472226) – *44 varieties of apple plus pears, plums, cherries, nuts and soft fruit, also rootstock, grafting scions and budding eyes.*

SCOTLAND

Butterworth's Organic Nursery, Garden Cottage, Auchinleck Estate, Cumnock, Ayrshire, KA18 2LR (01290 551088) – *more than 50 varieties of apples many originating in Scotland, plus plums and pears.*

J Tweedie Fruit Trees, Maryfield Road Nursery, Maryfield, Nr Terregles, Dumfries DG2 9TH (01387 720880) – *96 varieties of apple plus pears, plums, cherries.*

IRELAND

Irish Seed Saver Association, Capparoe, Scariff, County Clare – *38 Irish apple varieties and a few from England. Also stock Irish vegetable and other seeds, such as beans, kale, herbs and flowers.*

Suppliers of fruit

The following list gives details of fruit farms, growers and suppliers who grow several varieties of apples. Some produce mail order boxes and may be able to provide Apple Day Gift Packs. Please remember that those offering a mail order service need to be given as much notice as possible of your requirements so do place your order early. Remember also that the varieties you request may not always be available, due to the vagaries of the season, but most growers will replace them with something equally interesting.

BEDFORDSHIRE

Philip Worthington, Sheephill Orchard, Kiln Lane, Clophill, MK45 4DA – *a range of varieties grown and sold from the farm shop.*

BERKSHIRE

Gillian Franklin, Cross Lanes Fruit Farm, Mapledurham, Reading RG4 7UW (0118 972 3167) – *45 varieties of apples plus plums and pears grown and sold from farm shop.*

BUCKINGHAMSHIRE

Pat & Peter Hinde, Home Cottage Farm, Bangors Road South, Iver SL0 0BB (01753 653064) – *13 varieties of apples, plus pears, plums and soft fruit, sold through farm shop and pick your own.*

DORSET

Caroline Jackson, Elwell Fruit Farm, Waytown, Bridport DT6 5LF (01308 488283) – *15 varieties of apples and pears, plus apple juice, available from farm shop and pick your own.*

ESSEX

Crapes Fruit Farm, Rectory Rd, Aldham, Colchester C06 3RR (01206 212375) – *over 150 varieties of apple grown, available in mixed seasonal 7lb, 8lb, 13lb or 20lb boxes by mail order or from the farm shop. Some plums, cherries, pears and quince, also honey from orchard bees. Apple Day selections.*

Philip Taylor, Lathcoats Farm, Beehive Lane, Galleywood, Chelmsford CM2 8LX (01245 266691) – *25 varieties of apple plus 12 single variety juices available from farm shop.*

KENT

Brogdale Horticultural Trust, Brogdale Farm, Brogdale Road, Faversham ME13 8XZ (01795 535286) – *hundreds of varieties of apples, plums, pears, cherries, quince, medlar and soft fruit along with apple juices available in season from the Trust's shop.*

Perry Court, Bilting, Ashford TN25 4ES (01233 812408) – *over 100 varieties of apples and 10 pears grown, available from farm shop and at many local farmers markets, ring for details.*

Pippins Farm, Stonecourt Lane, Pembury, Tunbridge Wells TN2 4AB (01892 824544) – *30 varieties of apples available from the farm shop, can also offer boxes by mail order, ring for details.*

Nick Chard, Sepham Farm, Otford (01959 522774) – *18 varieties of apple grown for sale in farm shop.*

David H S Simmons, Whitehill House, Whitehill, Faversham ME13 0DN (01795 532100) – *no farm shop or pick your own, but happy to sell direct also presentation packs of around 7lbs of apples delivered by post anywhere (at a price!).*

LONDON

The Fresh Food Co., 341a Ladbroke Grove W10 6HA (020 8969 0351, email: toby.young@freshfood.co.uk) – *home delivery of seasonal fruit from organic and biodynamic growers, 20lb of 3-4 varieties.*

OXFORDSHIRE

Waterperry Gardens, Waterperry, nr Wheatley (01844 339254) – *range of varieties of apples, pears, plums, cherries and peaches grown and sold single variety juice and trees also available.*

SOMERSET

Charlton Orchards, Charlton Rd, Creech St Michael, Taunton TA3 5PF (01823 412979) – *wide range of seasonal apple varieties plus 14 single variety apple juices, available from farm shop, local farmers markets or by mail order.*

Stawell Fruit Farm, Stawell, Bridgwater TA7 9AE (01278 722732) – *more than 30 varieties of apple available as they ripen from PYO and farm shop, also have packs/boxes of 6, 10, 15, 20, 30 and 40lbs, apples can be individually wrapped or available loose, cell or traypacked. May be able to supply by mail order also press their own juice.*

West Bradley Orchards, Glastonbury BA6 8LT (01458 850227) – *17 dessert varieties available from farm shop, PYO on three weekends in September and presentation boxes available around Christmas ranging from 6 lb to 10 lb, plus a standard 20lb box.*

SUSSEX

English Farm Cider Centre, Middle Farm, Firle, Lewes (01323 811303/411) – *wide range of varieties on sale in Middle Farm shop and offer occasional presentation packs of apples, but don't operate a mail order system.*

Laurel Tree Fruit Farms, Boar's Head, Crowborough, TN6 3HD (01892 661637) – *range of varieties, including the Cherry Cox which originated at the farm, available direct, also gift and Christmas packs available to order.*

Ringden Fruit Farm, Flimwell TN19 7QY (01580 879385) – *wide variety of apples sold, plus 22 varieties of apple juice.*

WARWICKSHIRE

Snitterfield Fruit Farm, Kings Lane, Snitterfield, Stratford- upon-Avon CV37 0QA (01789 731711) – *25 varieties of apple grown plus a range of other fruit. Large orders only.*

WORCESTERSHIRE

Walsgrove Farm, Egdon, Spetchley WR7 4QL (01905 345371, website - http://welcome.to/walsgrove) – *seasonal selection of the 60+ varieties of apples, plus plums, available from farm shop, also offer presentation boxes.*

WALES

Robert Peel, Berryhill Farm, Coedkernew, Newport, Gwent NP1 9UD (01633 681590) – *16 varieties of apple grown and sold through farmshop and pick your own.*

SCOTLAND

Bruce Bennet, Pillars of Hercules, Falkland, Cupar, Fife KY15 7AD – *organic fruit grower.*

Fruit Identification

Fruit Identification is one of the most popular activities offered at Apple Day events, people will queue for hours to find out the name of the delicious fruit produced by the gnarled old tree in their garden. The identification of fruit has often been the starting point for surveys or maps of fruit trees in an area.

The Royal Horticultural Society and the Brogdale Horticultural Trust both offer a fruit identification service for a small fee. To make use of these services choose 3 samples of typical mature fruit with a shoot and leaves. Don't send misshapen, damaged or poor specimens, which are difficult to name. Provide as much detail about the tree as possible, age and habit of tree, whether the fruit is dessert or culinary, or both, season of use, the locality of the tree if different from your address. If you have information on the soil type this would also be useful.

If sending fruit from more than one tree, number each sample and make a note which tree it comes from as the fruit cannot be returned. Apples and pears are best numbered gently on the fruit skin with a ballpoint pen or marker pen, don't use stick on labels as these can get lost. Try to ensure that the fruit arrives in as good condition as possible. Wrap fruit in newspaper, bubble wrap, polystyrene granules, etc. and pack in a strong box to avoid crushing. Do not use boxes that have previously contained strongly smelling products such as soap as this can mask the characteristic scent and flavour of the fruit. Samples should be sent with an s.a.e. and the appropriate fee to:

The Director of Horticulture (Fruit Naming), RHS Garden, Wisley, Woking, Surrey, GU23 6QB

Fruit Naming, Brogdale Horticultural Trust, Brogdale Road, Faversham, Kent, ME13 8XZ.

While these are excellent services, before using them it is always worthwhile finding out if there is a local expert who can help you. Horticultural societies and colleges, fruit growers and specialist nurseries may all be able to help with identification. Some groups, such as the Northern Fruit Group and the Marcher Apple Network are beginning to establish basic identification and variety computer databases.

You might like to try your hand at identifying the fruit yourself. Fruit books contain photographs, drawings and detailed descriptions of a number of varieties and may be a good starting point - but don't rely on them to contain more than a few of the many varieties.

The number of people with fruit identification skills is rapidly diminishing and it takes many years of experience to accumulate such knowledge, we therefore need to begin sharing this knowledge before it is lost. If you are interested in learning the basic skills of fruit identification contact your local experts to find out if such training is available. If not, try to persuade them that it is necessary.

Finally, remember that, in most cases, if the fruit has been grown from a pip or stone it is likely to be a completely new variety and no expert will be able to name it, instead take delight in naming the fruit yourself or simply enjoy its flavour and anonymity.

A brief history

Common Ground	Parallel Events
1987 Research for the *Trees, Woods and the Green Man* programme shows up the anomaly of lack of conservation interest in orchards as cultural landscapes or wild life habitats.	Somerset County Council explores ways of saving standard orchards as part of the Levels and Moors Scheme: grants initiated.
1988 14 September. *Save our Orchards* Campaign launched with the publication of first campaign leaflet which outlines what is happening to orchards, why they are important and what can be done to conserve them.	*The English Apple* by Rosanne Sanders published by Phaidon & RHS
1989 7 June. Publication of *In a Nutshell – A Manifesto for trees and a guide to growing and protecting them*. The book includes a chapter on growing fruit trees and community woods and orchards. Publication of *Manifesto for Trees*, a leaflet which includes a section on saving old orchards and fruit trees. 2 August. Publication of *PULP!* a 56-page one-off newspaper all about trees and woods to accompany the Common Ground/Crafts Council touring exhibition 'Out of the Wood'. Contents include 'Liquidating Apples' by Omar Sattaur, 'The Pruning of Diversity' by Neil Sinden, 'Pippins, Biffins & Codlins' by Joan Morgan, and 'Fruit Trees in Small Gardens' by Harry Baker. 28 October. *Orchards – photographs from the West Country* by James Ravilious. Launch of a Common Ground touring exhibition starting at the Royal Memorial Museum, Exeter. October. *Orchards – a guide to local conservation* published. The book contains sections on plums, apples, cobnuts, cherries and how to find and conserve local varieties of fruit with descriptions of local initiatives and photographs by James Ravilious. Contributors: Roger Deakin, Meg Game, Francesca Greenoak, Rebecca Hubbard, Joan Morgan and Neil Sinden. Photographic commission of orchards in Kent as a part of the Cross Channel Photographic Mission.	First Big Apple festival in Herefordshire. Common Ground offered advice and suggested that the festival organisers hold an Apple Roadshow. South Hams District Council in Devon starts work on Orchard Conservation.

Common Ground	Parallel Events
November. 'Under the Apple Boughs', feature by Brian Jackman on Common Ground published in *Country Living*.	

Common Ground	Parallel Events
1990	
Spring/Summer. 'The Case for Orchards', by Neil Sinden is published in *Natural World*.	Somerset County Council extends grants for orchard conservation for the Somerset Levels and Moors for the whole county.
September. 'Fruits of the Earth' by Sue Clifford in *Tree News*.	September. Marks & Spencer launch its range of 12 varieties of 'old fashioned' apples.
Save our Orchards, a 12-page campaign pamphlet including a county gazetteer of fruit varieties is published.	20 September. MAFF Fruit Trials at Brogdale reprieved – charitable trust in formation.
8 October. Exhibition of James Ravilious photographs and 100 varieties of apples comes to the Piazza at Covent Garden, London, for two weeks.	
17 October. Comments to the Minister of State, Department of the Environment, on James Batho's report on Tree Preservation Orders, making the case for wider TPO protection for non-commercial fruit trees.	
21 October. Apple Day initiated and organised by Common Ground in The Old Apple Market, Covent Garden, London.	
Apple Day poster published listing 592 varieties. Printed for Common Ground by Marks & Spencer plc.	

Common Ground	Parallel Events
1991	
25 April. Apple Day pamphlet published to help launch the idea across the country.	April. South Hams District Council publishes the booklet *Saving our Orchards – a practical guide to managing and caring for traditional orchards in the South Hams*.
24 June. Meeting with the Countryside Commission about orchard conservation.	17 April. Brogdale Horticultural Trust opens to the public.
15 October. *The Apple Source Book* launched at Smith's, Covent Garden, with Tony Baldry MP, Parliamentary Under Secretary of State for the Environment and Michael Barry, BBC TV Food and Drink programme.	4 May. *Save our Orchards Campaign* started in north Devon by the Dartington North Devon Trust.
21 October. Apple Day first launched countrywide, with more than 50 events from Truro, Cornwall to Melrose, Roxburghshire.	June. Gwent County Council gives grant aid for orchard rehabilitation.
Apple Day celebrated for the first time in the House of Commons with MPs devouring almost one tonne of English apples.	August. Council for the Protection of Rural England argues for traditional orchard conservation in *Saw Points*.
Sainsbury's celebrates Apple Day by featuring a selection of English apples with the Apple Day logo.	Sainsbury's stock 20 traditional apple varieties.
November. *Apple Day News* (1) – a resume of events around the country.	22 August. Kentish Cobnuts Ltd, Britain's first ever co-operative of cobnut growers, is launched.
	September. Marks & Spencer increase the number of 'Old Fashioned Apples' stocked to 18.

Common Ground	Parallel Events
	2 October. Safeway celebrates the apple season with 53 varieties.
	21 October. Somerset Cider Brandy Company launches Somerset Royal Cider Brandy.
	December. *Devon Orchards Initiative* discussion document, published by Devon County Council.
1992 February. *Apple Day News* (2) published 5 June. Presentation to and joint meeting with the Countryside Commission and nine county councils about orchard conservation. 26 June. *Community Orchards* pamphlet published. July. *Save our Orchards* displays including photographs by James Ravilious and text by Common Ground produced for hire. 21 October. Apple Day. More than 80 events countrywide. Creation of new Community Orchard at Colnbrook, Surrey, to commemorate the Cox's Orange Pippin and Richard Cox who 'created' this apple and installation of three metal seats by Richard Farrington in the shape of the letters COX. North Yorkshire County Caterers take Apple Day to the 300+ schools which they serve. The first of many local authority caterers to use Apple Day to encourage healthy eating among schoolchildren. Forty Groundwork Trusts celebrate Apple Day by creating 63 Community Orchards. The New National Forest plants a Community Orchard within a hospital.	6 January. Prime Minister John Major MP makes a speech on the value of traditional varieties of British apples. January. Kent Orchards Liaison Group's first meeting. May. Devon County Council launches the Devon Orchards Initiative. Cornwall County Council starts Orchard Campaign. June. Countryside Commission extends grant aid to old orchards through the Countryside Stewardship Scheme. 2 August. Safeway promises a range of 53 varieties of apple on sale this season. October. Julian Temperley, Somerset Cider Brandy Company, purchases a 28-hectare cider apple orchard at Over Stratton in Somerset, the largest single standard orchard in the country. October. Perry pear orchard in Combe Florey, Somerset, the largest in Britain, is felled with all its pears.
1993 4 February. *Apple Day News* (3) 7 June. *The Cox's Orange Pippin Community Orchard for Colnbrook* leaflet published. September. *Apple Day News* (4) 13 September. *The Common Ground Apple Map* published. 21 October. Apple Day. More than 100 events countrywide from Cornwall to Stirling, Cardiff to Norfolk. Publication of new Apple Day leaflet, flyers and stickers.	1 October. Safeway produces a leaflet to promote Apple Day in their stores. 21 October. Publication of *The Book of Apples* by Joan Morgan and Alison Richards, Ebury Press.

Common Ground	Parallel Events
1994	Safeway create special apple shaped biscuits for Apple Day.
February. *Apple Day News* (5).	Jacobs Cream Crackers link local apples with cheese and run a competition for Apple Day.
Summer. *The Apple Broadcast*, a unique 16-page newspaper all about orchards published.	Somerset County Council produce the *Orchard Video*.
September. *Apple Day News* (6).	BSBI/Plantlife launch the National Mistletoe Survey.
October. *Apple Games and Customs* published by Common Ground. Sculptor Jim Partridge commissioned to make a game board for Apple Tree Man game played with apples. Fruit growers and sellers encouraged to promote the tradition of Apple Gifting for Apple Day. Two art colleges set their students the task of designing packaging for apple gift boxes.	
21 October. Apple Day. 150 events including one in France and one in Holland.	
1995	Cheshire Orchards Project, a joint venture by the WI, Wildlife Trust and Cheshire Landscape Trust, launched. Their book *Orchards of Cheshire* published.
February. *Apple Day News* (7).	European Union announce further grubbing grants for orchards under 20 years old.
August. *Apple Day News* (8) including the launch of Orchard Observances a year-long survey of the wild life found in orchards.	CAMRA sets up APPLE, its cider committee, and publishes *Cider Press*, an insert in its *What's Brewing* newspaper.
Common Ground win a Special Glenfiddich Award for work on promoting apples and orchards. Other special award winner is Delia Smith.	*Burcombes, Queenies and Colloggetts* by Virginia Spiers with illustrations by Mary Martin published, describing the orchards of the Tamar Valley in Cornwall.
21 October. Apple Day 160 events countrywide. Common Ground and CPRE issue a joint press release and report on the plight of orchards in the landscape.	Countryside Council for Wales publishes the booklet *Traditional Orchards*.
	Orchards our Native Bounty published by the Arnside & Silverdale AONB.
	June Small of Charlton Orchards creates the *Apple Map of Somerset* and begins research on a list of apples originating in the county.
1996	New Road Cyderists win Henry Ford Conservation Award (Heritage). *Apples, Berkshire, Cider...* by Duncan Mackay of New Road Cyderists published.
April. *Apple Day News* (9).	Orchards included in the Biodiversity Action Plan for Kent.
September. *Apple Day News* (10).	Marcher Apple Network formed to carry out research into orchards of the Welsh Marches.
21 October. Apple Day. 160 events countrywide.	Westmorland Damson Association established.
November. Revised *Community Orchards* pamphlet published.	

Common Ground	Parallel Events
	Organic Fruit Focus Group formed by HDRA and other organic growers.
	County collections established in Hampshire, Gloucestershire, Somerset, Cheshire, Devon and Cornwall.
	Surveys of orchards begun in Cumbria, Norfolk, Yorkshire and the Scottish Borders.
	Fruits of the Forest published by the Red Rose Community Forest.
	Ripest Apples, an anthology of poetry and prose on apples and orchards by Roy Palmer published and launched at the Big Apple.
	Coordination of Countryside Stewardship transferred from Countryside Commission to MAFF.
	MAFF figures for total orchard area for 1995/6 show a decline of 3,500ha from previous year.
1997	
Spring/Summer. *Apple Day News* (11).	Bath City Council holds three trial farmers' markets through September and October, one especially for Apple Day.
21 October. Apple Day 200+ events countrywide.	Cider-makers Bulmers and Matthew Clark assist farmers to plant more orchards of cider apples in Herefordshire and the south west.
Common Ground/Learning Through Landscapes launch *The School Orchard Pack.*	
	CAMRA launches the Pomona Awards for cider and perry.
	Cheshire Orchards project works with British Waterways on the planting of canalside orchards.
	The Armagh Orchards Trust begin working with Irish Seed Savers to establish a collection of Irish apple varieties.
1998	
Summer. *Orchards & Apple Day News* (12).	MAFF Central Science Laboratory publish the results of their survey on bird populations in orchards, *Bird populations in traditional and modern orchards.*
September. At last, someone to work full time on orchards – Dan Keech starts work as the first Community Orchards Officer. Funded by Department for the Environment, Transport and the Regions, the Tedworth Trust and others.	The All Party Cider Group is set up in the Houses of Parliament, headed by Paul Keetch, MP.
21 October. Apple Day. 350 events countrywide including many more farmers' markets.	22 October. Kent stops issuing licences to kill bullfinches in orchards countywide.

Common Ground	Parallel Events
Autumn. First of the series of Orchard Advice Notes published. Subjects covered: Specialist nurseries, Fruit growers, Sources of funding, Suggested reading, Useful contacts and Wassailing.	Orchards included in the Biodiversity Action Plan for Essex.

1999

Spring. *Orchard News* (1).

March. Orchard laminated panels exhibition updated with more information on Community Orchards.

April. *Orchards Slide Pack* produced.

Summer. *Save our Orchards* and *Community Orchards* pamphlets revised and reprinted.

More Orchards Advice Notes published: Plant pears for your heirs, Gazetteer of local varieties, Community Orchards as local nature reserves, Fruit identification, Arts and crafts in orchards.

September. Orchards and Wild Life conference organised jointly by Common Ground and English Nature, held in Herefordshire.

October. Common Ground website goes live with details of Apple Day events and information on the Save our Orchards and Community Orchards projects.

21 October. Tenth Apple Day celebrated with more than 600 events countrywide. James Crowden appointed the first Apple Day Poet Laureate.

November. Old Orchards in the Landscape conference, held in York. Organised by the College of Ripon and York St John, Northern Fruit Group and Common Ground.

Winter. *Orchards News* (2)

Sustain publish *The Pear Essentials* and *How Green are our Apples*.

February. Survey of orchards in the City of Worcester published by Worcester City Council.

May. Orchards included in the Biodiversity Action Plan for Worcestershire.

September. *Apples: a social history* by Sally Twiss published by the National Trust.

English Nature begins investigation into invertebrates and old orchards.

October. *Cider: the forgotten miracle* by James Crowden published.

October 21. Devon County Council launch *Orchards – a practical guide for management*.

November. Centenary Fields in Surrey containing a Community Orchard, declared a Local Nature Reserve.

Funding for Countryside Stewardship grants increased by £1 million.

Woodland Trust agree to consider the purchase of old orchards as part of its reserve portfolio.

National Trust restoring and planting more orchards on their properties.

Orchards can be included in Local Nature Reserves designations.

The National Forest launches its Orchards Campaign to support Community Orchards old and new in the forest area.

Hertfordshire Orchards Initiative launched.

Worcestershire Traditional Orchards Forum established.

Chichester District Council offer grants for orchard conservation and planting in their West Sussex area.

Tewkesbury District Council institute Environmental Improvement Grants which include funding for orchards.

Orchard training days being organised by Field Studies Council, British Trust

Common Ground	Parallel Events
	for Conservation Volunteers, Federation of City Farms and Community Gardens, Workers Educational Association in addition to those already run by the Brogdale Horticultural Trust and Royal Horticultural Society.

Common Ground	Parallel Events
2000	
Spring. *Orchard News* (3).	February. Local Heritage Initiatives launched. National grant scheme which includes orchards in the Natural Heritage section.
Spring. Orchards Advice Notes published on: Small-scale juicing, Small-scale cider-making, Infant fruit tree care, Orchard groups by county and Apple Day ideas.	April. Orchards included in the Biodiversity Action Plan for Gloucestershire.
April. Common Ground nominated by listeners and reach the finals of the BBC Radio 4 Food Programme Awards in the Campaigner/Educator category.	May. Orchards included in the Biodiversity Action Plan for Herefordshire.
1 May. Common Ground selected to be part of ITV's Year of Promise. 60-second film among 13 shown throughout the day.	
May. *Orchards and Wild Life Conference Report* published by Common Ground.	
June. A set of 13 apple postcards with watercolours by Charles Raymond published.	
June. Common Ground present at the Bath and West Show and plant the two millionth cider apple tree in the show ground.	
November. *The Common Ground Book of Orchards – community, conservation and culture* published by Common Ground.	

Useful publications

You may find the following publications of interest. Some may be out of print, but your local library should be able to obtain them for you:

Arbury, Jim & Pinhey, Sally – *Pears,* Wells and Winter, 1997

Atkins, David – *The Cuckoo in June: Tales of a Sussex Orchard,* Toat Press, 1992

Baker, Harry – *The Fruit Garden Displayed,* Ward Lock, 1998

Barratt, Victoria – *A Taste of Damsons,* Westmorland Damson Association, 1997

Beacham, Peter & Ravilious, James - *Down the Deep Lanes,* Devon Books, 2000

Blackburne-Maze, Peter – *The Apple Book,* Collingridge Books, 1996

Bruning, Ted – *Guide to Real Cider,* CAMRA Books, 1996

Bunker, Bob – *Farmhouse Cider and Scrumpy,* Bossiney Books, 1999

Bultitude, John – *Apples: a guide to the identification of international varieties,* Macmillan Reference Books, 1983

Bush, Raymond – *A Fruit Grower's Diary,* Faber and Faber, 1948

Bush, Raymond – *Tree Fruit Growing – I. Apples,* Penguin, 1943

Bunyard, Edward – *A Handbook of Hardy Fruits More Commonly Grown in Great Britain,* First published in two volumes 1920 &1925. Reprinted by Picton Publishing (Chippenham) Ltd, 1994

Cheshire Federation of Women's Institutes, *Orchards of Cheshire,* CFWI, 1995

Countryside Council for Wales – *Orchards and Parkland Scheme Handbook,* CCW, 1997

Countryside Council for Wales – *Traditional Orchards,* CCW, 1995

Crowden, James – *Cider: The Forgotten Miracle,* Cyder Press 2, 1999

French, Roger – *The History and Virtues of Cyder,* Robert Hale, 1982

Game, Meg – *In a Nutshell: the story of Kentish cobnuts,* Chris Howkins, 1999

Garner, Robert – *The Grafter's Handbook,* Cassell/RHS, 1988

Grigson, Jane – *Jane Grigson's Fruit Book,* Penguin, 1982

Greenoak, Francesca – *Forgotten Fruits: the English orchard and fruit garden,* Andre Deutsch, 1983

Grubb, Norman – *Cherries,* Crosby Lockwood & Son, London, 1949

Hills, Lawrence – *The Good Fruit Guide,* Henry Doubleday Research Association, 1984

Hinchcliffe, Dorothy & Colley, Dan – *Apples from Appleby,* Appleby-in-

Westmorland Society & Cumbria Countryside Forum, 1993

King, Angela & Clifford, Sue – *Holding Your Ground: an action guide to local conservation,* Wildwood House, 1985

Legg, Philippa & Binding, Hilary – *Somerset Cider: the complete story,* Somerset Books, 1998

Luckwill, L & Pollard, A, – *Perry Pears,* J W Arrowsmith Ltd, Bristol, 1963

Mabey, David – *In Search of Food: traditional eating and drinking in Britain,* Book Club Associates, 1978

Mackay, Duncan – *Apples, Berkshire, Cider: the A to Z guide to apples, apple-growing and cider-making in Berkshire,* Two Rivers Press, 1996

Merryweather, Roger – *The Bramley: a world famous cooking apple,* Newark & Sherwood District Council, 1992

Miles, Archie – *Silva: the tree in Britain,* Ebury Press, 1999

Morgan, Joan & Richards, Alison – *The Book of Apples,* Ebury Press, 1993

Newton, John – *Ground Rules: a guide to some of the legal aspects of community land ownership and management,* Rural Action, 1994

Palmer, Roy (compiler) – *Ripest Apples: an anthology of verse, prose and song,* Big Apple Association, 1996

Pillans, Craig – *Lincolnshire to the Core,* Lincolnshire County Council, 1992

Pooley, Michael & Lomax, John – *Completely Touched by Human Hand: real cidermaking on a small scale,* Smallscale Cidermakers Association, 1997

Readman, Joanna – *Fruity Stories: all about growing, storing and eating fruit,* Boxtree/Channel 4, 1996

Roach, Frederick – *The Cultivated Fruits of Britain,* Blackwell, 1985

Sanders, Rosanne – *The English Apple,* Phaidon Press, 1988

Smith, Muriel – *The National Apple Register of the United Kingdom,* Ministry of Agriculture, Fisheries and Food, 1971

Spiers, Virginia – *Burcombes, Queenies and Colloggetts: the makings of a Cornish orchard,* West Brendon, 1996

Taylor, H. – *The Apples of England,* 3rd edition, Crosby Lockwood & Son, London, 1946

Taylor, H. – *The Plums of England,* Crosby Lockwood & Son, London, 1949

Twiss, Sally – *Apples: a social history,* National Trust, 1999

Ward, Ruth – *A Harvest of Apples,* Sage Press, 1997

William-Davies, John – *Cider Making in Wales,* Welsh Folk Museum, 1984

References

Local Distinctiveness

Clifford, Susan & King, Angela - *Local Distinctiveness: place, particularity and identity*, Common Ground, 1993.

Community Orchards

Casey, Mary – From 'Not after Plutarch, Comfort Me with Apples' published in *Full Circle*, Enitharmon Press, 1981

Common Ground – *Community Orchards*, Common Ground, updated 1999

Luckwill, L. & Pollard, A (eds) – *Perry Pears*, J W Arrowsmith Ltd, Bristol, 1963

Thoreau, Henry David – *Wild Fruits*, W W Norton, 1999

Saving Orchards

Common Ground – *Orchards and Wild Life: Conference Papers*, Common Ground, 2000

Common Ground – *Save Our Orchards*, Common Ground, updated 1999

Department for the Environment Transport & the Regions – *Tree Preservation Orders: A Guide to the Law and Good Practice*, DETR, 1999

Gloucestershire County Council – *Orchards: conserve our orchards, restore our landscape*, GCC, 1998

Richardson, Simon – *Community Orchards as Local Nature Reserves*, Orchards Advice Note No. 10, Common Ground, 1999

Smith, Muriel – *The National Apple Register of the United Kingdom*, Ministry of Agriculture, Fisheries and Food, 1971

Planting New Orchards

Fairs, Chris & Moss, Ben – *Selecting and Planting Standard Trees*, Orchards Advice Note No.5, Common Ground, 1998

Hardy, Thomas – *The Woodlanders*, Penguin, 1998

Hertfordshire Orchards Initiative – *Hertfordshire Orchards Initiative*, HOI, 1998

Phelps, Humphrey – 'Plum Crazy', published in *The Countryman*, 1989

Roach, Frederick – *The Cultivated Fruits of Britain*, Blackwell, 1985

City and Country

Hinchcliffe, Dorothy & Colley, Dan – *Apples from Appleby*, Appleby-in-Westmorland Society/Cumbria Countryside Forum, 1993

Mabey, Richard – *Flora Britannica*, Sinclair Stevenson, 1995

Morgan, Joan & Richards, Alison – *The Book of Apples*, Ebury Press, 1993

Williamson, Laureen – *An Illustrated History of the Maharaja's Well*, Maharaja's Well Trust, reprinted 1993

Orchard Fruits

Arbury, Jim & Pinhey, Sally – *Pears*, Wells & Winter, 1997

Beaford Arts Centre – *Discovering Landkey: a community catalogue*, Beaford Arts Centre, 1996.

Cheshire Federation of Women's Institutes (eds) – *Orchards of Cheshire*, CFWI, 1995

Crawford, Martin – *Walnuts: production & culture*, Agroforestry Research Trust, 1996

Fletcher, Simon – *The Cherry Trees of Wyre and Other Poems*, Angria Press, 1996

Game, Meg – *In a Nutshell:the story of Kentish cobnuts*, Chris Howkins, 1999

Greenoak, Francesca – *Forgotten Fruits: the English orchard and fruit garden*, Andre Deutsch, 1983

Grigson, Jane – *Jane Grigson's Fruit Book*, Penguin, 1982

Grubb, Norman – *Cherries*, Crosby Lockwood & Son, 1949

Holmes, Jim – *Apple Man*, Rushmere Publishing, 1998

Hubbard, Rebecca – 'Cherries' from *Orchards: a guide to local conservation*, Common Ground, 1989

Forsyth, William of Kensington the Elder – *On Gathering Apples and Pears and Preserving Them*, in Hunter, H.– *Georgical Essays*, Volume 2, imprint York, printed by T. Wilson and R. Spence for the author, 1803

Juniper, Barrie – *Tracing the Origins of the Apple*, from St Catherine's College Yearbook, 1998

Luckwill, L & Pollard, A – *Perry Pears*, J.W. Arrowsmith, 1963

Pomfret, Margaret – *Stone's Orchard Croxley Green*, Croxley Green Parish Council, 1994

Spiers, Virginia – *Burcombes, Queenies & Colloggetts: the makings of a Cornish orchard*, West Brendon, 1996

Taylor, H – *The Plums of England*, Crosby Lockwood & Son, 1949

Sharing with Nature

Common Ground – *Orchards and Wild Life: Conference Papers*, Common Ground, 2000

Briggs, Jonathan – *Kissing Goodbye to Mistletoe?* Plantlife/BSBI, 1999

Gilbert, Oliver – *Lichens*, Harper Collins, 2000

Jeffries, Richard – *Wildlife in a Southern County*, 1879

Leather, Simon & Bland, Keith – *Insects on Cherry Trees*, Richmond Publishing Company, 1999

Newton, Ian – *Studies of West Palearctic Birds: 192. Bullfinch*, British Birds, December 1993

Proctor, Michael & Yeo, Peter & Lack, Andrew – *The Natural History of Pollination*, Harper Collins, 1996

Prys-Jones, Oliver & Corbet, Sarah – *Bumblebees*, Richmond Publishing Company, 1991

Inspiration

Chekhov, Anton – *The Cherry Orchard*, (translated by Michael Frayn) Methuen, 1998

Clark, Leonard – *Apple Trees* from *Selected Poems 1940-57*, Hutchinson, 1958

Dury, Ian – *Apples: The Musical*, Faber & Faber, 1989

Fletcher, Simon – *The Cherry Trees of Wyre and other Poems*, Angria Press, 1996

Hamburger, Michael – from *Late*, Anvil Press, 1997

Keesing, Richard – *The History of Newton's Apple Tree*, Contemporary Physics, 1998

Lee, Laurie – *Cider with Rosie*, Penguin, 1962

Poliakoff, Stephen – *Talk of the City*, Methuen, 1988

Shakespeare, William – *Romeo & Juliet*, Penguin, 1994

Watson, Catherine – *Full and Plenty*, Twelvetrees Publishing Company, 1987

Apple Day

Common Ground – *Apple Games & Customs*, Common Ground, 1994

Common Ground – *The Apple Source Book*, Common Ground, 1991

School Orchards Pack, Learning Through Landscapes, 1996

Palmer, Roy (compiler) – *Ripest Apples – an anthology of verse, prose and song*, Big Apple Association, 1996

Small, June – *Apple Varieties of Somerset*, Somerset County Council, 1996

Spiers, Virginia – *Burcombes, Queenies & Colloggetts: the makings of a Cornish orchard*, West Brendon, 1996

Produce

Common Ground – *The Apple Source Book*, Common Ground, 1991

Countryside Council for Wales – *Traditional Orchards*, CCW, 1995

Crowden, James – *Cider: the forgotten miracle*, Cyder Press 2, 1999

French, Roger – *The History and Virtues of Cyder*, Robert Hale, 1982

Grigson, Jane – *Jane Grigson's Fruit Book*, Penguin, 1982

Hartley, Dorothy – *The Land of England*, Macdonald, 1979

Hartley, Dorothy – *Food in England*, Futura Publications, 1985

Mabey, David – *In Search of Food: traditional eating and drinking in Britain*, Book Club Associates, 1978

Mackay, Duncan – *Apples, Berkshire, Cider: the A to Z guide to apples, apple-growing and cider-making in Berkshire*, Two Rivers Press, 1996

Mason, Laura & Brown, Catherine – *Traditional Foods of Britain*, Prospect Books, 1999

Milk Marketing Board – *The Dairy Book of British Food*, Ebury Press, 1988

Ward, Ruth – *A Harvest of Apples*, Sage Press, 1997

Passing on Knowledge

School Orchards Pack, Learning Through Landscapes, 1996

An Apple a Day

Brewer, Ebenezer - *Brewer's Dictionary of Phrase & Fable*, (14th edition) Cassell, 1990

Crawford, Martin – *Directory of Apple Cultivars*, Agroforestry Research Trust, 1994

French, Roger – *The History and Virtues of Cyder*, Robert Hale, 1982

Grigson, Jane – *Jane Grigson's Fruit Book*, Penguin, 1982

Greenoak, Francesca – *Forgotten Fruits: the English orchard and fruit garden*, Andre Deutsch, 1983

Hoskins, Rosemary – *How Green are Our Apples?* SAFE Alliance, 1999

Hoskins, Rosemary – *The Pear Essentials*, SAFE Alliance, 1999

Everyday Tasks

Baker, Harry – *The Fruit Garden Displayed*, Royal Horticultural Society/Cassell, 1986

Bush, Raymond – *A Fruit Grower's Diary*, Faber and Faber, 1948

Common Ground – *Infant Fruit Tree Care – The First Five Years*, Orchards Advice Note No. 15, Common Ground, 1999

Grubb, Norman – *Cherries*, Crosby Lockwood & Son, London, 1949.

Acknowledgements

We are very grateful for the support of many foundations, trusts and individuals in helping to fund our work including: Cobb Charity, the Manifold Trust, Roger Raymond Charitable Trust, the Serve All Trust, J Sheridan, Stanley Smith Horticultural Trust, the Tedworth Charitable Trust, Zephyr Charitable Trust, Department of the Environment, Transport and the Regions Environmental Action Fund and a London based trust.

Many individuals and organisations have helped us as much as we have tried to help them, we thank them all: Ruth Alcock, Youth Hostels Association; Sue Anderson, National Forest; Peter Andrews, Bath Organic Group; Jim Arbury, Royal Horticultural Society; Steve Ashley; Hannah Bartram, Royal Society for the Protection of Birds; Bernard Bligh, London Borough of Lewisham; Bridgeman Art Library; Jonathan Briggs, Botanical Society of the British Isles; Jeremy Burgess, Medway Council; Simon Burnham-Slipper, West Sussex County Council; Pauline Buttery; Sheila Camplin, Tamar Valley Orchard Volunteers; Peter Cartmell, Westmorland Damson Association; Michael Cassin; Barry Champion, National Trust Trelissick Garden; Michael Clark, Tewin Orchard; Steve Clark, Department for the Environment, Transport and the Regions; Michael Clifford; Rebecca Coombes, National Trust Cotehele; Phil Corbett, Own Root Fruit Trees Project; Kevin Croucher, Thornhayes Nursery; James Crowden; James Denison, Groundwork Black Country; Peter Dewey; Graham Donachie, National Trust Oxburgh Hall; Ivor Dunkerton; Matt Dunwell, Ragman's Lane Farm; John Edgeley, Pershore College; John Ely, Shenley Park Trust; James Evans; Chris Fairs, HP Bulmer; Richard Fawcett, Gloucestershire County Council; Harriet Festing, Ashford Borough Council; Cathy Fitzroy, Orchard Link; Fitzwilliam Museum, Cambridge; Simon Fletcher; Lynn Fomison; Andrew Fraser, Worcestershire Wildlife Trust; Anya Gallaccio; Meg Game, Kentish Cobnuts Association; Michael Gee, Dartington North Devon Trust; John Gittins, Cheshire Landscape Trust; Gill Goddard, London Borough of Lewisham; Liz Godden, Stanmer Organic Group; Kristina Gould, Landmark Northwest; Sophie Grigson; Andrew and Terry Gunn; Michael Hamburger; Kevin Hand, Tree Council; Colin Harris, Warndon Villages WildWatch; Harris Museum and Art Gallery; Colin Hawke, Cornwall County Council; Pete Hay; Paul Hegley, Medway Council; Albert Henderson, Leeds University; Martin Hicks, Hertfordshire Biological Records Centre; Pat and Peter Hinde, Home Cottage Farm; Neil Holmes-Smith, Oaklands College; Nancy Holt, Carhampton Community Orchard; Barbara Horseman; Ian & Gill Horsley, Brandy Wharf Cider Centre; Rebecca Hubbard; Danny Hughes, Beaford Centre; Justine Hunt, Mid-Beds Council; Rosemary Jackson, British Horse Society; Maureen Jeffery, Sulgrave Manor; Dick Joy, Landkey Parish Council; Dr Barrie Juniper, Oxford University; Richard Keesing, York University; Tony Kendle, University of Reading; Roger Key, English Nature; Joe King, Gabriel's Community Orchard; John Kingsbury, Youth Hostels Association; George Kington, Veryan Cyder Company; John Langan, Kentish Town City Farm; Simon Leather, Imperial College London; Amanda Lebus; Teresa Lee, Newham City Farm; Sheila Leitch, Marcher Apple Network; Bob Lever, Norfolk Orchards & Apples Project; Mike Levett, London Borough of Barking & Dagenham; Catherine Lloyd; Peter Loosmore, Sturminster Mill; Richard Lutwyche, Gloucester Old Spot Pig Breeders Club; Duncan Mackay, New Road Cyderists; Pauline Markovits, Horfield Community Orchard; James Marsden, English Nature; Mary Martin; Amanda Matthews, Harrogate District Council; Andrina May, Mid-Beds Council; Alastair McLeod, Kentish Town City Farm; Hazel Mead, Rivers Nursery Orchard; Sarah Menear, Exmoor National Park Authority; Margaret Miller, Gartmore School; Joan Morgan, Brogdale Horticultural Trust; Deborah Morris, Bath & North East Somerset Council; Faith Moulin, Two Hoots Biodiversity Group; Pete Nalder,

South Court Environmental; Isobel Norris; Nancy O'Brien, La Sainte Union School; Tom Oliver, National Trust Croome Landscape Park; Kim Patterson, Bolton Wildlife Trust; Claire Peasnall; Dave Perkins, Roots & Shoots; Humphrey Phelps; Ian Pitcairn; Michael Pooley, Shropshire Apple Trust; Mark Powell; John Purves, Elder Stubbs Allotments; Paul Read; Mary Reid, Oxhey Allotment Society; Ann Richards, Centenary Fields Local Nature Reserve; Diana Richards, Rivers Nursery Orchard; Simon Richardson, English Nature; Sonia Ritter, Lions Part Theatre Company; Markus Rösler, Naturschutzbund; Charlie Rugeroni, Butterfly Conservation; Yvonne Sharp, Oaklands College; Colin Shawyer, Hawk & Owl Trust; Martin Skipper, Norfolk Apples and Orchards Project; Alison Sloane, National Trust Oxburgh Hall; June Small, Charlton Orchards; Michael Somers, Surrey Beekeepers Association; Virginia Spiers; Judy Steel, Henry Doubleday Research Association; Clare Stimson; Norfolk Apples and Orchards Project; Mr R Talbot, Northampton Borough Council; Andrew Tann, Crapes Fruit Farm; Julian Temperley; Sue Trim, Hedingham School; Trudy Turrell, South Hams District Council; Patricia Tutt, Bath & North East Somerset Council; Eddie Upton, Folk South West; Caroline Vulliamy, Tamar Valley Orchard Volunteers; Dave Walters, Maiden Lane Community Centre; Don & Linda Warren, Cleeve Prior Heritage Trust; Barry Watson, Becontree Organic Growers; William Watson; Claire Whistler; Rev'd Mervyn Wilson; Christine Wright; Bob Woodrofe, Cleeve Prior Heritage Trust.

Illustrators
Page: 12 David Nash; 18 Gordon Young; 19 Clifford Harper; 22 David Holmes; 28 Pete Hay; 29 Pete Hay; 46 Pupil at Gurnard School; 50 Mary Roberts; 61 Kate Charlesworth; 72 David Holmes; 86 Angela Hogg; 87 Stephen Turner; 96 Stephen Turner; 100 Stephen Turner; 106 Samuel Palmer; 108 Edward Burne-Jones and J. H. Dearle; 110 Abbey Weeks; 122 Peter Till; 124 Clifford Harper; 126 Beatrice

Mayfield; 129 Dovrat Ben-Nahum; 133 Stephen Turner; 136-7 Denis Gould; 141 Brian Grimwood; 142 Richard Allen; 144 Charles Raymond; 157 June Small; 164-5 David Holmes; 169 Charles Raymond; 178 Kate Charlesworth; 180 Robert J Garner; 182 Emma Mackett; 185 David Holmes.

Uncaptioned photographs by James Ravilious
Page: 4 Apple trees, West Park, Iddesleigh, Devon; 9 Cider apple orchard, West Park, Iddesleigh, Devon; 188 Mazzard cherry, Harford, Devon; 197 Sloping orchard, St Dominick, Cornwall; 198 Farm orchard, Shobrooke, Devon; 208 Apple orchard in fruit near Ilminster, Somerset; 219 A break from pruning in a bush orchard, East Cornworthy, Devon; 222 Miss Betty's orchard near Martock, Somerset.

James Ravilious

In 1988 Common Ground commissioned James Ravilious to create an exhibition of Orchards. He did so much more than we asked: he explored, talked to orchard owners, listened to their stories and retold them with care. He took and printed hundreds of photographs, the perfectionist always. They are beautifully framed – as a landscape painting would be, and he would wait for hours for the right light and to follow the jobs of the day – or return again and again until he was happy. He was able to convey the dignity of people and domestic animals absorbed in their daily round.

The exhibition *Orchards of the West Country* opened at the Royal Albert Museum in Exeter in 1989 and has travelled across the country. It has proved a beguiling way of showing the cultural depth of these places and the importance of the people who work them. The bank of prints and slides which James produced helped us to launch the Save our Orchards campaign. His images continue to be used in books, magazines and newspapers.

James travelled to Cornwall, Somerset and Dorset for us, but he was most at ease in North Devon where, over 20 years he had created an unparalleled record of working life and landscapes now held as the Beaford Archive in Barnstaple Library – it is a unique legacy. His own books include *The Heart of the Country* with his wife Robin, *A Corner of England, An English Eye* by Peter Hamilton and *Down the Deep Lanes* with Peter Beacham. James Ravilious died in 1999 at the age of 60, we miss his humility and wise counsel, but his genius for place and for people will continue to resound.